Jim C. DeLoach
DeVry Institute of Technology—Atlanta

Frank J. Ambrosio
Monroe Community College

LAB MANUAL
(A Troubleshooting Approach)

to accompany

DIGITAL SYSTEMS
Principles and Applications

Sixth Edition

Ronald J. Tocci
Monroe Community College

Prentice Hall
Englewood Cliffs, New Jersey   Columbus, Ohio

The data sheets included in this book have been reprinted with the permission of the following companies:

All materials reproduced courtesy of Analog Devices, Inc.
All materials reproduced courtesy of Fairchild-A Schlumberger Company.
All materials reprinted by permission of Intel Corporation. Intel Corporation assumes no responsibility for any errors which may appear in this document nor does it make a commitment to update the information contained herein.
All materials reprinted with permission of National Semiconductor Corp.
All materials reproduced courtesy of Texas Instruments, Incorporated.

Cover photo: Joshua Sheldon

Editor: Dave Garza
Production Editor: Mary Harlan
Cover Designer: Ruta Kysilewskyj
Production Buyer: Patricia A. Tonneman

This book was printed and bound by Press of Ohio. The cover was printed by Phoenix Color Corp.

 © 1995 by Prentice-Hall, Inc.
A Simon & Schuster Company
Englewood Cliffs, New Jersey 07632

Printed in the United States of America

10 9 8 7 6 5 4 3 2

ISBN: 0-13-303777-0

Prentice-Hall International (UK) Limited, *London*
Prentice-Hall of Australia Pty. Limited, *Sydney*
Prentice-Hall of Canada, Inc., *Toronto*
Prentice-Hall Hispanoamericana, S. A., *Mexico*
Prentice-Hall of India Private Limited, *New Delhi*
Prentice-Hall of Japan, Inc., *Tokyo*
Simon & Schuster Asia Pte. Ltd., *Singapore*
Editora Prentice-Hall do Brasil, Ltda., *Rio de Janeiro*

To my wife, Margaretta, whose patience and encouragement have been unending; to our son and daughter, John and Cheryl; and to Steve, Debbie, Sara, Justin, Heather, Stevie, and Sarah.

Jim C. DeLoach

To my wife, Ana, for her patience and understanding, and to the most wonderful son in the world, Filip.

Frank J. Ambrosio

CONTENTS

PREFACE

This manual is designed to provide practical laboratory experience for the student of digital electronics. There are forty-two experiments which are coordinated with the manual's companion text, *Digital Systems: Principles and Applications, 6th Edition*, by **Ronald Tocci**. The sequence of the experiments follows reasonably well with the text.

The manual includes experiments on digital fundamentals, design, and troubleshooting. There is enough material to cover a two-semester laboratory course stressing design or troubleshooting or even a combination of the two. It is not intended that all the experiments be completed or that every experiment be done in its entirety. Instructors will probably want to make certain exercises optional to the student.

The troubleshooting exercises take the student from digital IC fault recognition (Experiments 3 and 6) to troubleshooting combinatorial circuits (Experiment 14), flip-flops (Experiment 19), counters (Experiment 25), and systems (Experiment 35). There are also exercises using a logic analyzer (Experiments 31,32, and 40). The logic analyzer is discussed in Appendix B of this manual. Logic probes and logic pulsers are discussed in Experiment 3 and are needed in most of the troubleshooting exercises. The specifications for the Elenco Model LP-700 logic probe and LP-600 logic pulser may be found in Appendix A.

The design exercises include simplification exercises (Experiment 8), a majority tester (Experiment 13), a programmable counter (Experiment 18), a system clock, variable timer, and serial interface with handshake (Experiment 28), a word recognizer (Experiment 36), a synchronous counter (Experiment 40), and a programmable function sequencer (Experiment 42). Also included in the exercises is an example of a control waveform generator, a synchronous data transmission system, a frequency counter, a 2-digit digital voltmeter, and a data bus system.

Each experiment begins with a set of stated objectives, text references, and required equipment, followed by a procedure for meeting each objective. Most experiments specify logic circuits needed to perform the experiment, while a few require that the student design and draw the circuit(s). Almost all experiments end with a set of review questions for the student to complete.

There are several improvements made in this edition of the lab manual. Most of the changes were necessary because of diminished supply of some of the integrated c ircuits and escalating cost of others. For example, the 74111 can not be obtained by many sources, and the 74178 will continue to increase in cost as supplies decrease. We have left the 74111 experiment intact for this edition since it can be simulated very easily. For those interested, the solutions manual will contain a circuit for this simulation. The 74178 is replaced by the 74194 in this edition. Finally, the AD561 is replaced by the MC1408 (or DAC0808).

Most of the TTL ICs can be replaced by the 74LS or 74HCT series versions without loss of function. The only experiments where substitution of the ICs called for is not a good idea are Experiment 16 and Experiment 29. Incidentally, a 74F10 has been added to Experiment 29 as an instructor's option. We believe it is not necessary to compare all of the different IC families in a single experiment, but comparing CMOS to one or two of the more popular TTL families is instructive.

Appendix A covers several topics which should be helpful to the student. Included in the material are general hints on proper breadboarding, digital troubleshooting, and information on typical digital system and IC faults. The student is encouraged to become familiar with the contents of the appendix early, even though serious reading of much of the information on troubleshooting and digital faults can be deferred until it is needed.

Appendix B covers the basic principles of logic analyzers. The operation of a typical logic analyzer, the Tektronix Model 7D01, is also discussed. Most of the material covered here can be transferred to another logic analyzer, providing the instructor explains the differences between that logic analyzer and the 7D01.

The circuits in the experiments will work with most digital trainers. As a minimum, the trainer should have the following features:

1) Buffered LED monitors (8)
2) Toggle switches (8)
3) Normally HIGH debounced pushbutton switch (1)
4) Normally LOW debounced pushbutton switch (1)
5) TTL-compatible clock, 1 Hz–100 kHz (1)

There will be occasional requirements for additional LED monitors and toggle and pushbutton switches. Figure 0-1 shows a circuit for wiring an additional Light Emitting Diode (LED) monitor and Figure 0-2 shows a circuit for converting the output of a conventional square wave generator (SWG) so that it is compatible with TTL levels. A circuit for obtaining both normally HIGH and normally LOW debounce switches is shown in Figure 0-3.

There are some forty-two different IC's covered in this manual. It is not anticipated that there will be any difficulty obtaining the ICs. LS-TTL ICs may be

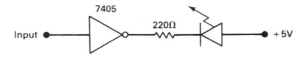

Figure 0-1

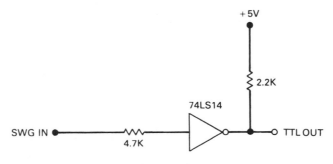

Figure 0-2

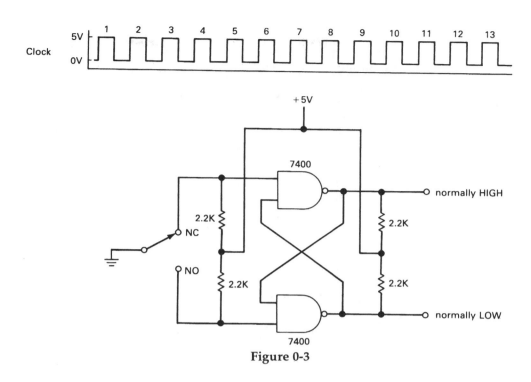

Figure 0-3

substituted for all TTL ICs except the 7476. The data sheets for all digital ICs are found either in Appendix C of this manual or Appendix II of the text.

A list of all integrated circuits, parts, and laboratory equipment, required and optional, is found in the Equipment List that follows the preface.

We would like to express our appreciation to the author of the companion text, *Professor Ronald Tocci* of Monroe Community College, for writing such an outstanding text, for his many contributions to the development of this manual, including some of the experiments, and for being a tireless reviewer and critic.

We would like to thank several firms which provided up-to-date information that was helpful in preparing this manual, and for permission to use the data sheets which appear in this manual:

Analog Devices, Inc.
Elenco Electronics, Inc.
Fairchild Semiconductor, Inc.
Intel Corporation
Motorola Semiconductors
National Semiconductor Corporation
R.S.R. Electronics, Inc.
Texas Instruments Incorporated

EQUIPMENT LIST

Laboratory Equipment

1) Power supplies: 0 to +5 V, 50 mA, regulated; 0 to +15 V, 50 mA, regulated; 0 to -15 V, 50 mA, regulated; 6.3 VAC, 60 Hz.
2) Dual trace oscilloscope
3) Storage oscilloscope (optional)
4) Pulse or square wave generator (SWG), 0 to 1 MHz
5) Time interval counter (optional)
6) Volt-ohm-milliameter (VOM)
7) Logic probe
8) Logic pulser
9) Logic analyzer (optional)
10) Digital voltmeter (DVM) or Digital Multimeter (DMM)

Integrated Circuits

IC	Qty	IC	Qty	IC	Qty
555	1	7432	4	74LS139	1
2114	1	7442	1	74147	1
4016	1	7446	2	74151	1
7400	2	7474	4	74173	3
				74174	1
7402	2	7475	1	74192	1
7404	2	7476 [1]	1	74193	1
7405	1	74LS76	4	74194	4
7406	1	7483A	1	74273	1
7408	2	7486	2	74293 [4]	2
7410 [1]	1	7490	2	LM324	1
74F10 [2]	1	7493	2	MC1408	
74LS10	1	74111 [3]	1	or DAC0808	2
74LS11	1	74LS121	2		
74LS13	1	74LS125	1		
7427	1	74LS138	1		

[1] Do NOTsubstitute.
[2] Instructor's option.
[3] The 74111 may be simulated if it is not available.
[4] The 74293 may be used to replace the 7493 if desired.

Other components and material

Resistors	Qty	Capacitors	Qty	Diodes	Qty
150 ohm	14	270 F	1	1N457	1
1 k-ohm	1	330 pF	1	1N914	2
2.2 k-ohm	2	560 pF	1	4.7 V zener	1
6.8 k-ohm	1	680 pF	1	LEDs	3
10 k-ohm	1	0.01 μF	1	FND507 7-segment	
18 k-ohm	1	1 μF	1	display units	2
33 k-ohm	1	100 μF	1		
180 k-ohm	1				

Potentiometers	Qty	Switches	Qty
1 k-ohm		SPDT	10
(ten-turn recommended)	2	Pushbutton	6
5 k-ohm			
(ten-turn recommended)	2		

Miscellaneous
Decimal or hexadecimal keyboard
SK-10 circuit board

NOTE: ICs and other components listed are available in bulk or in prepackaged
          kits from **RSR Electronics, INC. Telephone (908) 381-8777.**

Experiment 1

PRELIMINARY CONCEPTS

OBJECTIVES

1. To observe differences between analog and digital devices.
2. To learn binary-to-decimal conversions.
3. To learn decimal-to-binary conversions.
4. To investigate basic pulse characteristics.

TEXT REFERENCES

Read sections 1.1 through 1.6 and section 2.5. Also read Appendix A of this manual.

EQUIPMENT NEEDED

Components
74147 IC;
7404 IC;
7442 IC;
4 toggle switches;
4 LED monitors;
1 k-ohm resistors (9).

Instruments
volt-ohm-milliameter (VOM);
digital multimeter (DMM);
pulse or square wave generator (SWG);
triggered oscilloscope;
0–5 volt DC power supply.

DISCUSSION

In this experiment, you will discover the major difference between analog and digital quantities by using both an analog and a digital measuring device to measure the output voltage of a power supply. Keep in mind that analog measuring devices display their measurements continuously on a scaled meter, which can be difficult to read with precision. On the other hand, digital devices display their measurements in steps using digits and therefore are capable of being read with much greater precision.

You will also observe how decimal quantities are represented in binary and, conversely, how binary numbers are represented by a decimal number by constructing special circuits called decimal-to-binary encoders and binary-to-decimal decoders. If this is your first experience working with integrated circuits (ICs), you should not be intimidated by your lack of knowledge of what is inside the IC. Concentrate on the experiment at hand, that is, to show that each decimal digit (0–9) has a unique binary representation, and that these same binary numbers have a unique decimal representation.

Finally, you will discover some of the characteristics of pulses and learn how to use an oscilloscope to measure these characteristics.

PROCEDURE

a) *Analog vs. digital:* Turn on the power supply and set it to +5 volts. Set the VOM to measure +5 volts DC, and connect the VOM probes to the output of the power supply, being careful to observe correct polarity. Note the smooth swing of the VOM needle as it swings from zero toward +5 volts. Note also that the amount of deflection of the needle is determined by, and therefore proportional to, the voltage at the VOM's probes. Record the value indicated by the VOM: _____.

Now set the DMM to measure +5 volts DC, and touch the probes to the output of the power supply, being careful to observe correct polarity. Note that the readout displays its measurement in one or more values before it settles near +5 volts. In other words, it displays increasing values in a number of steps. Finally, note that voltage is represented by digits. Record the readout value: _____.

b) *Decimal-to-binary:* In this step, a 74147 IC and a 7404 IC will be combined to convert decimal digits to binary coded decimal (BCD). Refer to the data sheet for the 74147 and 7404, and draw the pin layout diagram for each:

Use the 74147 and 7404 and connect the circuit in Figure 1-1 according to the procedure outlined in Appendix A. There are nine inputs to this circuit (I_1–I_9), each representing a decimal digit (1–9, respectively) and each connected through a spdt

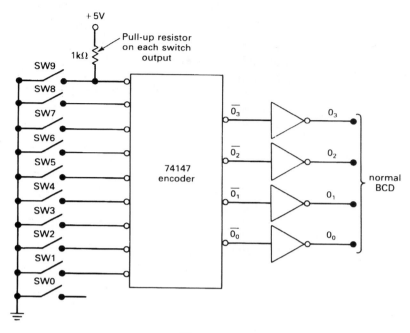

Figure 1-1

switch to either ground (input activated) or V_{cc} (input-deactivated, or normal). If nine spdt input switches are not available, leave all input connections open, then connect a single wire to ground. You will use this wire to activate each input as is called for below by touching the wire to the appropriate input pin on the 74147.

The BCD output of this circuit will be monitored by connecting an LED monitor, DMM, or VOM to the outputs of the circuit labelled 0_0–0_3. If LED monitors are used to monitor the output, you will interpret a lighted LED as a binary 1 and an unlighted LED as a binary 0. If a DMM or VOM is used, interpret each output as follows:

$$0 \text{ to } + 0.8 \text{ volt} = \text{binary } 0$$

$$+2 \text{ to } + 5 \text{ volts} = \text{binary } 1$$

The Least Significant Bit (LSB) of the output is 0_0; the Most Significant Bit (MSB) is 0_3. The output of this circuit is normally 0000 when none of the 74147 inputs are activated. Turn on the power supply and check to see that this is the case. If so, then proceed with the experiment; otherwise, turn off the power supply, check your circuit wiring, correct any faults, and repeat this step.

Once you have have verified that the circuit is initially working correctly, activate each of the inputs, one at a time, and record the BCD output observed in Table 1-1 on page 4.

c) *Binary-to-decimal*: Refer to the data sheet for the 7442 IC, and draw the pin layout diagram:

Table 1-1

Input Activated	Decimal Digit	BCD Output			
		O_0	O_1	O_2	O_3
None	0	0	0	0	0
I_1	1				
I_2	2				
I_3	3				
I_4	4				
I_5	5				
I_6	6				
I_7	7				
I_8	8				
I_9	9				

Turn the power supply off, and disassemble the circuit used in step b. Use the 7442, and connect the circuit in Figure 1-2, which is a circuit for converting BCD to decimal. Connect a separate spdt switch to each of the inputs A, B, C, and D of the 7442 so that each can be switched to ground (binary 0) or V_{CC} (binary 1). Input A is LSB, and input D is MSB. To monitor the outputs, connect an LED monitor, DMM, or VOM to each 7442 output O_0–O_9, representing decimal digits 0–9, respectively. One (and only one) output will be activated (indicated by an unlighted LED or a reading of near 0 volts DC) for each combination of input switch conditions. Use the binary equivalences given in step b above to interpret the input and output levels of the 7442.

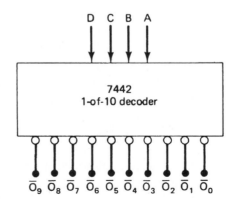

Figure 1-2

Set all of the input switches to the ground position (all inputs binary 0). Monitor the 0_0 output (pin 1 of the 7442): it should be activated. Now check all of the other outputs 0_1–0_9 (pins 2–7 and 9–11, respectively), and verify that they are all inactive (all LED monitors connected to these outputs should be lighted or show voltage readings 2.4 V). If this is not the case, recheck the input switches. If the switches are all set to ground position, turn the power supply off and recheck your circuit wiring. If a fault is found, correct it, and repeat this step. If you have problems getting the right results, call your instructor.

Refer to Table 1-2, and toggle the input switches so that each BCD number from 0001 to 1001 is entered into the 7442, recording the output conditions for each BCD number in the table.

d) *Pulse characteristics*: Set up an oscilloscope as follows:

DC vertical input at 1 volt/division
Horizontal sweep rate at 1 millisecond/division

Table 1-2

BCD Input				7442 Output Conditions										Decimal
D	C	B	A	0_0	0_1	0_2	0_3	0_4	0_5	0_6	0_7	0_8	0_9	Digit
0	0	0	0	0	1	1	1	1	1	1	1	1	1	0
0	0	0	1											
0	0	1	0											
0	0	1	1											
0	1	0	0											
0	1	0	1											
0	1	1	0											
0	1	1	1											
1	0	0	0											
1	0	0	1											

Auto triggering
Negative trigger slope

Set up a pulse, function, or square wave generator to 200 Hz. The output of the generator should be TTL compatible (i.e., LOW level of pulse should be 0 to +0.8 volt and HIGH level of pulse should be +2.0 to +5.0 volts). Connect the output of the generator to both the vertical and external trigger inputs of the scope. Adjust the generator frequency until the oscilloscope display shows two repetitions of the generated pulse. Sketch the display on Timing Diagram 1-1.

Adjust the vertical position control so that the leading edge of a positive-going pulse intersects a convenient vertical graticule at 2.5 volts (50% point). Measure the distance between this point and the 50% point of the trailing

Timing Diagram 1-1

edge along the horizontal graticule. Record your result: _____. Multiply the distance observed by the setting on the horizontal sweep control. Record your calculation: _____. The calculated result is the *pulse duration* (t_p). Now measure the distance between the leading edges of two consecutive pulses, and convert the distance into time by multiplying by the horizontal sweep setting. Record your computation: _____. This measurement is called the *period* (T) of the waveform. The duty cycle of the waveform can now be calculated using the formula:

$$\text{Duty Cycle} = \frac{(t_p)}{T} \times 100\%$$

Record your computation for the duty cycle: _____.

Set the pulse generator to 1 kHz, and adjust the oscilloscope to display the leading edge of a positive-going pulse. Use the highest horizontal speed possible (magnified, if available). Adjust the oscilloscope's positioning controls so that the 0.5 V (10%) point of the pulse intersects a convenient vertical graticule. Estimate the distance between this point and a vertical line passing through both the 4.5 V (90%) point of the pulse and the main horizontal graticule. Multiply your measurement by the horizontal sweep speed, and record your computation: _____. This is the pulse's *rise time* (t_r). Repeat this procedure on the trailing edge of the pulse. Record your measurement: _____. This is the *fall time* of the pulse (t_f).

One more important pulse characteristic is *propagation delay*. This measurement will be performed in a future experiment.

e) *Review*: This concludes the exercises on preliminary concepts of digital systems. To test your understanding of the principles covered by this experiment, complete the following statements:

1. Based on your observations [analog, digital] voltmeters are the easiest to read because voltage is represented by _____. [Analog, Digital] representations are continuous (smooth) while [analog, digital] representations are discrete (in steps).

2. In this experiment, a binary 0 is represented by _____ volts. An LED monitor is [unlighted, lighted] when indicating a binary 0.

3. In this experiment, a binary 1 is represented by _____ volts. An LED monitor is [unlighted, lighted] when indicating a binary 1.

4. When input I_5 of the 74147 IC is activated, the outputs of the IC will indicate a binary _____.

5. A 7442 IC has a BCD input of 0110. Its output will indicate a decimal ____.

6. For a series of pulses, T = 8 microseconds and t_p = 3 microseconds. The duty cycle of the waveform is ____%.

Experiment 2

LOGIC GATES I: OR, AND, AND NOT

OBJECTIVES

1. To investigate the behavior of the OR gate.
2. To investigate the behavior of the AND gate.
3. To investigate the behavior of the NOT gate (inverter).

TEXT REFERENCES

Read sections 3.1 through 3.5.

EQUIPMENT NEEDED

Components
7404 IC;
7411 IC;
7432 IC;
4 toggle switches;
1 LED monitor.

Instruments
VOM;
0–5 volt DC power supply;
logic probe (optional).

DISCUSSION

In general, logic circuits have one or more inputs and only one output. The circuits respond to various input combinations, and a truth table shows this relationship between a circuit's input combinations and its output. The truth table for a particular circuit explains how the circuit behaves under normal conditions. Familiarization with a logic circuit's truth table is essential to the technologist or technician before he or she can design with or troubleshoot the circuit.

In this experiment, three logic circuits are covered: the OR, AND, and NOT gates. The OR operation can be summarized as follows:

1) When any input is 1, the output is also 1.
2) When all inputs are 0, the output is also 0.

The AND operation can be summarized similarly:

1) When any input is 0, the output is also 0.
2) When all inputs are 1, the output is also 1.

Finally, the NOT operation is said to be complementary. In other words:

1) If the input is 0, the output is 1.
2) If the input is 1, the output is 0.

You should recall that the logic levels, 0 and 1, have voltage assignments. For TTL circuits, a logic 0 can be anywhere from 0 V to +0.8 V, and a logic 1 is in the range of +2.0 V to +5.0 V.

PROCEDURE

a) *The OR gate*: Refer to the data sheet for the 7432 IC and draw its pin layout diagram:

A	B	x = A + B
0	0	0
0	1	1
1	0	1
1	1	1

(a)

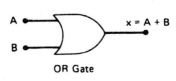

OR Gate

(b)

Figure 2-1

b) Figure 2-1 shows the logic symbol and truth table for the OR logic gate. The 7432 contains four of these gates. Wire one of them as follows:

1) V_{cc} to +5 volts; GND to power ground.
2) Inputs A and B to separate toggle switches.
3) The output to the VOM.

Table 2-1

Data Switches A B	VOM (Volts)	Logic Level (0/1)
0 0		
0 1		
1 0		
1 1		

c) You will now verify the OR operation by setting inputs A and B to each set of logic values listed in the truth table of Figure 2-1, recording the output voltage observed, and converting the output voltage to a logic level. Use

$$0 \text{ V--}0.8 \text{ V} = 0 \text{ and } 2 \text{ V--}5 \text{ V} = 1$$

for the conversions and record your observations in Table 2-1.

d) Disconnect the VOM from the circuit, and use an LED monitor to observe the output. Repeat step c using the conversion rule LED OFF (unlighted) = 0 and LED ON (lighted) = 1.

e) Disconnect one of the inputs, and set the remaining one to 0. Is the output level 0 or 1? Based on your observation and knowledge of the OR operation, what level does the unconnected input act like? _____.

f) *The AND gate:* Refer to the data sheet for the 7411 IC, and draw its pin diagram:

g) Figure 2-2 shows the logic symbol and truth table for the three input AND logic gate. The 7411 contains three 3-input AND gates. Wire one of the AND gates as follows:

1) V_{cc} to +5 V and GND to power ground.
2) Inputs A, B, and C to toggle switches.
3) Output to an LED monitor.

A	B	C	x = ABC
0	0	0	0
0	0	1	0
0	1	0	0
0	1	1	0
1	0	0	0
1	0	1	0
1	1	0	0
1	1	1	1

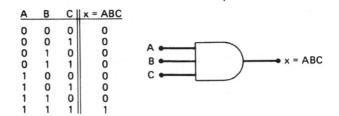

Figure 2-2

Table 2-2

Data Switches			Output LED Monitor (On/Off)	Output Logic Level (0/1)
A	B	C		
0	0	0		
0	0	1		
0	1	0		
0	1	1		
1	0	0		
1	0	1		
1	1	0		
1	1	1		

h) You will now verify the AND operation by setting toggle switches A, B, and C to each set of input values of the truth table in Figure 2-2 and recording the output level observed on the LED monitor using Table 2-2.

i) Disconnect input A from the toggle switch, and set inputs B and C to 1. Note the logic level indicated by the LED monitor. Based on your observation, what logic level does the unconnected input act like? _____

j) *The NOT gate*: Mount a 7404 IC on the circuit board. Refer to the data sheet for the 7404, and draw its pin layout diagram:

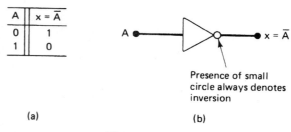

A	x = $\overline{A}$
0	1
1	0

(a)   (b)

Figure 2-3

Table 2-3

Data Switch A	Output LED Monitor (On/Off)	Output Logic Level (0/1)
0		
1		

k) Figure 2-3 shows the logic symbol and truth table for the NOT gate, also commonly called an inverter. The 7404 IC contains six inverters. Connect one of the inverters as follows:

1) V_{cc} to +5 V and GND to power ground.
2) Input A to a toggle switch.
3) Output to an LED monitor.

l) You will now verify the NOT operation given by the truth table in Figure 2-3 and record your observations in Table 2-3.

m) *Review:* This concludes the investigation of basic logic gate operation. To test your understanding of the logic gates, complete the following statements:

1. The output of an OR gate is LOW only when _____.
2. The output of an AND gate is _____ whenever any input is LOW.
3. The output of an inverter is always _____ the input.
4. Using the results obtained in step h, one could conclude that to use a three-input AND gate as a two-input gate, one input should be connected to [V_{cc}, GND].
5. If an OR gate input were accidentally shorted to V_{cc}, the output of the gate would always be _____, no matter what level the other input level might be.

DISCUSSION

Most digital systems incorporate numerous IC logic gates into their circuitry. IC gates are very reliable, but like all electronic devices they fail, and when they do fail, they must be isolated and replaced. Troubleshooting gates and their faults is essential to learning how to troubleshoot a digital system. The techniques employed at the gate level can be used to troubleshoot larger devices.

In this experiment, you will learn to use a logic probe and a logic pulser together to "discover" some typical gate faults. These two tools are probably the most popular of all digital test equipment. They are easy to use, small, and lightweight. They get their power from the power supply of the device being serviced. Figure 3-1 shows a Model LP700 logic probe, and Figure 3-2 shows a Model LP600 logic pulser, both manufactured by Elenco Electronics, Inc. Descriptions of these devices can be found in Appendix A of this manual.

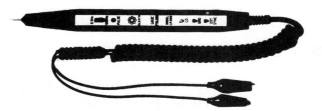

Figure 3-1

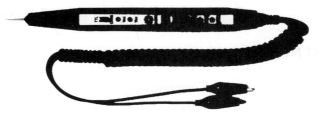

Figure 3-2

LOGIC PROBES

A logic probe is a small, hand-held instrument used to indicate the logic level at a point in a digital circuit. It is capable of indicating a logic 0, logic 1, and a level floating between logic 0 and 1. In many cases it is capable of detecting the presence of high speed pulses. Figure 3-3 shows a typical application of the logic probe, that is, static testing a logic gate by monitoring its output while the gate's inputs are switched through their various combinations.

LOGIC PULSERS

A logic pulser generates digital pulses. Like the logic probe, the pulser uses the logic power supply to get its own power. The tip of the pulser is placed on a circuit

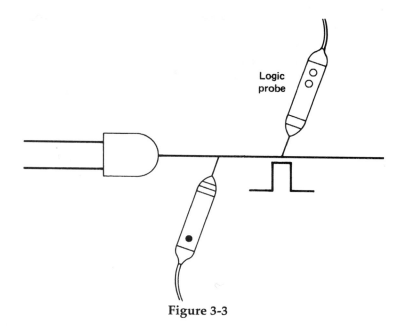

Figure 3-3

node where an injected pulse is desired. The pulser senses the logic state of the node and generates a pulse that will attempt to drive the node to the opposite state. This is a valuable aid in troubleshooting, since it permits the triggering of gates and other devices without removing them from their circuits.

PROCEDURE

   a) *Testing the logic probe:* First, make sure the lab power supply is OFF, then set the TTL/CMOS switch to TTL, and connect the logic probe power leads to the logic power supply of the device under test. For this experiment, we will be troubleshooting TTL IC gates, so the logic power supply will be our 0–5 volt DC lab power supply. Make sure to connect the red clip to +5 volts and the black clip to power supply ground. Turn the lab power supply ON. If your probe has a single LED to indicate logic levels, as in the case of the LP700, the LED should be blinking to indicate that the level at the probe tip is floating. (If your probe has two LEDs to represent the two logic levels, both should be out.) If you have a DMM available, connect its leads between the logic power ground and the probe tip. The DMM should read a value between 1.3 and 1.5 volts. This value is called by various names—"indeterminate," "bad," "invalid," and "floating." All refer to the fact that if a voltage value falls into a range of greater than 0.8 volts and less than 2.0 volts, the value cannot represent a logic 0 or a logic 1. These values all have a tolerance of 20%.

   Refer now to Figure 3-4. Turn the power supply off and connect a 1 k-ohm linear potentiometer and DMM to the power supply as shown. Set the potentiometer so that the DMM reads 0 volts. Touch the probe to the center tap, and turn the power supply ON. Its LED(s) should indicate logic 0. Now slowly turn the potentiometer away from ground and toward V_{cc}. When the LED(s) indicate a floating level, you have reached the top end of the range for logic 0. Now slowly continue to turn the potentiometer toward V_{cc}, this time until the LED(s) indicate a logic 1. This is the bottom end of the range for logic 1.

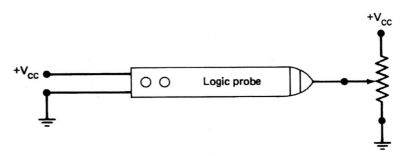

Figure 3-4

b) *Testing the logic pulser*: Install a 7404 IC, a 7408 IC, and a 7432 IC on the circuit board. Connect V_{cc} and ground to each IC. For this part of the experiment, we will use only the 7404 and 7408. Refer to Figure 3-5. Connect one vertical input of the oscilloscope to the output of one of the 7404 inverters. Select a horizontal graticule near the bottom of the oscilloscope display, and adjust the trace of the oscilloscope to that graticule. This marking will be your LOW reference.

Connect the black power connector of the pulser to the logic power supply ground and the red to V_{cc}. Place the pulser tip on the inverter output that is being observed. Adjust the oscilloscope timing until a stable pulse is displayed. You should note that the pulse is a positive-going pulse.

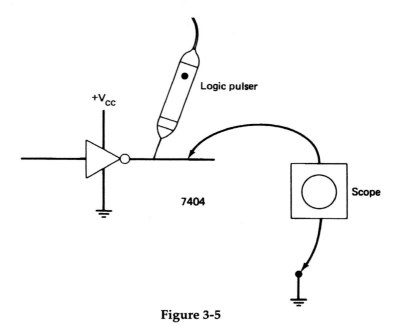

Figure 3-5

Refer now to Figure 3-6. Place the oscilloscope input on the output of one 7408 AND gate. Adjust the oscilloscope trace to a suitable horizontal graticule near the top of the screen. This will be your HIGH reference. Touch the pulser tip to the AND output being observed, and adjust the oscilloscope timing until a stable pulse is displayed. You should note that the pulse is negative-going. This confirms that the pulser will attempt to drive a node to its opposite state.

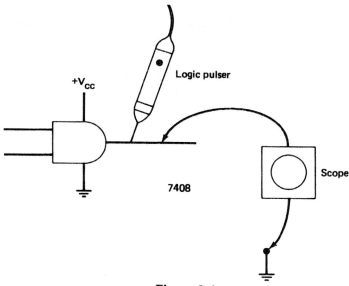

Figure 3-6

Finally, refer to Figure 3-7. Connect the oscilloscope input to V_{cc}. Adjust the oscilloscope trace to a convenient HIGH reference graticule. Touch the pulser tip to V_{cc}. You should note that the pulser cannot drive V_{cc} to a logic 0. Now connect the oscilloscope input to ground, and adjust the oscilloscope trace to a convenient LOW reference graticule. Touch the pulser to ground, and note that it cannot drive ground to a logic 1.

c) *Using the logic probe and logic pulser to troubleshoot gates:* In what follows, the probe-pulser combination will be used to aid in locating certain types of faults of IC gates. We will not look at every possible type of fault, but we can simulate most of the common ones and develop a procedure for testing for them. The faults will be shaded in the figures.

A word of caution: some of the fault simulations call for shorting gate inputs together and outputs together. **Never** short inputs together that are all connected to your trainer's data switches. **Never** short a trainer data switch directly to ground or to V_{cc}. **Never** short any gate output to ground or to V_{cc}. **Do** exercise care in following the instructions below and elsewhere in this manual. Do not substitute LS-TTL for TTL ICs in this exercise, since shorting LS-TTL outputs together for more than one second is not recommended. Voltages at shorted LS-TTL outputs cannot be measured with any consistency.

OR Gates

1) Refer to Figure 3-8, and wire a 7432 OR gate as shown. Recall that when all inputs to an OR gate are the same, the output is the same as the inputs. Touch the probe tip to one of the inputs and the pulser to the other input. You should observe that the pulsing on one of the inputs is detected by the probe on the other. Normally, unless the two inputs are purposely wired together, you should not observe this condition.

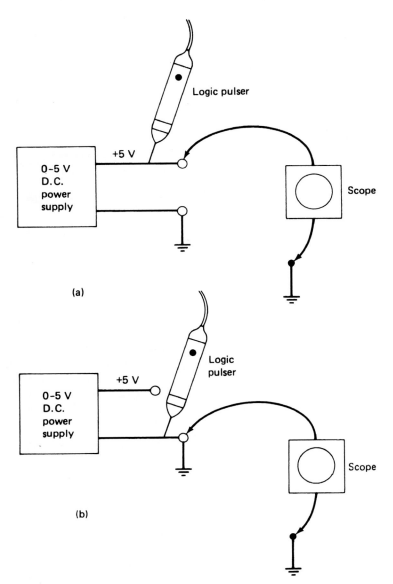

Figure 3-7

2) Refer to Figure 3-9, and wire a 7432 OR gate as shown. Connect point A to a data switch, but leave points B and C disconnected. Place the probe tip on point C, and observe that the output is HIGH. Toggle the data switch, and observe that it has no effect on the output. Now place the probe tip on point D. You should observe that the level there is floating. This tells you that either the input (point D) has an external open or an internal open. To verify that the open is external, place the pulser tip to point D and the probe tip to point C. Set the data switch at A to LOW. You should observe that the probe now indicates a pulsing condition. If the open had been internal, you would still see a HIGH at point C.

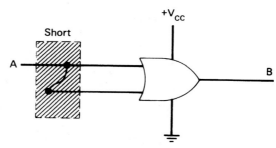

Figure 3-8

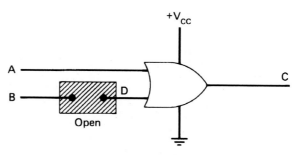

Figure 3-9

3) Refer to Figure 3-10, and wire three 7432 OR gates as shown. Note that a short between the outputs of gate 3 and gate 2 has been wired purposely. Connect data switches to inputs A, B, C, and D. Set switches A and B to LOW and switches C and D to HIGH. Place the tip of the logic probe on output E. You should observe that the level there is LOW. The HIGH output of gate 2 has no effect on the output of gate 1. This is because one of gate 1's inputs is LOW, and the LOW output of gate 3 is pulling the level at the other input of gate 1 down to LOW. Now toggle switch B several times while observing the output at E with the logic probe. You should observe that the output at E toggles also.

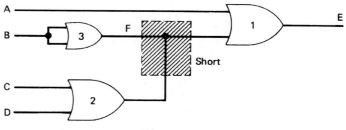

Figure 3-10

Set switches C and D to LOW. Now toggle switch B several times, again monitoring output E with the logic probe. You should observe that the logic probe indicates a constant LOW. Why?

_____

_____

_____

Place the tip of your probe on point F, and toggle switch B several times. You should observe that switch B has no effect on point F. Measure the voltage at point F with the DMM. The voltage at that point should be near the midrange value for a LOW, which is 0.4 V. A typical reading would be about 0.38 V. Remove the short between the outputs of gate 2 and gate 3, and measure the voltage at point F. It should now measure less than 0.4 V, typically 0.15 V. Set switch B to HIGH and measure the voltage at point F with the DMM. Record this voltage: _____.

Finally, replace the short between the outputs of gate 2 and gate 3. Place the tip of the logic probe on the output of gate 1 and the tip of the logic pulser on point F. You should note that the logic probe indicates a pulsing output at E. Thus, the logic pulser can overcome a LOW produced by the output of a gate.

4) Refer to Figures 3-11 and 3-12. You will not wire these circuits. In step 3 above, when the output of gate 2 was HIGH, it had no effect on the output of gate 3. Switch B could be toggled, producing a toggling output at E if switch A was set to 0. A short to V_{cc} at point F could not be overcome by the output of gate 3. So point F would be stuck HIGH. Measuring the actual voltage level at point F can help you determine whether or not a circuit node is shorted to V_{cc}, since the outputs of TTL gates are normally lower than V_{cc}. A logic pulser cannot overcome a short to V_{cc}.

If point F measures 0 V, then it is likely that point F is shorted to ground. Also, a logic pulser cannot overcome this type of short.

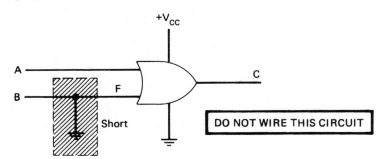

Figure 3-11

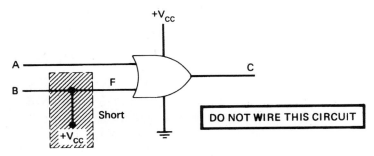

Figure 3-12

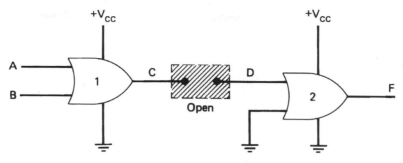

Figure 3-13

5) Refer to Figure 3-13, and wire two 7432 OR gates as shown.   Leave points A and B disconnected. We will assume that gate 2 is functioning normally.   Place your probe tip on point D. It should indicate a floating level. This is symptomatic of an open in the output circuit of gate 1. The question is whether it is an external or internal open. Place the probe on the output pin of gate 1.   If it is HIGH, then there is an external open somewhere between the IC and point C. If the output pin is floating, then an internal open in gate 1's output circuit could be the cause.

AND Gates

1) Refer to Figure 3-14, and wire a 7408 AND gate as shown. Recall that when all inputs to an AND gate are the same, the output is the same as the inputs. Touch the probe tip to one of the inputs and the pulser to the other input. You should observe that the pulsing on one of the inputs is detected by the probe on the other.

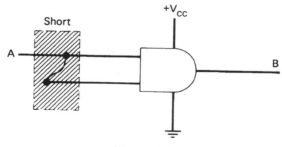

Figure 3-14

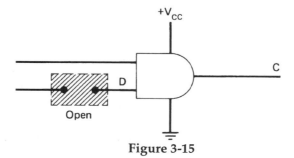

Figure 3-15

Normally, unless the two inputs are purposely wired together, you should not observe this condition.

2) Refer to Figure 3-15, and wire a 7408 AND gate as shown. Connect point A to a data switch, but leave points B and C disconnected. Place the probe tip on point C, and observe that the output is HIGH. Toggle the data switch, and observe that the output acts normally. Now place the probe tip on point D. You should observe that the level there is floating. This tells you that either the input (point D) has an external open or an internal open. To verify that the open is external, place the pulser tip on point D and the probe tip on point C. Set the data switch at A to HIGH. You should observe that the probe now indicates a pulsing condition. If the open had been internal, you would still see a HIGH at point C.

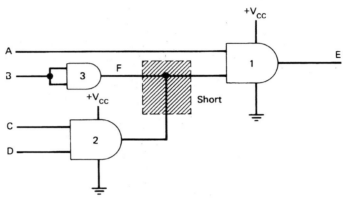

Figure 3-16

3) Refer to Figure 3-16, and wire three 7408 AND gates as shown. Note that a short between the outputs of gate 3 and gate 2 has been wired purposely. Connect data switches to inputs A, B, C, and D. Set switch A to HIGH and B to LOW and switches C and D to HIGH. Place the tip of the logic probe to output E. You should observe that the level there is LOW. The HIGH output of gate 2 has no effect on the output of gate 1. This is because one of gate 1's inputs is HIGH, and the LOW output of gate 3 is pulling the level at the other input of gate 1 down to LOW. Now toggle switch B several times while observing the output at E with the logic probe. You should observe that the output at E toggles also.

Set switches C and D to LOW. Now toggle switch B several times, again monitoring output E with the logic probe. You should observe that the logic probe indicates a constant LOW. Why?

_____

_____

_____

Place the tip of your probe on point F, and toggle switch B several times. You should observe that switch B has no effect on point F. Measure the voltage at point F with the DMM. The voltage at that point should be near the midrange value for a LOW, which is 0.4 V. A typical reading would be about 0.39 V. Remove the short between the outputs of gate 2 and gate 3, and measure the voltage at point F. It should now measure considerably less than 0.4 V, typically 0.10 V. Set switch B to

HIGH and measure the voltage at point F with the DMM. Record this voltage: _____ .

Finally, replace the short between the outputs of gate 2 and gate 3. Place the tip of the logic probe on the output of gate 1 and the tip of the logic pulser on point F. You should note that the logic probe indicates a pulsing output at E. Thus, the logic pulser can overcome a LOW produced by the output of a gate.

4) Refer to Figures 3-17 and 3-18. You will not wire these circuits. In step 3 above, when the output of gate 2 was HIGH, it had no effect on the output of gate 3. Switch B could be toggled, producing a toggling output at E. A short to V_{cc} at point F could not be overcome by the output of gate 3, so point F would be stuck HIGH. Measuring the actual voltage level at point F can help you determine whether or not a circuit node is shorted to V_{cc}, since the outputs of TTL gates are normally lower than V_{cc}. A logic pulser cannot overcome a short to V_{cc}.

If point F measures 0 V, then it is likely that point F is shorted to ground. A logic pulser cannot overcome this type of short either.

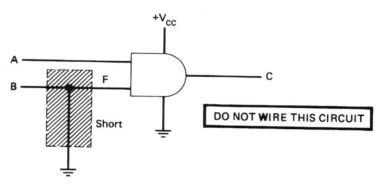

Figure 3-17

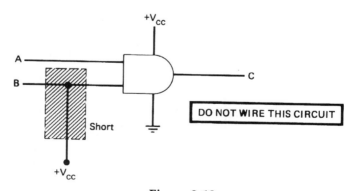

Figure 3-18

5) Refer to Figure 3-19, and wire two 7408 AND gates as shown. Leave points A and B disconnected. We will assume that gate 2 is functioning normally. Place your probe tip on point D. It should indicate a floating level. This is symptomatic of an open in the output circuit of gate 1. The question is whether it is an external or internal open. Place the probe on the output pin of gate 1. If it is HIGH, then there is an external open somewhere between the IC and point C. If the output pin is floating, then an internal open in gate 1's output circuit could be the cause.

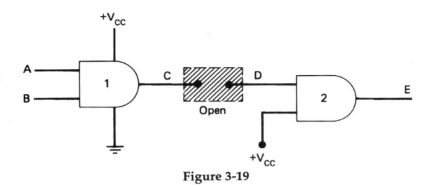

Figure 3-19

NOT Gates

1) Refer to Figure 3-20, and wire a 7404 NOT gate as shown. Connect point A to a data switch, but leave points B and C disconnected. Place the probe tip on point C, and observe that the output is LOW. Toggle the data switch, and observe that it has no effect on the output. Now place the probe tip on point C. You should observe that the level there is floating. This tells you that the input (point C) has either an external open or an internal open. To verify that the open is external, place the pulser tip to point C and the probe tip on point B. You should observe that the probe now indicates a pulsing condition. If the open had been internal, you would still see a LOW at point B.

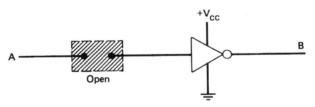

Figure 3-20

2) Refer to Figure 3-21, and wire two 7404 NOT gates as shown. Note that a short between the outputs of the two inverters has been wired purposely. Connect data switches to inputs A and C. Set switch A to HIGH and C to LOW. Place the tip of the logic probe on output B. You should observe that the level there is LOW. The HIGH output of gate 2 has no effect on the output of gate 1. This is because the LOW output of gate 1 is pulling the level of the output of gate 2 down to LOW. Now toggle switch A several times while observing the output at B with the logic probe. You should observe that the output at B toggles also.

Set switch C to HIGH. Now toggle switch A several times, again monitoring output B with the logic probe. You should observe that the logic probe indicates a constant LOW. Why?

_____

_____

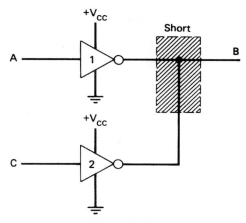

Figure 3-21

Measure the voltage at point B with the DMM. The voltage at that point should be near the midrange value for a LOW, which is 0.4 V. A typical reading would be about 0.39 V. Remove the short between the outputs of gate 1 and gate 2, and measure the voltage at point B. It should now measure considerably less than 0.4 V, typically 0.10 V. Set switch A to LOW and measure the voltage at point B with the DMM. Record this voltage: _____.

Finally, replace the short between the outputs of gate 2 and gate 3. Place the tips of the logic probe and the logic pulser on point C. You should note that the logic probe indicates a pulsing output at E. Thus, the logic pulser can overcome a LOW produced by the output of a gate.

3) Refer to Figures 3-22 and 3-23. Do not wire these circuits. As with the AND and OR gates above, shorts to V_{cc} and ground can be found by making a voltage measurement at the point that is stuck. You should never measure exactly V_{cc} or ground unless there is a short to one or the other.

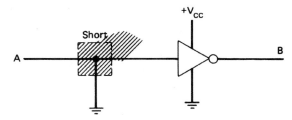

Figure 3-22

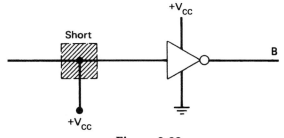

Figure 3-23

Summary

In the preceding exercises, you have learned several techniques for isolating problems in digital systems. These techniques can help you to isolate the problems to a small area in the system. Many times, you will hit it lucky and isolate one or more defective ICs in sockets by using these techniques. Other times, you will isolate several defective ICs that must be desoldered, removed, tested, and then replaced. Since digital systems can contain hundreds of ICs (and thousands of gates!), these techniques are extremely important in the field.

Experiment 5

Name_____

LOGIC GATES II: NOR AND NAND

OBJECTIVES

1. To investigate the behavior of the NOR gate.
2. To investigate the behavior of the NAND gate.

TEXT REFERENCE

Read section 3.9.

EQUIPMENT NEEDED

Components
7400 IC;
7402 IC;
7404 IC;
7408 IC;
7432 IC;
4 toggle switches;
1 LED monitor.

Instruments
0–5 volt DC power supply;
pulse or square wave generator;
oscilloscope.

DISCUSSION

In Experiment 2, you learned the characteristics of three of the fundamental logic gates: the AND, OR, and NOT. You will now be introduced to two of the remaining logic gates: the NAND and NOR. The NAND and NOR gates are nothing more than inverted AND and OR gates, respectively. That is important, but not the most important thing. The fact that a NAND or a NOR can be used to create all other gates is important, because this fact has made them more popular in use than the others.

PROCEDURE

a) *The NOR gate:* Figure 5-1 shows the logic symbol for a two-input NOR gate and its truth table. Examine the truth table, and familiarize yourself with the NOR operation.

b) Refer to the data sheet for a 7402 IC, and draw the pin layout diagram:

c) Mount a 7402 on the circuit board. Connect V_{cc} to +5 V and GND to power ground. Connect toggle switches to inputs A and B of one of the 7402 NOR gates. Observe the output of the gate with an LED monitor.

d) Set the toggle switches to each input combination listed in Table 5-1, observe and record the output state of the LED monitor in the table.

Table 5-1

Data Switch A B	Output LED Monitor (On/Off)	Output Logic Level (0/1)
0 0		
0 1		
1 0		
1 1		

Verify that your results agree with the truth table in Figure 5-1.

e) Disconnect input B from the toggle switch. Set toggle switch A alternately to 0 and 1, and observe the effect on the output. Based on your observations, the disconnected NOR input acts like a ____ input level.

and V_{cc} to an input labelled "1." Monitor the output with one vertical input of the oscilloscope and the pulse generator with the other.

b) Connect the circuit for theorem 1, and observe the output displayed on the oscilloscope. The display should be constant with a level of 0 V. You probably suspect that a circuit like this one could be replaced with a single wire connected to ground, and you would be right. Theorem 1 permits this simplification.

c) Connect the circuit for theorem 2. The output should now be identical to the signal from the pulse generator. Confirm this by comparing the two waveforms on the oscilloscope. It should be plain that this circuit can be replaced by a single wire connected to signal x.

d) Connect the circuit for theorem 3. Again, the output should be identical to the signal from the pulse generator. Verify that this is so. This circuit, like that of theorem 2, can be replaced by a single wire to signal x.

e) Connect the circuit for theorem 4. Observe that the output is constant at 0 V. This circuit can be replaced by a wire to ground.

f) All of the univariate theorems involving AND gates have now been verified. You should now verify the remainder of the theorems, all of which involve OR gates.

g) *Theorem 14*: Figure 7-2 shows the circuit for testing another Boolean theorem, $x + xy = x$. Using $A = C = x$ and $B = y$, connect a toggle switch to input y and the pulse generator to x. Monitor both the pulse generator and the output of

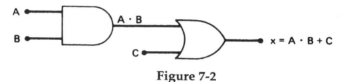

Figure 7-2

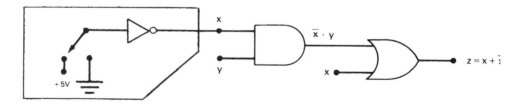

Figure 7-3

this circuit on the oscilloscope. You should observe that the two waveforms are identical.

h) Set switch y alternately to 0 and to 1. Switch y should have no effect on the output. This implies that input y serves no purpose, and since signal x is passed through the circuit unchanged, the entire circuit can be replaced with a single wire connected to x.

i) *Theorem 15*: Modify the circuit on the board by removing the pulse generator connection to the AND gate and inserting an inverter between a toggle switch and the AND gate input just disconnected. The Boolean expression for the new circuit is $x + \bar{x}y$. You are to verify that this circuit is equivalent to an OR gate with x and y as its inputs. Connect an LED monitor to the output of the circuit.

j) Set toggle switches x and y to all the input combinations listed in Table 7-1, and record the output observed in the table.

Compare Table 7-1 with the truth table for an OR gate. They should be identical, which shows that the circuit tested can be replaced by a single OR gate with inputs x and y.

Table 7-1

Input Data Switches		Output LED Monitor (On/Off)	Output Logic Level (0/1)
x	y		
0	0		
0	1		
1	0		
1	1		

k) *Review:* This concludes the experiment on Boolean theorems. To test your understanding of the results of this experiment, complete the following statements:

1. In Experiment 4, enabler and inhibitor circuits were discussed. The Boolean theorem that describes the AND inhibitor is _____.
2. The OR enabler circuit is described by theorem _____.
3. In troubleshooting a circuit containing an AND with one input shorted to LOW, one would discover [a signal, a constant HIGH (stuck-HIGH), a constant LOW (stuck-LOW)] at the output of the gate. The Boolean theorem that explains this is _____.
4. Theorem 6 guarantees a _____ output if an input to an OR gate is shorted to V_{cc}.

Experiment 10

THE UNIVERSALITY OF NAND AND NOR GATES

OBJECTIVES

1. To demonstrate the universality of the NAND gate.
2. To demonstrate the universality of the NOR gate.
3. To construct a logic circuit using all NOR gates.
4. To construct a logic circuit using all NAND gates.

TEXT REFERENCE

Read section 3.12.

EQUIPMENT NEEDED

Components
7400 IC;
7402 IC;
7410 IC;
7427 IC;
3 toggle switches;
1 LED monitor.

Instruments
0–5 volt DC power supply.

DISCUSSION

Most digital circuits consist of combinations of the basic logic gates. In this experiment, you will investigate the use of NAND and NOR gates in constructing digital circuits. You will demonstrate that NAND gates can be used to obtain all the other gates, and, similarly, NOR gates can be used to do the same thing. For example, you will show that an AND gate is simply an inverted NAND or a NOR gate with inverters in its inputs. These simple facts help a designer to design simpler circuits by reducing chip count, and they help a troubleshooter to understand and troubleshoot them.

PROCEDURE

a) Install a 7400 IC on the circuit board. Connect V_{cc} to +5 V and GND to power ground.

b) *NOT from NAND:* Connect the circuit shown on the left side of Figure 10-1(a). Connect a toggle switch to circuit input A and an LED monitor to output x. Verify that the circuit is an inverter by setting the input switch to 0 and then 1 and observing the output LED.

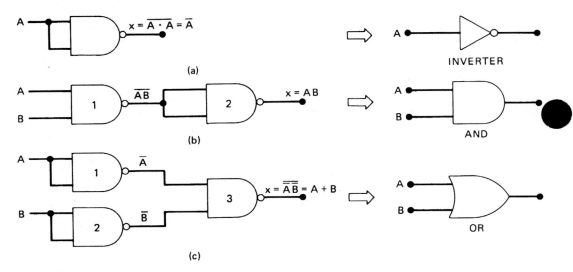

Figure 10-1

c) *AND from NAND:* Connect the circuit on the left side of Figure 10-1(b). Connect toggle switches to circuit inputs A and B. Connect an LED monitor to output x. Verify that the circuit performs the AND function by setting the toggle switches to each set of input combinations in Table 10-1 and observing the output LED monitor. Record your observations in the table.

Table 10-1

Inputs		Output
A	B	X
0	0	
0	1	
1	0	
1	1	

d) *OR from NAND*: Connect the circuit on the left side of Figure 10-1(c). Connect toggle switches to circuit inputs A and B. Connect an LED monitor to output x. Verify that the circuit performs the OR function by setting the toggle switches to each set of inputs in Table 10-2 and observing the output. Record your observations in the table

Table 10-2

Inputs		Output
A	B	X
0	0	
0	1	
1	0	
1	1	

e) Mount a 7402 IC on the circuit board. Connect V_{cc} to +5 V and GND to power ground.

f) *NOT from NOR*: Connect the circuit on the left-hand side of Figure 10-2(a). Connect a toggle switch to circuit input A and an LED monitor to output x. Verify that the circuit is an inverter by setting the input switch to 0 and then to 1 and observing the output.

g) *OR from NOR*: Connect the circuit on the left-hand side of Figure 10-2(b). Connect toggle switches to circuit inputs A and B and an LED monitor to output x. Verify that the circuit performs the OR function by setting the toggle switches to each input combination listed in Table 10-3 and observing the output LED monitor. Record your observations in the table.

Table 10-3

Inputs		Output
A	B	X
0	0	
0	1	
1	0	
1	1	

h) *AND from NOR*: Connect the circuit on the left-hand side of Figure 10-2(c). Connect toggle switches to circuit inputs A and B and an LED monitor to output x. Verify that the circuit performs the AND function by setting the toggle switches to each input combination listed in Table 10-4 and observing the output LED monitor. Record your observations in the table.

Table 10-4

Inputs		Output
A	B	X
0	0	
0	1	
1	0	
1	1	

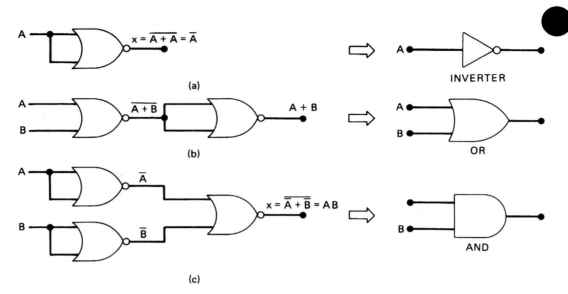

Figure 10-2

i) *Constructing a circuit using all NORs:* Use Table 10-5 to make a truth table for the circuit in Figure 10-3(a). Redraw and construct the circuit in Figure 10-3(a) using only NOR gates.

Table 10-5

Inputs			Output
A	B	C	X
0	0	0	
0	0	1	
0	1	0	
0	1	1	
1	0	0	
1	0	1	
1	1	0	
1	1	1	

Connect toggle switches to circuit inputs A, B, C, and D. Connect an LED monitor to output x. Verify that the circuit is equivalent to the original circuit by setting the toggle switches to each input combination in Table 10-5 and observing the output. Compare the outputs to the corresponding values for x in the truth table.

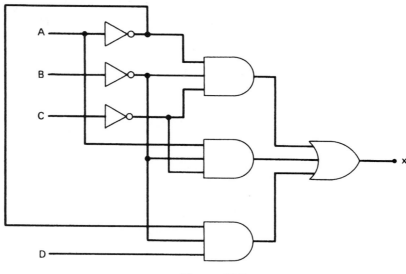

Figure 10-3

j) *Constructing a circuit using all NANDs:* Use Table 10-6 to make a truth table for the circuit in Figure 10-3. Redraw and construct the circuit of Figure 10-3 using only NAND gates.

Connect toggle switches to circuit inputs A, B, C, and D. Connect an LED monitor to output x. Verify that the circuit is equivalent to the original circuit by setting the toggle switches to each input combination in Table 10-6 and observing the output. Compare the outputs to the corresponding values for x in the truth table.

Table 10-6

Inputs				Output
A	B	C	D	X
0	0	0	0	
0	0	0	1	
0	0	1	0	
0	0	1	1	
0	1	0	0	
0	1	0	1	
0	1	1	0	
0	1	1	1	
1	0	0	0	
1	0	0	1	
1	0	1	0	
1	0	1	1	
1	1	0	0	
1	1	0	1	
1	1	1	0	
1	1	1	1	

k) *Review:* This concludes the exercises on the universality of NAND and NOR gates. To test your understanding of the experiment, answer the following questions:

1. Draw a circuit for a NOR gate using all NANDs:

2. Draw a circuit for a NAND gate using all NORs:

Experiment 11

Name_____

IMPLEMENTING LOGIC CIRCUIT DESIGNS

OBJECTIVE

To design and construct logic circuits given either a truth table or a set of statements that describe the circuit's behavior.

TEXT REFERENCES

Read sections 4.1 through 4.4.

EQUIPMENT NEEDED

Components
Selected NAND and/or NOR ICs;
4 toggle switches;
1 LED monitor.

Instruments
0-5 volt DC power supply

DISCUSSION

In this experiment, you are asked to design several combinatorial circuits. A combinatorial circuit is, as the name suggests, a circuit composed of a combination of logic gates. It acts on its inputs and gives an output based on its logic function. A combinatorial circuit can be designed directly from a truth table or from a description of its logic function. In either case, you are called upon to derive the simplest circuit possible. You should ask your instructor which circuits you will be required to build.

PROCEDURE

a) Table 11-1 is a truth table that describes the logic circuit you are to design and construct in this step. Study it carefully, and then draw a logic circuit in the space below using a *minimum* number of logic gates. Show your circuit to the instructor before constructing it. When you have completed the construction, test the circuit and compare your results with the truth table.

Table 11-1

Inputs			Output
A	B	C	X
0	0	0	1
0	0	1	0
0	1	0	1
0	1	1	1
1	0	0	1
1	0	1	0
1	1	0	0
1	1	1	1

b) Design a circuit whose output is HIGH only when a majority of inputs A, B, and C are LOW. Use Table 11-2 to make a truth table for the circuit, then draw a logic diagram that corresponds to the truth table. Show your circuit design to the instructor before constructing it. Test the circuit using the truth table you made for it.

Table 11-2

Inputs			Output
A	B	C	X
0	0	0	1
0	0	1	0
0	1	0	1
0	1	1	1
1	0	0	1
1	0	1	0
1	1	0	0
1	1	1	1

c) Design a logic circuit that has two signal inputs A_0 and A_1 and a control input S so that it functions according to the requirements given in Figure 11-1. This type of circuit is called a *multiplexer* (covered in Experiment 34). Show your circuit design to the instructor before constructing it. Test the completed circuit using the truth table given in Figure 11-1.

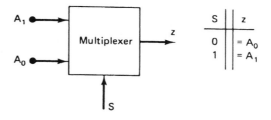

Figure 11-1

d) In step b, you designed a simple majority tester. There are many variations of this problem, one of which is the following:

A board of directors has four members—a president, vice president, a secretary, and a treasurer. In order that voting by the board members never results in a tie, the president is given two votes, and all members must vote. For a motion to carry, three "yes" ("yes" = logic 1; "no" = logic 0) votes are required. Otherwise, the motion fails to carry. Design this tester using all NAND gates.

Experiment 12

Name_____

EXCLUSIVE-OR AND EXCLUSIVE-NOR CIRCUITS

OBJECTIVES

1. To investigate the operation of the exclusive-OR circuit.
2. To investigate the operation of the exclusive-NOR circuit.
3. To investigate the operation of the 7486 quad exclusive-OR IC.

TEXT REFERENCE

Read section 4.6.

EQUIPMENT NEEDED

Components
7400 IC (2);
7486 IC;
2 toggle switches;
1 LED monitor.

Instrument
0–5 volt DC power supply.

DISCUSSION

Two Boolean expressions occur quite frequently in designing combinatorial circuits:

$$1) \ x = \overline{A}B + A\overline{B}$$

and

$$2) \ y = AB + \overline{A} \ \overline{B}$$

Expression 1 defines the Exclusive-OR function to be one that yields an output that is HIGH whenever its inputs are different. Similarly, expression 2 defines the exclusive-NOR function to be one that yields an output that is HIGH whenever its inputs are the same. While these circuits are combinatorial circuits, they have been given their own symbols, and both have been implemented with integrated circuits. In this experiment, you will investigate the behavior of both circuits and the exclusive-OR integrated circuit implementation.

PREPARATION

Part (c) of this experiment requires the student to design a binary comparator circuit. This may take a substantial amount of time to do, and therefore the student is encouraged to do this work prior to the laboratory class for a more efficient use of the laboratory time.

PROCEDURE

a) Figure 12-1(a) shows the sum-of-products circuit for the exclusive-OR function and its associated truth table. The equivalent logic symbol for the circuit is shown in Figure 12-1(b).

b) *Sum-of-products exclusive-OR:* Implement the circuit of Figure 12-1 using all NAND gates. Draw your circuit in the space provided below. Connect toggle switches to circuit inputs A and B. You will monitor the output with an LED monitor. Using Table 12-1, set the toggle switches to each input combination listed, and observe the effect on the circuit output. Record your observations in the output column of the table. Your observations should be the same as those of the truth table in Figure 12-1.

Table 12-1

Inputs		Output
A	B	X
0	0	
0	1	
1	0	
1	1	

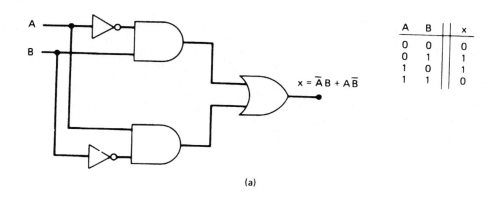

A	B	x
0	0	0
0	1	1
1	0	1
1	1	0

$x = \overline{A}B + A\overline{B}$

(a)

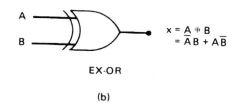

$x = A \oplus B$
$= \overline{A}B + A\overline{B}$

EX-OR

(b)

Figure 12-1

c) *Sum-of-products exclusive-NOR:* Disconnect the monitor from x and reconnect x to an inverter. Connect the monitor to the output of the inverter. The new circuit performs the exclusive-NOR function and is equivalent to the one illustrated in Figure 12-2. Using Table 12-2, verify that this is so by setting the toggle switches to each combination listed and recording the output states that you observe in the table.

Table 12-2

Inputs		Output
A	B	X
0	0	
0	1	
1	0	
1	1	

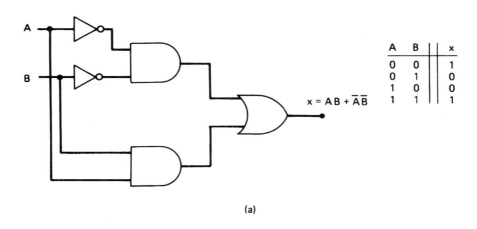

(a)

$$x = \overline{A \oplus B} = AB + \overline{A}\,\overline{B}$$

EX-NOR

(b)

Figure 12-2

d) *7486 IC exclusive-OR:* Refer to the data sheet for a 7486 IC. This IC contains four exclusive-OR circuits. Draw the pin layout diagram for the 7486:

e) Mount a 7486 on the circuit board. Connect V_{cc} to +5 V and GND to power ground. Connect toggle switches to one of the exclusive-OR circuits of the IC, and connect an LED monitor to its output. Using Table 12-3, verify that the circuit performs the exclusive-OR function. Record your observations in the table.

Table 12-3

Inputs		Output
A	B	X
0	0	
0	1	
1	0	
1	1	

f) Disconnect the LED monitor from the output of the 7486 circuit under test, and insert an inverter between the monitor and the circuit. Verify that the new circuit performs the exclusive-NOR function. Use Table 12-4 to record your results.

Table 12-4

Inputs		Output
A	B	X
0	0	
0	1	
1	0	
1	1	

g) You will now demonstrate that the placement of the inverter in steps c and f could just as well have been in one of the inputs in order to obtain the exclusive-NOR function from an exclusive-OR circuit. Remove the inverter added to the 7486 IC circuit in step f, and insert it between the toggle switch and input A. Reconnect the LED monitor to the output of the 7486 circuit under test. Now verify that the circuit still performs the exclusive-NOR function. Record your observations in Table 12-5.

Table 12-5

Inputs		Output
A	B	X
0	0	
0	1	
1	0	
1	1	

h) *Review:* This concludes the investigation of the exclusive-OR and exclusive-NOR circuits. To test your understanding of the circuits, answer the following questions:

1. The exclusive-OR function can be described as a circuit whose output is HIGH only when its two inputs are _____.
2. The exclusive-NOR function can be described as a circuit whose output is HIGH only when its two inputs are _____.
3. A simple application of the exclusive-OR circuit is in the addition of two 1-digit binary numbers. The output of the exclusive-OR is called the SUM bit. However, the exclusive-OR cannot always indicate the true sum since the circuit cannot indicate the carry that results in the case of $1 + 1$. Design a circuit which can add any two 1-bit numbers and indicate both the sum and carry of such an addition. This circuit will have two inputs and two outputs. It is called a *half adder*.
4. Use Boolean algebra to prove the results obtained in step g.

Name _____

DESIGNING WITH EXCLUSIVE-OR AND EXCLUSIVE-NOR CIRCUITS

OBJECTIVES

1. To investigate the application of an exclusive-OR circuit in a parity generator circuit.
2. To investigate the application of an exclusive-OR as a controlled inverter.
3. To investigate the application of an exclusive-NOR circuit in a digital comparator circuit.

TEXT REFERENCE

Read section 4.6.

EQUIPMENT NEEDED

Components
7404 IC (2);
7408 IC (2);
7411 IC;
7427 IC;
7486 IC (2);
6 toggle switches;
3 LED monitors.

Instruments
0–5 volt DC power supply;
pulse or square wave generator;
dual trace oscilloscope.

DISCUSSION

In the previous experiment, you were introduced to the exclusive-OR and exclusive-NOR circuits. You discovered that these circuits can be used to compare the level of two inputs. Indeed, the exclusive-OR and exclusive-NOR are basically digital comparators. In the current experiment, you will design several circuits using the exclusive-OR and exclusive-NOR circuits. In practice, you will probably invert an exclusive-OR to get an exclusive-NOR, since the common TTL IC implementation of the exclusive-NOR (74LS266) requires special output wiring and is used in very special applications.

PROCEDURE

a) *Parity generator application:* Design a four-bit even parity generator that uses exclusive-OR circuits. This circuit should have four inputs and an output that is HIGH only when an odd number of inputs are HIGH. Use Table 13-1 to make a truth table for the circuit. Draw your logic circuit in the space provided below. Have your instructor approve the circuit design before you construct and test it.

b) *Controlled inverter application:* Disassemble the circuit of step a except for a single 7486 IC. Connect the output of the square wave generator to one input of a 7486 exclusive-OR circuit. Connect a toggle switch to the other input. Monitor both the generator output and the output of the exclusive-OR with the dual trace oscilloscope. Trigger the oscilloscope on the generator output. Set the toggle switch to LOW, and observe the relationship between the two waveforms. They should be the same. Now set the toggle switch to HIGH, and observe the relationship between the two waveforms. Compare the two waveforms.

Table 13-1

Inputs				Output
A	B	C	D	X
0	0	0	0	
0	0	0	1	
0	0	1	0	
0	0	1	1	
0	1	0	0	
0	1	0	1	
0	1	1	0	
0	1	1	1	
1	0	0	0	
1	0	0	1	
1	0	1	0	
1	0	1	1	
1	1	0	0	
1	1	0	1	
1	1	1	0	
1	1	1	1	

c) *Binary comparator application:* Figure 13-1 represents a three-bit relative magnitude detector that determines if two numbers are equal and, if not, which number is larger. There are three inputs, defined as follows:

1) $M = 1$ only if the two input numbers are equal.
2) $N = 1$ only if $X_2 X_1 X_0$ is greater than $Y_2 Y_1 Y_0$.
3) $P = 1$ only if $Y_2 Y_1 Y_0$ is greater than $X_2 X_1 X_0$.

Design the circuit for the detector. Since the circuit is too complex to use a truth table, you might want to refer to Example 4.16 in the text to get an idea about how to get started. Draw your logic diagram in the space provided. Show the circuit to your instructor before constructing and testing the circuit.

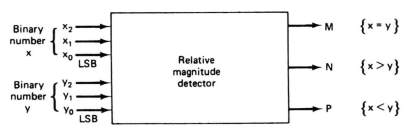

Figure 13-1

    d) *Review:* This concludes the investigation of exclusive-OR and exclusive-NOR applications. To test your understanding of this experiment, answer the following questions:

1. How would you modify the even parity generator circuit you designed to produce an *odd* parity generator?

2. If a signal is applied to input A of an exclusive-OR gate and input B is controlled with a toggle switch, then whenever input B is HIGH, the output is [A, $\overline{A}$, 1, 0]. When B is LOW, the output is [A, $\overline{A}$, 1, 0].

3. The exclusive-OR circuit may be used to simplify some sum-of-products designs. Give an example of this.

TROUBLESHOOTING EXCLUSIVE-OR AND COMBINATORIAL CIRCUITS

OBJECTIVES

1. Troubleshoot 7486 IC faults.
2. Troubleshoot combinatorial circuits.

TEXT REFERENCES

Read sections 4.6 and 4.9 to 4.13. Also read Appendix A of this manual, and review Experiment 3.

EQUIPMENT NEEDED

Components
7486 IC;
2 toggle (spdt) switches.

Instruments
0–5 volt DC power supply;
logic pulser;
logic probe.

DISCUSSION

In Experiment 3, you learned how to troubleshoot the basic gates. You repeated this exercise in Experiment 6 with NAND and NOR gates. Before proceeding to troubleshoot combinations of these gates, you should spend a few minutes learning to troubleshoot the exclusive-OR, since it is found in many digital applications. Since the IC faults of the 7486 are isolated by using the techniques developed in the earlier troubleshooting exercises, we will concentrate on the faults that produce symptoms peculiar to the exclusive-OR circuit. You will then be asked to troubleshoot a combination circuit using the procedures found in this lab manual and the text.

PROCEDURE

a) Refer to Figure 14-1, and wire a 7486 EX-OR gate as shown. Recall that when the inputs to an EX-OR gate are both the same, the output is LOW. Therefore, if the output of an EX-OR appears to be stuck LOW, one possible trouble might be shorted inputs. Touch the probe tip to one of the inputs and the pulser to the other input. You should observe that the pulsing on one of the inputs is detected by the probe on the other. This indicates a short in the EX-OR's inputs.

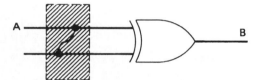

Figure 14-1

b) Refer to Figure 14-2, and wire a 7486 EX-OR gate as shown. Connect point A to a data switch and set the switch HIGH, but leave points B and C disconnected. Place the probe tip on point C, and observe that the output is LOW. Toggle the data switch, and observe that the output is always the inverse of the level at A. If the EX-OR is connected as a controlled inverter, this gate would be behaving properly. Now place the probe tip on point D. You should observe that the level there is floating. This tells you that the input (point D) is open. To verify that the open is external, place the pulser tip on point D and the probe tip on point C. Set the data switch at A to LOW. You should observe that the probe now indicates a pulsing condition. (If the open had been internal, you would still see a LOW at point C. You would also not detect a floating condition at the suspect input's pin.)

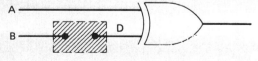

Figure 14-2

c) *Troubleshooting combinatorial circuits*:

1) Tear off the circuit diagram (Figure 14-2) and study it carefully, including the notes in the lower right-hand corner. Note the following:

- D, C, B, and A are inputs to the logic circuit.

- Each IC is identified as Z1, Z2, etc. Logic gates with the same Z number are on the same IC chip. For example, the two NAND gates labeled "Z4" are on the same 7400 NAND gate chip.

- The numbers on each logic gate input and output are pin numbers on the IC chip.

- The "balloons" TP1, TP2, etc., indicate test points that will be checked during testing or troubleshooting.

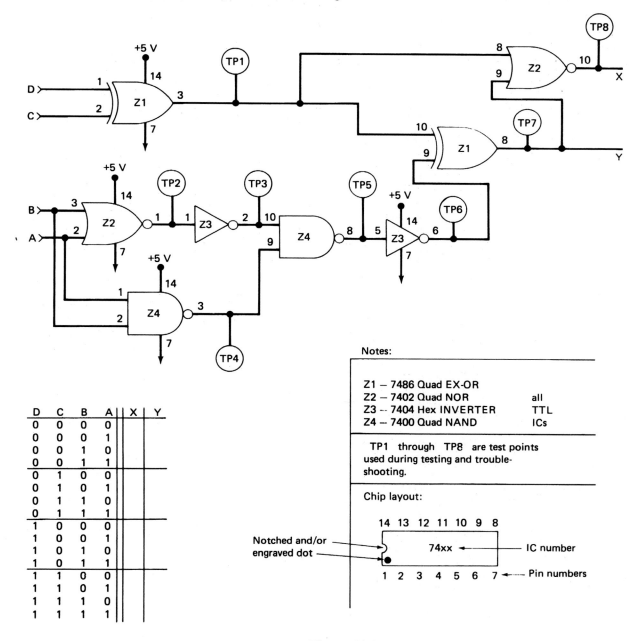

D	C	B	A	X	Y
0	0	0	0		
0	0	0	1		
0	0	1	0		
0	0	1	1		
0	1	0	0		
0	1	0	1		
0	1	1	0		
0	1	1	1		
1	0	0	0		
1	0	0	1		
1	0	1	0		
1	0	1	1		
1	1	0	0		
1	1	0	1		
1	1	1	0		
1	1	1	1		

Notes:

Z1 — 7486 Quad EX-OR
Z2 — 7402 Quad NOR   all
Z3 -- 7404 Hex INVERTER   TTL
Z4 — 7400 Quad NAND   ICs

TP1 through TP8 are test points used during testing and trouble-shooting.

Chip layout:

14 13 12 11 10 9 8

Notched and/or engraved dot

74xx   IC number

1 2 3 4 5 6 7 ← Pin numbers

Figure 14-3

2) The four ICs used in this circuit should be inserted into the circuit board with a left-to-right orientation (i.e., Z1 on the left, then Z2 and Z3, with Z4 on the right). Wire the circuit according to Figure 14-3.

3) Connect inputs A, B, C, and D to toggle switches. Use your logic probe to test the circuit operation by trying each of the 16 input conditions and monitoring the outputs X and Y with the logic probe.

4) If the results do not match your predicted values, you will have to troubleshoot your circuit by following the logic levels through the circuit, starting at the inputs. Use your logic probe and pulser to locate the fault.

5) Once the circuit is operating normally, have your instructor or lab assistant introduce a fault, then use your troubleshooting procedure to locate this fault.

6) Repeat step 5 as frequently as time permits.

Name _____

FLIP-FLOPS I: SET/CLEAR LATCHES AND CLOCKED FLIP-FLOPS

OBJECTIVES

1. To investigate the operation of the NOR gate SET/CLEAR latch.
2. To investigate the operation of the NAND gate SET/CLEAR latch.
3. To investigate the operation of an edge-triggered J-K flip-flop, the 74LS76 IC.
4. To investigate the operation of an edge-triggered D flip-flop, the 7474 IC.

TEXT REFERENCES

Read sections 5.1, 5.2, 5.4 through 5.7, and 5.9.

EQUIPMENT NEEDED

Components
7400 IC (2);
7402 IC (2);
7474 IC;
74LS76 IC;
normally HIGH pushbutton switch (2) and normally LOW pushbutton switch (2), all debounced;
2 LED monitors.

Instruments
0–5 volt DC power supply;
pulse or square wave generator;
dual trace oscilloscope;
logic probe (optional).

DISCUSSION

All of the previous experiments have been concerned with learning the fundamentals of logic gates and combinatorial circuits. Recall that an output of such a device or circuit responds to changes in its inputs and that when its inputs are removed, the output may not be sustained. In this experiment, you will be introduced to a device that can sustain a given output even when its inputs are removed. Such a device is said to possess memory. Examples of memory devices include flip-flops, which are the topic for this experiment. The following classes of flip-flops are investigated in this experiment:

- SET/CLEAR latches
- Edge-triggered J-K flip-flops
- Edge-triggered D flip-flops

SET/CLEAR Latches

The most fundamental flip-flop is the SET/CLEAR latch. Two types of SET/CLEAR latches are investigated in the current experiment:

- NAND gate SET/CLEAR latch
- NOR gate SET/CLEAR latch

The input levels to these devices determine the outputs. SET/CLEAR latches do not have a clock input, and so they are said to operate *asynchronously*.

Edge-Triggered J-K Flip-Flops

The J-K flip-flop eliminates the ambiguous condition. In place of this invalid condition, the J-K has a "toggle" condition, a characteristic of this flip-flop. Normally, a J-K flip-flop can be operated synchronously, since its J and K inputs need a separate clock to cause the flip-flop to change states. A J-K flip-flop can also be operated asynchronously and have SET and CLEAR inputs to facilitate this.

Edge-Triggered D Flip-Flops

The D flip-flop is a J-K flip-flop with an inverter between the J and the K inputs. This causes the flip-flop to SET or CLEAR with only one synchronous signal input. Like the J-K flip-flop, the D flip-flop also has an asynchronous mode.

PROCEDURE

a) *NOR gate SET/CLEAR latch:* Examine closely and then wire the NOR gate latch shown in Figure 15-1. Connect normally LOW pushbutton switches to the CLEAR and SET inputs to the circuit. You will monitor circuit outputs Q and $\overline{Q}$ with LED monitors.

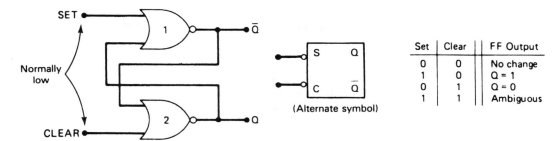

Figure 15-1

b) Turn the power supply on, and note the states of both LEDs: Q = _____;
$\overline{Q}$ = _____.

Predicting the states of a latch when power is first applied is impossible, so
the values just recorded are random.

Clear Q by momentarily pulsing the CLEAR input HIGH. If Q is already
HIGH, pulsing the CLEAR input will have no effect on the circuit.

c) Pulse the SET input HIGH, and observe the effects on the circuit outputs:
Q = _____; $\overline{Q}$ = _____.

Note that releasing the pushbutton does not cause Q to change from its new
state. Why? _____.

Now pulse the SET input HIGH again. What effect does this have on the
circuit outputs? _____.

d) Pulse the CLEAR input HIGH, and observe that Q changes back to LOW
and stays LOW even after the pushbutton is released.

e) Alternately pulse the SET and CLEAR inputs HIGH several times. Note
that the outputs are always at opposite states.

f) Press and hold the SET and CLEAR inputs HIGH at the same time. Note
that both outputs are now LOW. Release the pushbuttons, and note the states of
the outputs. Are they both still LOW? _____.

Now pulse both SET and CLEAR inputs simultaneously several times, and
note the effects on the outputs. If you pulse the circuit in this manner enough times,
you will probably get random results. This is because the circuit response to this
input condition is unpredictable.

g) *NAND gate SET/CLEAR latch:* Examine closely and then wire the NAND
gate SET/CLEAR latch shown in Figure 15-2. Connect normally HIGH pushbutton
switches to the SET and CLEAR inputs of the circuit.

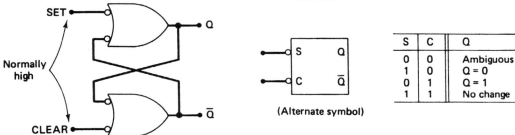

Figure 15-2

h) Turn the power supply on. Pulse the SET input LOW, and verify that Q is HIGH and $\overline{Q}$ is LOW. Now pulse the CLEAR input LOW, and observe that the latch is cleared (Q = 0) and stays cleared even after the pushbutton is released.

i) Alternately pulse the SET and CLEAR inputs LOW several times. Observe that the outputs are always at opposite states.

j) Pulse both SET and CLEAR inputs LOW simultaneously, and observe the effects on the circuit outputs.

k) *Edge-triggered J-K flip-flop—74LS76 IC:* Refer to the data sheet for a 7476 IC. Note that there are three versions of this flip-flop: the 7476 and the 74H76 dual pulse-triggered master/slave J-K, and the 74LS76 dual edge-triggered J-K. The pin layout diagram given by the data sheet is the same for all three, but the operation of the edge-triggered and pulse-triggered versions are slightly different. You will test a 7476 IC in Experiment 16.

Draw the pin layout diagram for the 74LS76 IC:

Install a 74LS76 IC on the circuit board, and make the following connections:

1) Connect V_{cc} and DC SET to +5 V, GND to power ground.
2) Connect toggle switches to J and K inputs.
3) Connect a normally LOW pushbutton switch to the clock (CLK) input.
4) Connect a normally HIGH pushbutton switch to DC CLEAR.
5) Connect LED monitors to outputs Q and $\overline{Q}$ (or use a logic probe to monitor the outputs).

Turn the power supply on, and observe the states of Q and $\overline{Q}$. If Q = 1, then pulse DC CLEAR momentarily LOW. Note that this input clears the flip-flop immediately without a clock signal and that the input is active LOW.

l) *74LS76 synchronous operation:* In this step, you will observe that the J and K inputs can be used to change the output state of the flip-flop. You will also observe that in order for these inputs to effect a change, a clock pulse must be applied. For this reason, the J , K, and CLK inputs are referred to as *synchronous* inputs. Verify this by performing the following steps:

1) Change the J and K input switch settings, and observe that nothing happens to Q.
2) Set J = 1 and K = 1, and apply a positive-going transition at CLK. Do this by pressing and holding the CLK pushbutton switch. What happens to Q?_____.

3) Repeat step 2 using a negative-going transition at CLK. Do this by releasing the pushbutton switch. What happens to Q? _____. This proves that the flip-flop responds to only negative-going transitions. Apply several more pulses to the CLK input. What happens? _____.

4) If Q is LOW, pulse the CLK input so that Q is HIGH. Set J = K = 0, and note that nothing happens to Q. Pulse the CLK input momentarily, and observe that nothing happens to Q. Why?

_____

5) Set J = 0 and K = 1, and note that nothing happens to Q. Pulse the CLK input momentarily. What happens to Q?

_____

Apply several more pulses to the CLK input, and observe that Q remains in the LOW state.

6) Change J to 1 and then back to 0, and note that nothing happens to Q. Pulse the CLK input momentarily. You should observe that Q remains LOW. This proves that the J and K input states present *at the time of the proper clock transition* are the ones transferred to the flip-flop output.

7) Set J = 1, K = 0. Note that nothing happens to Q. Apply a clock pulse, and observe that Q will go HIGH. Apply several more clock pulses. What happens to Q?

_____

m) Disconnect the pushbutton switch at the CLK input, and replace it with the output of a square wave generator set to 1 MHz (or the highest frequency obtainable). Connect the oscilloscope to observe the clock signal and output Q. Draw the waveforms displayed on the oscilloscope on Timing Diagram 15-1.

Verify that the flip-flop changes states on the negative-going transitions and does not change states on the positive-going transitions. What is the frequency of the Q waveform compared to the clock waveform? _____.

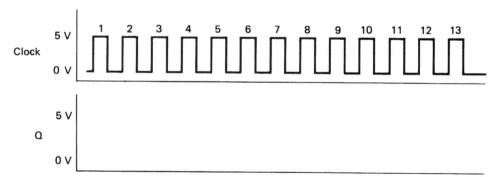

Timing Diagram 15-1

n) *74LS76 asynchronous operation:* The DC SET and DC CLEAR inputs are *asynchronous* inputs that operate independently from the synchronous inputs (J, K, CLK). The asynchronous inputs *override* the synchronous inputs when activated. Verify this by holding the DC CLEAR input LOW and observe that the flip-flop output stops toggling even though clock pulses are still being applied. Q will remain LOW, until the first clock pulse after the DC CLEAR pushbutton is released.

o) Disconnect the jumper connection from DC SET to V_{cc} at the V_{cc} end only, and touch this wire to ground. You should now observe that the flip-flop output stops toggling and remains HIGH as long as DC SET is held LOW.

p) *Edge-triggered D flip-flop—7474 IC:* Refer to the data sheet for a 7474 IC, and draw its pin layout diagram:

The 7474 IC has two individual positive edge-triggered D flip-flops with separate clock inputs and DC SET and DC CLEAR inputs.

Install a 7474 IC on the circuit board, and make the following connections to one of the D flip-flops:

1) Connect V_{cc} and DC SET to +5 V, GND to power ground.
2) Connect a toggle switch to the D input.
3) Connect a normally HIGH pushbutton switch to the CLK input.
4) Connect a normally HIGH pushbutton switch to DC CLEAR.
5) Connect LED monitors to Q and $\overline{Q}$ (or monitor the outputs with a logic probe).

q) *7474 synchronous operation:* Apply power and monitor the Q output. Observe that nothing happens when you toggle the D input switch back and forth. This is because the D input is a synchronous input that operates with the CLK input.

Clear Q to 0 by momentarily pulsing the DC CLEAR input LOW. Set D to 1, and apply a negative-going transition at CLK. Do this by pressing and holding the CLK pushbutton LOW. What happens to Q?

_____

Now apply a positive-going pulse at CLK by releasing the pushbutton switch. What happens? _____. This proves that the flip-flop responds only to positive-going transitions.

Make D = 0, and pulse CLK momentarily. This should clear Q back to 0.

r) *7474 asynchronous operation:* For both DC SET and DC CLEAR, verify the following:

1) The inputs are active LOW and do not require a pulse at CLK to become activated.
2) The inputs override the synchronous input signals.

s) *Review:* This concludes the first set of exercises on flip-flops and latches. In Experiment 16, you will continue your investigation of latches and flip-flops with D latches and master/slave flip-flops. To test your understanding of the principles demonstrated in this experiment, answer the following questions:

1. The Q output of a NAND gate latch can change from 1 to 0 only when S = _____ and C = _____, while a NOR gate latch can change from 1 to 0 only when S = _____ and C = _____.
2. The CLEAR conditions for a NAND gate latch are S = _____ and C = _____, while the CLEAR conditions for a NOR gate latch are S = _____ and C = _____.
3. The J and K input levels of a 74LS76 J-K flip-flop are transferred to the Q and $\overline{Q}$ outputs on the _____ at CLK.
4. The DC SET and DC CLEAR inputs to a 74LS76 J-K flip-flop are active _____ inputs and [operate with, operate independently from] the CLK signal.
5. The D input level of a 7474 D flip-flop is transferred to the Q output of the flip-flop on the _____ at CLK.

FLIP-FLOPS II: D LATCH; MASTER/SLAVE FLIP-FLOPS

OBJECTIVES

1. To investigate the operation of a D latch, the 7475 IC.
2. To investigate the operation of a master/slave flip-flop, the 7476 IC.
3. To investigate the operation of a master/slave flip-flop with data lock-out, the 74111 IC.

TEXT REFERENCES

Read sections 5.8, 5.9, and 5.13.

EQUIPMENT NEEDED

Components
7475 IC;
~~7476~~ IC; 74112
74111 IC;
normally HIGH pushbutton switch and normally LOW pushbutton switch, both debounced;
2 LED monitors.

Instruments
0–5 volt DC power supply;
logic probe (optional).

DISCUSSION

In this experiment, you are to investigate the behavior of the 7475 D-latch and master/slave flip-flops. The D latch is level-triggered and is frequently used to interface one processing unit with another. You will be asked to compare this flip-flop with the 7474 D flip-flop you examined in Experiment 15. Also in Experiment 15, you investigated edge-triggered flip-flops. Recall that these flip-flops have set-up and hold times that must be satisfied if the circuits which employ them are to work properly. In this experiment, you will examine the 7476 and 74111 J-K flip-flops. Both of these flip-flops have a set-up time of zero. But you will also discover that the 7476 is susceptible to input glitches and that the 74111 uses a data lockout feature to reduce its susceptibility to glitches. While master/slave flip-flops are still being used, they are being replaced in newer equipment with improved edge-triggered flip-flops.

PROCEDURE

a) *7475 IC D latch operation*: Refer to the data sheet for a 7475 IC, and draw its pin layout diagram:

Note that the 7475 has four D latches. The latch CLK inputs are tied together in pairs resulting in dual two-bit D latches. You will use only one of the D latches for this experiment, so examine Figure 16-1 closely for the proper connections to be made.

b) Install a 7475 IC on the circuit board, and make the connections shown in Figure 16-1. Connect a toggle switch to D_1, a normally LOW pushbutton switch to CLK, and LED monitors to Q_1 and $\overline{Q}_1$. When the circuit is completed, perform the following steps:

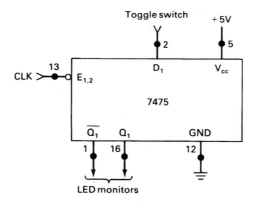

Figure 16-1

1) Turn the power supply on and monitor the outputs of the latch. Change the toggle switch back and forth a few times, and note that there is no effect on Q_1. This is because the latch is in the latch mode, and the data inputs are not enabled. Set $D_1 = 0$.
2) Press and hold the CLK input HIGH. Observe that Q_1 is LOW. Change D_1 back and forth a few times. What happens to Q_1? _____.
   Now set $D_1 = 1$, and release the CLK pushbutton. What happens to Q_1?

   _____

3) Change D_1 back and forth several times. Observe that Q_1 does not change. This proves that the data at D_1 is *latched* on the negative-going transition of the clock signal and that the output at Q_1 *follows* the data at D_1 while the clock signal is HIGH.

   c) *7476 master/slave J-K flip-flop operation*: The 7476 IC is identical to the 74LS76 IC that was tested in Experiment 15, except that the flip-flop circuits are pulse-triggered instead of edge-triggered. This will permit you to observe the differences between edge-triggered flip-flops and master/slave flip-flops.

   Install a 7476 IC on the circuit board, and make the following connections to one of the J-K flip-flops:

1) Connect V_{cc} and DC SET to +5 V, GND to power ground.
2) Connect toggle switches to the J and K inputs.
3) Connect a normally LOW pushbutton to CLK.
4) Connect a normally HIGH pushbutton switch to DC CLEAR.
5) Connect LED monitors to Q and $\overline{Q}$ (or monitor the outputs with a logic probe).

   d) *7476 synchronous operation*: To test the synchronous operation of the 7476, do the following steps:

1) Set J = 1 and K = 0. Turn the power on and note the states of Q and $\overline{Q}$. If the flip-flop is not cleared (Q = 0), then pulse the DC CLEAR input LOW momentarily.
2) Press and hold the CLK input HIGH. You should observe that this has no effect on the outputs. Now release the pushbutton. What happens to Q?

   _____

Pulse the CLK input several more times, and note that this has no effect on the outputs.
3) Change J to 0. Note that this has no effect on the outputs. Pulse the CLK input several times. You should observe that this also has no effect on the outputs. Why?

   _____

4) Change K to 1, and note that Q does not change. Press and hold the CLK input HIGH. What happens to Q? _____. Now release the CLK pushbutton. What happens to Q now?

   _____

Pulse the CLK input several more times, and note that Q does not change.

5) Change J to 1. Note that Q remains LOW. Press and hold the CLK
pushbutton HIGH. What happens to Q? _____.
Release the pushbutton. What happens to Q now? _____.
Pulse the CLK input several more times. You should observe that Q changes
states on each CLK pulse.

---

e) In step d, you should have observed that the flip-flop loaded the J and K
inputs only when the CLK is HIGH, and they were transferred to Q and $\overline{Q}$ on a
negative-going transition at CLK. Now you will observe the chief disadvantage of
the master/slave: data at the J and K inputs can affect the flip-flop outputs any time
while the CLK input is HIGH.

Set J = 0 and K = 1. Clear the flip-flop by momentarily pulsing DC CLEAR
to LOW. Press and hold the CLK pushbutton HIGH. Change J to 1 and then back
to 0. Now release the pushbutton. You should observe that Q changes to 1 even
though J = 0 and K = 1 at the time of the negative-going transition. This demonstrates
that, should an unwanted glitch or noise spike occur on J or K while the CLK input
is HIGH, it may cause the flip-flop outputs to be invalid when CLK goes LOW.

f) *7476 asynchronous operation:* The DC SET and DC CLEAR inputs to the
7476 operate in the same manner as the asynchronous inputs of the 74LS76. Verify
that this is so.

g) *74111 master/slave J-K flip-flop operation:* Refer to the data sheet for a 74111
IC, and draw its pin layout diagram:

Note that this IC has dual J-K flip-flops similar to the 7476. However, the two
ICs are not pin compatible, and the 74111 has the data lockout feature. It is this
feature that we need to investigate.

Install a 74111 on the circuit board, and make the following connections to
one of the flip-flops:

1) Connect V_{cc} and DC SET to +5 V, GND to power ground.
2) Connect toggle switches to the J and K inputs.
3) Connect a normally LOW pushbutton switch to CLK.
4) Connect a normally HIGH pushbutton switch to DC CLEAR.
5) Connect LED monitors to Q and $\overline{Q}$ (or monitor the outputs with a logic
probe).

Verify that the flip-flop operates according to its state table by repeating step
d above.

Set J = 0 and K = 1. Clear the flip-flop by momentarily pulsing DC CLEAR to LOW. Press and hold the CLK pushbutton HIGH. Change J to 1 and then back to 0. Now release the CLK pushbutton. You should observe that Q does not change. How does this differ from the 7476? _____.
Does this demonstrate that the 74111 J-K flip-flop is not susceptible to glitches while the clock is HIGH? _____.

h) *Review:* This concludes the exercises on flip-flops. To test your understanding of the principles covered in this experiment, answer the following questions:

1. The data input of a 7475 D latch is enabled when the CLK input is _____.
   The data present at the D input is latched to the output when

   _____.

2. A 7476 J-K flip-flop transfers the data at the J and K inputs to Q and $\overline{Q}$ when

   _____.

3. Based on your observations, explain how a single 7475 D latch operates differently from a 7474 D flip-flop.

4. Based on your observations, explain how a 7476 J-K flip-flop operates differently from a 74LS76 J-K flip-flop.

5. Discuss how the data lockout feature works.

Experiment 17

Name _____

SCHMITT TRIGGERS, ONE-SHOTS, AND ASTABLE MULTIVIBRATORS

OBJECTIVES

1. To investigate the operation of a 7414 IC Schmitt trigger inverter.
2. To investigate the operation of a 74121 IC nonretriggerable one-shot (OS) multivibrator.
3. To investigate the application of the one-shot multivibrator in timing and control circuits.
4. To investigate the operation of a 555 IC timer in the astable mode.

TEXT REFERENCES

Read sections 5.20, 5.21, and 5.23.

EQUIPMENT NEEDED

Components
555 IC;
7400 IC;
7414 IC;
74121 IC (2);
1N914 diode (2);
normally LOW pushbutton switch (2);
100 µF capacitor;

0.01 µF capacitor;
680 pF capacitor;
6.8 k-ohm resistor;
10 k-ohm resistor;
33 k-ohm resistor;
student-selected resistors and capacitors;
2 LED monitors.

Instruments
0–5 volt DC power supply;
12.6 VAC power supply;
pulse or square wave generator;
dual trace oscilloscope.

DISCUSSION

In Experiments 15 and 16, you investigated the behavior of flip-flop or bistable devices. In the current experiment, you will turn your attention briefly to devices that are somewhat related to flip-flops: the Schmitt trigger, one-shot, and astable multivibrator.

Schmitt Trigger

When logic circuit inputs have slow rise or fall times, the circuits can fail to operate correctly. For this reason, devices are necessary to square up the incoming signals. One device is the Schmitt trigger, whose symbol and response is shown in Figure 17-1. Note that as the input waveform exceeds the positive-going threshold, V_{t+}, the output changes from HIGH to LOW. Once the output goes LOW, it stays there even after the input drops back below V_{t+}. The input must drop below V_{t-}, the negative-going threshold voltage, before the output can change from LOW to HIGH. In the current experiment, you will demonstrate that a 74LS14 Schmitt trigger may be used to produce a clock signal from a sine wave source.

One-Shots

A one-shot (OS) is a monostable device, that is, a device with one stable state. It may be triggered by an input signal to switch to the opposite states, at which it will remain for a fixed amount of time, usually dependent on some external RC time constant. After the fixed time has elapsed, the one-shot returns to its stable state. You will investigate the behavior of the 74121 IC one-shot.

Astable Multivibrators

Astable multivibrators have no stable state. Instead, they can be wired to oscillate and produce clock signals. One popular IC that can be wired as an astable multivibrator is the 555 timer, which you will investigate in the current experiment.

PROCEDURE

      a) *7414 Schmitt trigger inverter operation:* Refer to the data sheet for a 7414 IC, and draw its pin layout diagram:

      b) Construct the circuit illustrated in Figure 17-1. Make sure that the protective diodes D1 and D2 are connected properly before applying power.

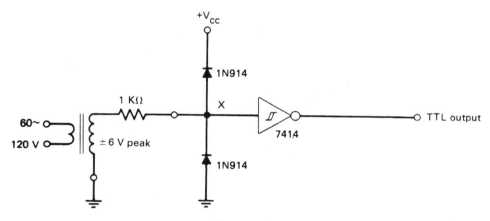

Figure 17-1

      c) Connect one vertical input of the oscilloscope to point "x" of the circuit and the other vertical input to the TTL output. Apply power and adjust the oscilloscope for a few cycles' display. With the vertical position controls, superimpose the two waveforms on one another. Be sure to keep the vertical gain of the two inputs the same. Draw the resulting oscilloscope display using Timing Diagram 17-1.

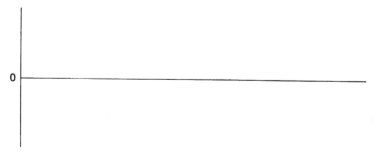

Timing Diagram 17-1

d) Estimate the values of the two threshold points:

$$V_{t+} = \text{_____}$$

$$V_{t-} = \text{_____}$$

Look up the values for V_{t+} and V_{t-} given on the data sheet for the 7414 and compare these values to your estimated values.

e) Refer to the data sheet for a 74121 IC, and draw its pin layout diagram:

The 74121 IC is a one-shot circuit that is complete except for an external timing capacitor, the value of which may be as large as 1000 µF. The 74121 has an internal timing resistor, which has a nominal value of 2 k-ohm. This resistor is effective when pin 9 is connected to V_{cc}. An external resistor (2 k-ohm to 40 k-ohm) may be used by connecting the resistor between pin 11 and V_{cc}, bypassing the internal resistor.

f) *74121 IC operation:* Install a 74121 IC on the circuit board. Connect V_{cc} to +5 V and GND to power ground.

You are to bypass the 2 k-ohm internal resistor of the 74121 and use an external resistor. Using the formula

$$T_p = 0.7R_tC_t$$

compute T_p if R_t = 33 k-ohm and C_t = 100 µF: _____ seconds.

g) Connect R_t and C_t to the 74121. Connect a normally LOW pushbutton switch to input B of the 74121. Connect A_1 and A_2 to LOW. Connect LED monitors to Q and $\overline{Q}$ of the 74121.

h) Turn the power supply on. Note that Q = 0 and $\overline{Q}$ = 1. Pulse input B HIGH, and observe that the outputs have changed states. In a time approximately equal to that computed in step b above, the outputs should return to their original states. When Q has returned to 0, pulse input B repeatedly several times. You should observe that once Q has changed to 1, the OS does not respond to any more triggering until Q returns to 0.

i) Disconnect the pushbutton switch from input B, and replace it with the output of a square wave generator. Change R_t and C_t so that T_p = 5 milliseconds (close as possible). Remember that R_t can range from 2 to 40 k-ohm, and C_t can be as large as 1000 µF. Use a x10 probe, and connect one vertical input of the oscilloscope to output Q of the OS. Connect the output of the generator to the other vertical input. Trigger the oscilloscope on the positive-going transition of the square wave signal. Set the generator to 50 Hz. Draw the waveforms displayed on the oscilloscope using Timing Diagram 17-2.

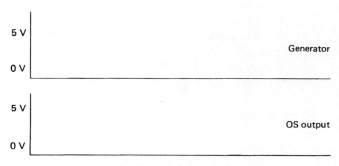

Timing Diagram 17-2

Change the generator frequency to 1 kHz. What effect does this have on the frequency of the OS output? _____. Does the pulse width of the OS output change? _____.

j) *Using one-shots to delay a pulse:* In this step, you will cascade another one-shot to the circuit of the first one-shot already on the circuit board. The purpose of this circuit is to produce a pulse that is *delayed* (with respect to the generator signal) by an amount of time that is approximately equal to the T_p of the first OS (5 m sec). The width of the delayed pulse will be approximately equal to the T_p of the second OS. For this exercise, you will use a T_p of 1 millisecond for the second OS.

Install another 74121 IC on the circuit board. Connect V_{cc} to +5 V and GND to power ground. You will cascade the second OS (OS2) to the first (OS1). Choose R_t and C_t so that T_p = 1 millisecond. Connect inputs A_1 and A_2 to ground and the B input to the Q output of OS1. Monitor the output of the generator, which is set to 50 Hz, and the output of OS2 with the dual trace oscilloscope. Draw the waveforms displayed, using Timing Diagram 17-3.

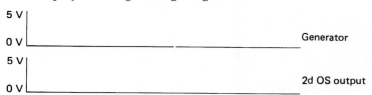

Timing Diagram 17-3

k) *555 IC timer operation:* Refer to the data sheet for a 555 IC timer, and draw its pin layout diagram:

l) Examine the circuit in Figure 17-2. Using the formulas given in the text, compute the following, given that R_A = 6.8 k-ohm, R_B = 10 k-ohm, and C = 680 pF:

1) t_1 = _____
2) t_2 = _____
3) T = _____
4) f = _____
5) duty cycle = _____

m) Construct the circuit in Figure 17-2. Connect one vertical input of the oscilloscope to the circuit output. Apply power to the circuit, and adjust the oscilloscope to display a few cycles. Draw the waveform using Timing Diagram 17-4.

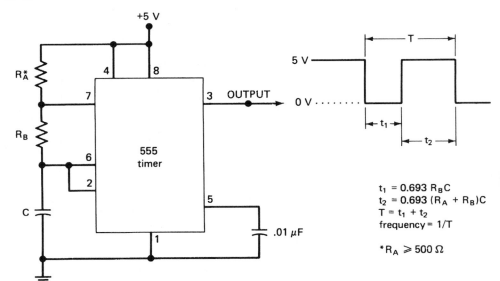

Figure 17-2

Timing Diagram 17-4

n) Estimate the period of the output waveform: _____. Is this value close to the value computed in step l? If not, recheck the values you computed in step l, and then, if the period estimated in this step is still appreciably different, check your circuit.

o) *Review:* This concludes the exercises on the Schmitt trigger, one-shot, and astable multivibrator. To test your understanding of the principles covered in this experiment, answer the following questions:

1. a) Why are the 1N914 diodes in Figure 17-1 necessary?

    b) What type of input signal to the circuit would make the diodes unnecessary?

2. Show how you would wire the 74121 IC inputs to respond to a
   Negative-Going Transition (NGT).

3. The maximum value for R_t is _____, while the maximum value for C_t is

   _____.
4. If R_t = 10 k-ohm, what value must C_t be to produce a pulse having a width of
   7 seconds? C_t = _____.
5. Explain the pulse delay circuit of step j.

6. An OS always returns to the Q = _____ state.
7. True or false: the output pulse width of a nonretriggerable OS is independent
   of the input frequency and pulse width.

8. In Figure 17-2, if R_A = 10 k-ohms, R_B = 2.2 k-ohms, and C = 680 pF, compute
   the following values:

$$t_1 = \underline{\hspace{2cm}}$$

$$t_2 = \underline{\hspace{2cm}}$$

$$T = \underline{\hspace{2cm}}$$

$$f = \underline{\hspace{2cm}}$$

Duty cycle = _____

DESIGNING WITH FLIP-FLOP DEVICES

OBJECTIVES

1. To investigate the application of J-K flip-flops in counting circuits.
2. To investigate the application of D flip-flops in data registers.
3. To investigate parallel data transfer.
4. To investigate the application of J-K flip-flops in shift register circuits.
5. To design a programmable counter.

TEXT REFERENCES

Read sections 5.17 through 5.19.

EQUIPMENT NEEDED

Components
7400 IC;
7404 IC;
7476 IC (3);
3 toggle switches;
normally HIGH pushbutton switch;
normally LOW pushbutton switch;
6 LED monitors.

Instruments
0–5 volt DC power supply;
pulse or square wave generator;
dual trace oscilloscope.

DISCUSSION

Now that you have become acquainted with the fundamentals of flip-flops, you are ready to apply your knowledge in designing and constructing circuitsthat use flip-flops. Two very important applications of flip-flops are counters and registers.

Counters

A counter is a digital device capable of producing an output which represents a sequence of numbers. The output count of the counter is binary and is usually triggered by a clock signal. Each bit of the binary count is produced by a flip-flop. Among the various types of counters used in digital circuits is the so-called MOD counter. The MOD counter has a count sequence that may start at 0 and end at some number N - 1 and repeat. The number N is called the modulus (MOD-number) of the counter and is equal to 2^M, where M is the number of flip-flops. The number N can be changed for a given MOD counter. In the current experiment, you will investigate these principles and also be asked to design a counter whose MOD-number can be changed by "programming" the counter.

Registers

While counters are a very important application of flip-flops, probably the most common application is the register. A register is simply a collection of flip-flops used for storing information (data) temporarily. In the current experiment, you will construct a simple register for storing data, and then investigate two methods of transferring data to and from such registers.

PROCEDURE

a) *Counter application:* Figure 18-1 shows the circuit for a three-bit binary counter. Examine the circuit closely, then construct it. Arrange the order of the flip-flops exactly as the diagram shows it.

b) Connect a normally HIGH pushbutton switch to the clock input of flip-flop X_0. Connect LED monitors to the Q outputs of each flip-flop. The order of the LEDs is important, since the output of the rightmost flip-flop will represent the LSB of the count and the leftmost the MSB. Connect all DC SET inputs to V_{cc} and all DC CLEAR inputs to a single normally HIGH pushbutton switch.

c) Turn the power on, and clear the counter by pulsing the DC CLEARs LOW momentarily. The number stored in the counter is indicated by the LEDs, which should all be OFF (i.e., the number should be 000_2). Test the counter circuit by pulsing the clock input and observing the count indicated by the LED monitors. Record your observations in Table 18-1.

Your results should indicate that the counter counts to a maximum of 7 and recycles to 000 on the eighth clock pulse.

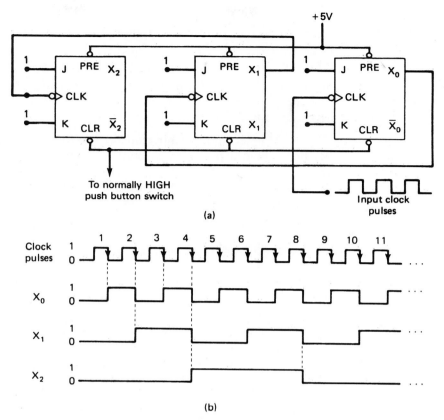

Figure 18-1

Table 18-1

Clock	Output State		
Pulse	X_2	X_1	X_0
0	0	0	0
1			
2			
3			
4			
5			
6			
7			
8			

Disconnect the pushbutton switch from the clock input of the counter. Connect the output of a square wave generator, set at 10 kHz, to the clock input of the counter and to one vertical input of a dual trace oscilloscope. Connect the other vertical input of the oscilloscope to the Q output of flip-flop X_0. Trigger on output Q of flip-flop X_0. What is the frequency of the signal at X_0? _____. Move the oscilloscope input from X_0 to X_1. Trigger on X_1. What is the frequency of this signal? _____. Finally, move the oscilloscope input from X_1 to X_2. Trigger on X_2. What is the frequency of this signal? _____. Based on your observations, what is the MOD-number of this counter? _____.

Disconnect the oscilloscope and the square wave generator from the counter, and reconnect the pushbutton to the counter clock input. You will use the counter in the next step.

d) *Changing the MOD-number of a counter:* In the preceding step, you investigated a three-bit counter. You determined its MOD-number and its count sequence. You will now modify the counter so that it has a new count sequence and a new MOD-number.

Disconnect the pushbutton switch from the DC CLEAR inputs of the flip-flops. Modify the counter circuit so that the wiring is like that shown in Figure 18-2. Clear the counter by pulsing it until the LED monitors indicate a count of 000, or by lifting the DC CLEAR line connection from the NAND gate output and grounding it momentarily, then reconnecting it to the NAND gate. Using Table 18-2, record the counter output states you observe as you pulse the counter through its new count sequence. Determine the MOD-number of this counter by examining the counter sequence: _____.

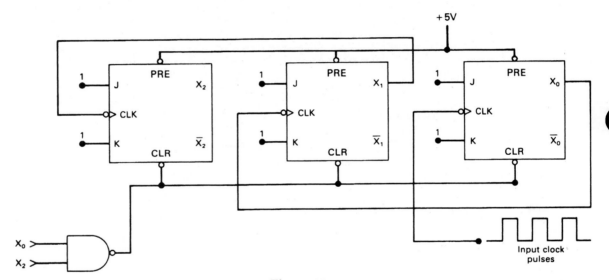

Figure 18-2

Table 18-2

Clock Pulse	Output State		
	X_2	X_1	X_0
0	0	0	0
1	0	0	1
2	0	1	0
3	0	1	1
4	1	0	0
5	1	0	1
6	1	1	0
7	1	1	1
8	0	0	0

e) *Parallel data transfer:* Many times it is necessary to store binary data temporarily. A device that performs this function is called a *register*. A register can be a set of D flip-flops, one for each bit to be stored. Figure 18-3 shows two 3-bit registers, X and Y. While each has the same storage capacity, the data in X may be transferred to Y, where it may be stored as long as necessary, thus permitting register X to receive new data. All three bits are transferred simultaneously whenever register Y receives the transfer pulse.

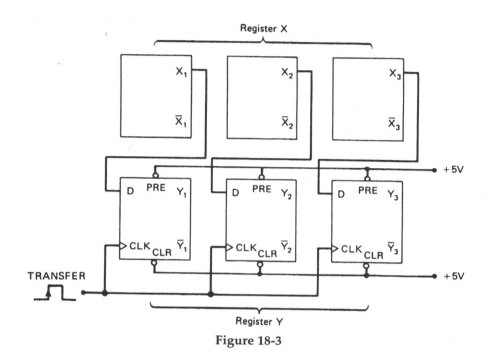

Figure 18-3

f) Build register Y using 7474 D flip-flops. Connect the D inputs of register Y to the outputs of the three-bit counter on the circuit board. Connect LED monitors to the outputs of register Y. Finally, connect all clock inputs of register Y together to a single normally LOW pushbutton switch.

g) Clear the counter by using the method of step d, then pulse the transfer pushbutton switch HIGH momentarily. You should observe that the LEDs of the counter and the register are OFF. Now pulse the counter once, and again pulse the transfer pushbutton HIGH momentarily. You should observe that the contents of the counter (001) are transferred to the register, all three bits simultaneously. Repeat this procedure several times, verifying that the data in the counter is transferred to the register each time.

h) *Serial shift register application:* In steps e–g you constructed and tested a parallel shift register. Actually, the proper name for this register is a parallel in/parallel out (P.I.P.O.) register. In this step, you will investigate another type of shift register, a serial shift register. Examine the circuit in Figure 18-4 closely, then modify and construct the circuit using one 7474 D flip-flop and three 7476 J-K flip-flops.

Connect a toggle switch to the data input and a normally HIGH pushbutton switch to the shift pulse input. Connect LED monitors to the Q outputs of each flip-flop. Finally, connect all DC SET inputs to V_{cc} and all DC CLEAR inputs to a single normally HIGH pushbutton switch.

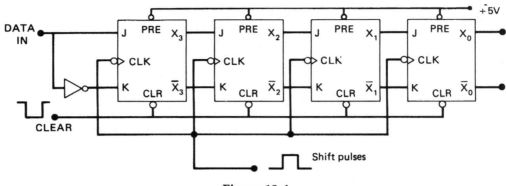

Figure 18-4

Table 18.3

Shift	Output State			
Pulse	X_3	X_2	X_1	X_0
0	0	0	0	0
1	1	0	0	0
2				
3				
4				
5				

Clear the register by pulsing the CLEAR line LOW momentarily. Set the data toggle switch HIGH and pulse the shift line once. The LEDs should indicate 1000, reading from left to right. Set the data switch LOW, and pulse the shift line four more times, each time observing the output LEDs. Record your observations in Table 18-3.

You should have observed that the 1, which was shifted into the flip-flop X_3 on shift pulse 1, was subsequently shifted to the right until it was shifted out of flip-flop X_0 on the last shift pulse applied (shift pulse 5). Each time the 1 was shifted, a 0 replaced it.

If the purpose of the serial shifting is to load a number into the register, this may be accomplished by setting or resetting the data input toggle switch after each shift pulse is applied. For example, to shift the number 0101 into the register, you would set the toggle switch to 1 before the first shift pulse is applied, then reset the switch before applying the next shift pulse. Repeating this procedure one more time will leave the desired number in the register. Try shifting this number into the register. Next, try shifting other numbers into the register, such as 1011.

Data can be taken from this register in two ways, parallel or serial. The serial output can be taken at the Q output of flip-flop X_0, while parallel data can be taken from the Q outputs of each flip-flop in a manner like that of steps e–g.

i) *A programmable counter:* Design a four-bit counter which is controlled by two control lines x and y and that behaves according to Table 18-4.

Table 18-4

Program Switch X Y	Counter Mode
0 0	No Count
0 1	Mod 5
1 0	Mod 10
1 1	Mod 12

Draw the logic diagram in the space provided below.

j) *Review:* This concludes the exercises on flip-flop applications. To test your understanding of the principles investigated in this experiment, answer the following questions:

1. The counter you constructed in this experiment was called a MOD-8 counter or a divide-by-8 counter. Using the results recorded in Table18-1, explain how the counter can be used to divide the frequency of a signal by 8.

2. Suppose you were to add another flip-flop to the circuit, making a total of four flip-flops. The maximum count this counter would indicate would be ____, and the MOD number would be ___. Its frequency division capability would be ___.

3. The text explains the use of the DC SET and CLEAR inputs to transfer data *asynchronously* into a J-K flip-flop. Explain the difference between this type of transfer and the parallel transfer method employed in steps e–g.

4. Making use of your observations recorded in Table 18-3, how many shift pulses are necessary to serially transfer data from one 8-bit register to another? _____.

5. Based on your knowledge of parallel and serial data transfer, does this experiment verify the relative speeds of the two methods? _____.

6. Explain how the modification you made to the counter in step d changed the count sequence.

7. How would you modify a binary counter to cause it to stop counting at a particular count even though clock pulses are continually applied?

Experiment 19

Name_____

TROUBLESHOOTING FLIP-FLOP CIRCUITS

OBJECTIVES

1. To practice troubleshooting counting circuits containing IC flip-flops.
2. To practice troubleshooting register circuits containing IC flip-flops.
3. To investigate a flip-flop device timing problem, clock skew.

TEXT REFERENCES

Read sections 5.3 and 5.24.

EQUIPMENT NEEDED

Components
7400 IC;
7474 IC (2);
74LS76 IC (2);
normally HIGH pushbutton switch (2) and normally LOW pushbutton switch (2), all debounced;
4 LED monitors.

Instruments
0–5 volt DC power supply;
pulse or square wave generator;
dual trace oscilloscope;
ohmmeter;
logic pulser;
logic probe.

DISCUSSION

Circuits containing flip-flops can develop many of the faults that occur in combinatorial circuits. For example, flip-flops can develop opens and shorts at their inputs and outputs the same as gates do. Unlike gates, however, flip-flops possess memory, and it is this characteristic that can cause flip-flop circuits to behave differently than combinatorial circuits. For example, when trying to determine the cause for a given flip-flop output condition, you must remember that the signals causing the condition may not be present at the inputs to the flip-flop.

In the current experiment, you will first construct a simple asynchronous counting circuit and verify that the counter operates properly. Remember, it is rather difficult to troubleshoot a circuit without knowing how the circuit normally works. You will then have someone put a "bug" (fault) into the circuit for you to find. As always, do not look for the bug, and even if you should suspect what the bug is, use your troubleshooting techniques to isolate the problem. Also, before coming into the lab to perform the experiments, place various bugs into the circuit on paper and try to predict the response of the circuit.

The second exercise is similar to the first. The device used here is a shift register that is synchronous. The last exercise will give you an opportunity to investigate one type of timing problem in flip-flop circuits referred to as clock skew.

PROCEDURE

a) *Troubleshooting flip-flop counters:* Examine the circuit and its timing diagram in Figure 19-1. Since you will be clocking the counter manually at first, use Table 19-1 to make a state table for the counter. Construct the counter. Use a pushbutton switch to clear the counter. Use a logic pulser, if available, to clock the counter and a logic probe to monitor the output of each flip-flop. If a pulser is not available, use a debounced pushbutton switch.

Table 19-1

Clock Pulse	Output State		
	X_2	X_1	X_0
0	0	0	0
1			
2			
3			
4			
5			
6			
7			
8			

b) To begin the exercise, have your instructor or lab assistant place a fault into your counter while your back is turned. Now test the circuit and make a state table using Table 19-2. If the two are different, your circuit is indeed not operating correctly. In the space provided below, list as many possible faults as you can which could cause the circuit to malfunction in this manner.

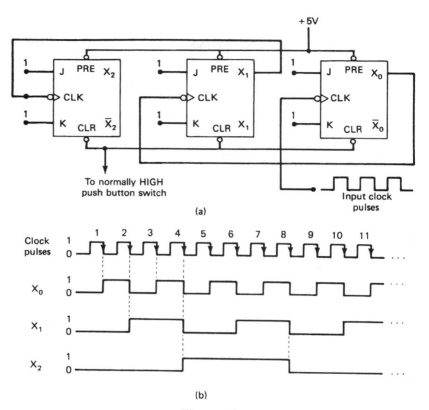

(a)

(b)

Figure 19-1

Table 19-2

Clock	Output State		
Pulse	X_2	X_1	X_0
0	0	0	0
1			
2			
3			
4			
5			
6			
7			
8			

c) Once you have listed as many faults as you can, proceed to troubleshoot the circuit. When you have isolated the bug, remove it and check the circuit once again. When you have done this, write a description of the bug in the space provided below.

d) In the preceding steps, you clocked the counter manually and used a state table to troubleshoot the circuit. In practice, some counters are used to divide the frequency of a signal, and in some counters it is not easy to clock the circuit manually. In fact, in many cases it is desirable to use the clock of the system that is being examined whenever troubleshooting a counter circuit. In these cases, a timing diagram and a dual trace oscilloscope could be used to troubleshoot the counter. Connect a square wave generator to the counter and use the oscilloscope to monitor the outputs. Compare the waveforms on the oscilloscope to those of Figure 19-1. If you removed the bug from steps b and c successfully, they should be the same. If they are not the same, you still have not removed the bug and should do so now. Now have your instructor or laboratory assistant introduce a new bug into your circuit. Draw a timing diagram for the counter in the space provided below and compare these waveforms to those of Figure 19-1 They should differ depending on the bug that was installed. Use the oscilloscope to isolate the circuit fault.

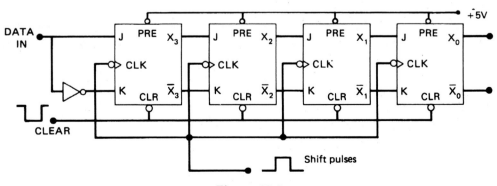

Figure 19-2

Table 19-3

Shift	Output State			
Pulse	X₃	X₂	X₁	X₀
0	0	0	0	0
1	1	0	0	0
2				
3				
4				
5				

e) *Troubleshooting flip-flop shift registers:* Examine the circuit and timing diagram of Figure 19-2. Use Table 19-3 to make a state table for the circuit. Construct the circuit. If a pulser is available, use the pulser for the clock. If a pulser is not available, connect a normally HIGH pushbutton switch (debounced) to the circuit's clock input. Connect the circuit's CLEAR input to a normally HIGH pushbutton switch. Connect a toggle switch to the data input (DATA IN).

f) Pulse the CLEAR input LOW momentarily to clear the register. Set the data input switch to HIGH. Pulse the clock input once and then set the data input switch LOW. Test the register by pulsing the clock enough times to cause the register to go through all of its remaining states, and check the output of each flip-flop after each clock pulse. Compare your observations with Table 19-3. When the register is operating correctly, have your instructor introduce a fault into the register circuit.

g) Test your circuit, and make a state table using Table 19-4. Compare your observations with Table 19-3. If they are not the same, you must troubleshoot. Begin by listing in the space provided below as many possible faults as you can that would cause the circuit to behave the way it currently does.

Table 19-4

Shift	Output State			
Pulse	X_3	X_2	X_1	X_0
0	0	0	0	0
1	1	0	0	0
2				
3				
4				
5				

h) Use the pulser (or debounced switch) and probe to isolate the fault. When you believe you have found the fault, write a brief description of the bug below.

i) *Troubleshooting timing problems—clock skew:* Construct the circuit in Figure 19-3. If a logic pulser is available, use the pulser to clock the circuit. Connect a normally HIGH pushbutton switch to the CLEAR circuit. You will monitor the flip-flop outputs with a logic probe.

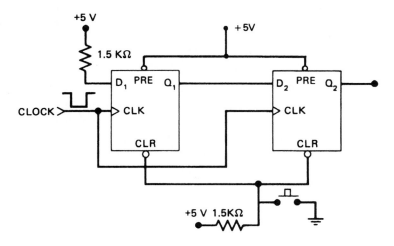

Figure 19-3

j) Test the circuit using the timing diagram provided in Figure 19.4. When the circuit is operating correctly, modify the circuit according to Figure 19.5. Now retest the circuit. You should notice that the circuit may not be functioning correctly, due to the additional propogational delay inserted in this step. If it still works correctly, add two inverters between the NAND gate and the CLK input of FF2, and retest the circuit operation.

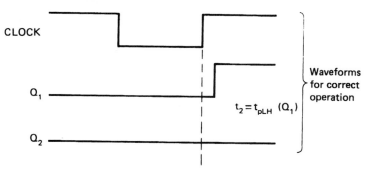

Figure 19-4

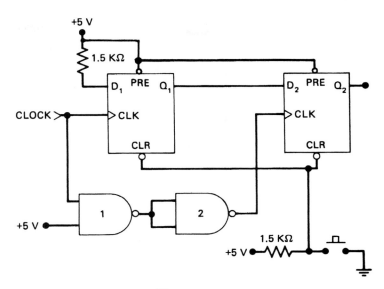

Figure 19-5

k) *Review*: This concludes the exercises on troubleshooting flip-flop devices. To test your understanding of the principles investigated in this experiment, answer the following questions:

1. What would happen to the counter in Figure 19-1 if $\overline{X}_1$ becomes shorted to ground?

2. In Figure 19-3, if FF$_1$ and FF$_2$ are both 74LS74 IC D flip-flops, and G$_1$ and G$_2$ are 74L00 IC NAND gates, would it seem likely that clock skew could be a problem? _____.

3. Answer review question 2 if FF$_1$ and FF$_2$ are both 74LS74 IC D flip-flops and G$_1$ and G$_2$ are 7400 IC NAND gates. _____

Experiment 20

Name _____

BINARY ADDERS AND 2'S COMPLEMENT SYSTEM

OBJECTIVES

1. To investigate the operation of a half adder.
2. To investigate the operation of a full adder.
3. To investigate the operation of a two-bit ripple adder.
4. To investigate the operation of a 7483A IC adder.
5. To investigate the operation of a 2's complement adder/subtractor circuit.

TEXT REFERENCES

Read sections 6.1 through 6.4 and sections 6.9 through 6.15.

EQUIPMENT NEEDED

Components
7400 IC;
7404 IC;
7432 IC;
7474 IC (4);
7483A IC;
7486 IC;
6 toggle switches;
normally HIGH pushbutton switch;
normally LOW pushbutton switch (2);
10 LED monitors.

Instrument

0–5 volt DC power supply.

DISCUSSION

At the heart of digital computers and calculators is the arithmetic unit. Depending on the system, this unit can range in complexity from the very simple, such as an adder, to a unit that possesses the capabilities of computing values for special functions, such as trigonometric and logarithmic functions. No matter how complex the unit is, its most important function is still addition.

At a minimum, arithmetic units usually consist of two flip-flop registers, one of which is called the *accumulator,* and the arithmetic circuits, which are special combinatorial circuits. The arithmetic circuit is fed data (operands) by the two registers and stores its answer into the accumulator.

In the current experiment, you will investigate one type of arithmetic circuit, the parallel binary adder. This circuit adds two binary numbers by operating on pairs of bits (a bit from one operand and the corresponding bit from the other operand) with units called full adders or half adders and generating carry bits that are fed to the next highest significant adder. Full adders have a third input to receive the carry bit output of the previous adder. Half adders do not and are thus used only to add the least significant bits of the two numbers being added. You will then investigate an IC four-bit parallel adder, the 7483A, and use this IC to construct a 2's complement adder/subtractor.

PROCEDURE

a) *Half adder:* In review question 3, Experiment 12, you were asked to design the circuit for a half adder. Redraw your circuit in the space provided below.

b) Construct the half adder. Connect toggle switches to the two inputs and LED monitors to both outputs. When construction is completed, test the half adder, using Table 20-1 to record your observations on the Sum and Carry outputs.

Table 20-1

Inputs			Outputs	
A	B		S	C
0	0			
0	1			
1	0			
1	1			

c) *Full adder:* Draw the circuit for a full adder:

d) Construct the full adder. Connect toggle switches to each input and LED monitors to both outputs. When construction is completed, test the full adder, using Table 20-2 to record your observations on the sum and carry outputs.

Table 20-2

Inputs				Outputs	
A	B	C_i		S	C
0	0	0			
0	0	1			
0	1	0			
0	1	1			
1	0	0			
1	0	1			
1	1	0			
1	1	1			

e) *Two-bit ripple adder:* Connect the half adder and full adder together, according to the diagram shown in Figure 20-1 to form a two-bit ripple adder.

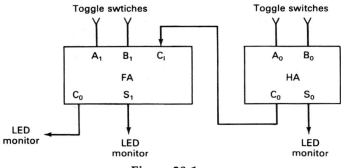

Figure 20-1

Test the operation of the adder by setting the toggle switches to several different values and observing the sum and carry indicated by the LED monitors. Demonstrate the circuit operation for your instructor.

f) *7483A IC adder operation:* Refer to the data sheet for a 7483A IC, and draw its pin layout diagram:

g) Install a 7483A IC on the circuit board, and make the following connections:

1) Connect V_{cc} to +5 V and GND to power ground.
2) Connect C_0 to power ground.
3) Connect toggle switches to inputs A_0 through A_3 and B_0 through B_3.
4) Connect LED monitors to sum outputs S_0 through S_3 and also to C_4.

Table 20-3

Inputs								Outputs				
A_3	A_2	A_1	A_0	B_3	B_2	B_1	B_0	C_4	S_3	S_2	S_1	S_0
0	0	1	1	0	0	0	1					
0	1	1	1	1	0	0	1					
1	0	1	1	0	1	0	1					
1	1	1	1	1	1	1	1					

h) Verify that the adder is operating correctly by entering the input values listed in Table 20-3 and recording your observations on the outputs in the table.

i) *Adder/Subtractor:* Examine the circuit of Figure 20-2. The circuit is for a parallel adder/subtractor using the 2's complement number system. Investigate the possibility of simplifying the circuit somewhat by examining the AND-OR circuits. The right simplification will permit you to replace the ADD and SUB control lines with a single control line, X. When X = 0, the circuit will function as an adder; when X = 1, it will function as a subtractor. When you believe that you

have found a way to simplify the circuit, draw the simplified diagram below, and show it to your instructor or laboratory assistant. HINT: consider using exclusive-OR circuits as controlled inverters.

j) Construct the circuit you drew in step i. Connect toggle switches to each D input of register B. Also, connect a toggle switch to control line X. Connect LED monitors to the 7483A sum outputs (S_3 through S_0) and carry output C_4, switch X, and register A outputs (A_3 through A_0).

The clock inputs of register A flip-flops should be connected to a single normally LOW pushbutton switch (ADD/SUB pulse input). The clock inputs of register B should all be tied to a single normally LOW pushbutton switch (TRANSFER line, not shown). Tie the DC SET inputs for both registers A and B HIGH. Finally, tie the DC CLEAR inputs for register A to a normally HIGH pushbutton switch, so that the register may be cleared to begin a new sequence of operations.

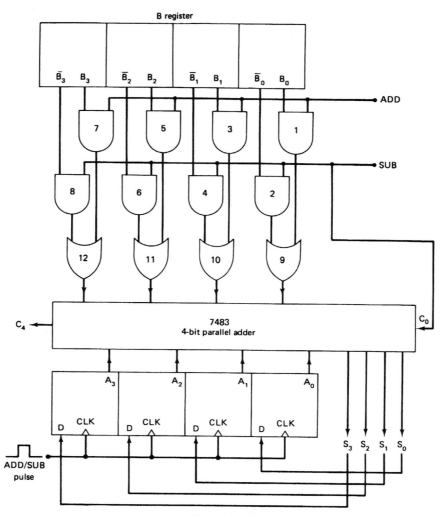

Figure 20-2

    k) The circuit operates in the following manner:

1) To clear the unit, pulse the DC CLEAR pushbutton switch momentarily LOW.

2) To ADD a number to register A, set X to 0. To SUBTRACT a number from register A, set X to 1.

3) To enter a number to be added or subtracted, set toggle switches B_3 through B_0 to the value of the number, then pulse the TRANSFER line momentarily HIGH to clock the data into register B. The LED monitors at the 7483A sum and carry outputs should now indicate the new sum (or difference) of [A] and [B].

4) Pulse the ADD/SUB line momentarily HIGH to clock the sum outputs from the 7483A into register A. The LEDs at the outputs of register A should now indicate the new accumulated sum (or difference).

5) Repeat steps 2–4 until all numbers have been added (or subtracted). The final result will be indicated by the register A output monitors.

l) Perform the following operations with the adder/subtractor unit:

1) 1 + 2 + 3 + 4 = _____.
2) +7 + (-1) + (-2) + (-3) = _____.
3) +1 - (-3) - (-2) = _____.
4) -3 + (-2) + (-3) - (+4) = _____.
5) 9 - 1 - 3 - 2 = _____.
6) +1 - (+5) - (+4) = _____.
7) 5 - 4 - 6 - 7 = _____.

m) *Review:* This concludes the exercises on binary adders. To test your understanding of the principles investigated in this experiment, answer the following questions:

1. A half adder may be made from a full adder by _____.
2. How many outputs must an adder have if it is to add two 8-bit numbers? _____.
3. What is the range of SIGNED numbers that a 7483A adder can operate on? _____.
4. Explain how register A, in the 2's complement adder/subtractor, acts like an accumulator in a digital arithmetic unit.

Experiment 21

ASYNCHRONOUS IC COUNTERS

OBJECTIVES

1. To investigate the operation of the 7493 IC counter.
2. To investigate a method of changing the MOD-number of the 7493 IC counter.
3. To investigate the cascading of 7493 IC counters.
4. To investigate propagation delays in asynchronous counters.

TEXT REFERENCES

Read sections 7.1 through 7.3 and section 7.5.

EQUIPMENT NEEDED

Components
7493 or 74293 IC (2);
4 LED monitors;
normally HIGH pushbutton switch (debounced).

Instruments
0–5 volt DC power supply;
pulse or square wave generator;
dual trace oscilloscope.

DISCUSSION

In Experiment 18, you investigated flip-flop asynchronous counters. Recall that in asynchronous counters, the output of one flip-flop serves as the clock for the next flip-flop. In the current experiment and the next one, you will investigate integrated circuit (IC) asynchronous counters.

The flip-flops in a typical asynchronous binary counter are connected in their toggle mode. That is, the flip-flops toggle on the arrival of the correct clock edge. The connections between flip-flop outputs and clock inputs determine the direction characteristics of the counter, that is, whether it counts up or down. The counting range is determined by the number of flip-flops and how the clear circuits are connected.

Counters are used not only for counting, but they also may be used to divide the frequency of digital signals and to time and sequence events in a control system. To meet these needs, IC manufacturers have provided counters with varying bit widths and MOD numbers. These counters can be cascaded to extend the counting range and the MOD number. Recall that the overall MOD number of cascaded counters is the product of the individual counter MOD numbers.

In the current experiment, you will investigate the 7493 IC counter. The 7493 consists internally of a single toggle flip-flop, a three-bit (MOD 8) counter, and a gated reset circuit. The flip-flop and counter may be wired together to form a four-bit counter. With appropriate external connections to the reset inputs, the counter's MOD number may be reduced. Finally, the 7493, as well as all asynchronous counters, produces a significant propogation delay between the input and output of the counter.

PROCEDURE

a) Refer to the data sheet for the 7493 IC. This IC contains four flip-flops that may be arranged as a MOD-16 ripple counter. To do this, Q_0 must be tied externally to $\overline{CP_1}$. The MSB of this counter is Q_3 and the LSB is Q_0. The counter's MOD-number may be changed by making the appropriate external connections.

Draw the pin layout diagram for this IC:

b) *7493 IC operation:* Connect the circuit of Figure 21-1. Connect a normally HIGH pushbutton switch to input $\overline{CP_0}$ and LED monitors to outputs Q_3 through Q_0.

c) Pulse $\overline{CP_0}$ and observe the counter sequence displayed on the LEDs. It should count from 0000 to 1111 and then recycle to 0000. Note that the NAND gate inputs $\overline{MR_1}$ and $\overline{MR_2}$ have no effect on the counter, since they are both tied LOW.

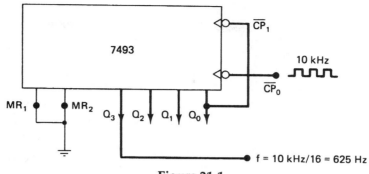

Figure 21-1

d) Disconnect the pushbutton switch at input $\overline{CP_0}$. Connect a square wave generator to this input, and set the generator to 10 kHz. Monitor the $\overline{Q_3}$ output with one vertical input of the oscilloscope and the generator output with the other input. Set the horizontal sweep so that you can verify that there is one $\overline{Q_3}$ pulse for every 16 generator pulses. Is the signal at $\overline{Q_3}$ a square wave? _____.

e) *Changing the 7493 MOD-number:* Disconnect the pulse generator from the counter, and reconnect the pushbutton switch in its place. Disconnect MR_1 and MR_2 from ground and connect one of them to Q_3 and the other to Q_2.

f) Pulse $\overline{CP_0}$ repeatedly, and observe the count sequence displayed on the LEDs. Record this sequence of output states in Table 21-1.

Table 21-1

Input Pulse Applied	Output States Q_3 Q_2 Q_1 Q_0	Decimal Number
None	0 0 0 0	0
1	0 0 0 1	1
2	0 0 1 0	2
3		
4		
5		
6		
7		
8		
9		
10		
11		
12		
13		
14		
15		

g) What is the MOD-number of the counter in step f? _____. Verify the MOD-number you gave by disconnecting the pushbutton switch at $\overline{CP_0}$ and applying a 10 kHz square wave to this input. Then measure the frequency of the signal at Q_3. Is this output a square wave? _____.

h) Now connect the 7493 IC as shown in Figure 21-2. Repeat steps c–f, using Table 21.2 to record your observations.

Based on the results recorded in Table 21-2, determine whether or not the signal at Q_3 is a square wave: _____.

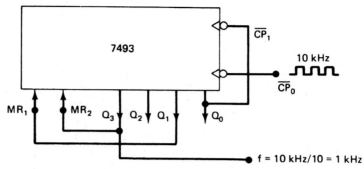

Figure 21-2

Table 21-2

Input Pulse Applied	Output States				Decimal Number
	Q_3	Q_2	Q_1	Q_0	
None	0	0	0	0	0
1	0	0	0	1	1
2	0	0	1	0	2
3					
4					
5					
6					
7					
8					
9					
10					
11					
12					
13					
14					
15					

i) *Cascading 7493 IC counters:* Connect the circuit shown in Figure 21-3. Apply a 6 kHz square wave to input $\overline{CP}_0$ of the MOD-10 counter. With the oscilloscope, determine the frequency of the signal at Q_3 of the MOD-6 counter: _____. What is the MOD-number of this counter arrangement? _____.

j) *Propagation delays in asynchronous counters:* Change the MOD-number of the cascaded counter of step i to 256. Adjust the frequency of the generator to 1 MHz. Monitor both the generator output and the counter output on the dual trace oscilloscope. Trigger the oscilloscope on Q_3 of the second MOD-16 counter. Measure the delay time t_d between the falling edge of the generator signal and the rising edge of the signal at Q_3. This measurement is for the TOTAL delay of the counter. Compute the *average* propagation delay (t_{pd}) for a single flip-flop using the following formula:

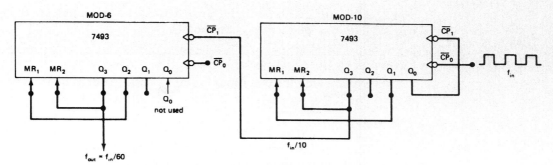

Figure 21-3

$$t_{pd} = \frac{t_d}{N}$$

where N is the number of flip-flops in the counter. What is f_{max} for this counter? _____.

k) *Review:* This concludes the exercises on asynchronous IC counters. To test your understanding of the principles covered in this experiment, answer the following questions:

1. Draw a diagram showing how a 7493 IC can be wired as a MOD-12 counter.

2. If the outputs Q_3 through Q_0 of a 7493 MOD-16 counter are each inverted, what is the count sequence at Q_3 through Q_0?

_____
.

3. Explain why the Q_3 output in steps e and f is not a square wave.

4. Three MOD-10 counters are cascaded together. If a 1 MHz signal is applied to the input of the resulting counter, the frequency of the output is _____.

Experiment 22

Name_____

BCD IC COUNTERS

OBJECTIVES

1. To investigate the operation of the 7490 IC counter.
2. To demonstrate that BCD counters may be displayed directly with seven-segment display units.
3. To investigate the cascading of 7490 IC counters.

TEXT REFERENCES

Read sections 7.1 through 7.3 and sections 7.11, 7.13, and section 9.3.

EQUIPMENT NEEDED

Components

7446 IC (2);

7490 IC (2);

FND507 seven-segment display units (2);

130 ohm resistors (14);

normally HIGH pushbutton switch (debounced).

Instruments

0–5 volt DC power supply;

pulse or square wave generator;

dual trace oscilloscope.

DISCUSSION

A special IC asynchronous counter is the 7490 BCD counter. There are many applications in digital systems for MOD-10 counters, and since many of these systems use BCD interfaces, counters like the 7490 are often included in the design. An example where BCD is employed is the output indicator of a frequency counter (see Experiment 24).

7490 IC Counter

The 7490 is similar to the 7493. It contains a single toggle flip-flop, a MOD-5 counter, and a gated reset circuit, which can be wired together externally to configure the counter as a BCD counter, which counts from 0 to 9. It may also be configured as a divide-by-10 counter, which does not count sequentially, and therefore is not a BCD counter.

Also, like the 7493, the counter can be wired to produce a counter that has a MOD-number less than 10, although this is not done often in practice. You should be aware that the MOD-5 counter internal to the 7490 is a three-bit counter with a MOD-number that has been reduced from 8 to 5 by internal wiring. The 7490 is often cascaded with other counters whenever the desired MOD-number has the numbers ten and/or five as factors. For example, cascading a 7493 wired as a four-bit counter with a 7490 wired as a BCD counter will result in a counter with a MOD-number of 16 x 10 = 160.

In the current experiment, you will investigate the 7490 operating in both of its primary modes, the symmetrical MOD-10 and BCD MOD-10 modes. You will also investigate cascading two BCD counters to form a MOD-100 counter.

BCD Displays

It is often desirable to display the count of a BCD counter. In many applications, a seven-segment LED display is used. The outputs of BCD counters must be converted from BCD into seven-segment codes and then applied to the seven-segment devices through current booster circuits called *drivers*. Both of these functions are found in the 7446 IC BCD-to-seven-segment decoder/driver. In this experiment, you will learn how to connect a 7446 and a seven-segment LED device to function as a BCD display unit.

PROCEDURE

a) Refer to the data sheet for the 7490 IC. This IC contains four flip-flops, which may be arranged as a BCD counter. To do this, the output of flip-flop A must be tied externally to the input of flip-flop B. The MSB of this counter is Q_3, and the LSB is Q_0. The counter's MOD-number may be changed by making the appropriate external connections. The operation of this counter is similar to that of the 7493, which was investigated in Experiment 21.

Draw the pin layout diagram for this IC:

b) *7490 IC operation—symmetrical MOD-10 configuration:* There are two ways to configure the 7490 as a MOD-10 counter. In this step you will investigate the symmetrical MOD-10 configuration. Install a 7490 IC on the circuit board, and wire the counter so that it is like that of Figure 22-1. Connect a normally HIGH pushbutton switch to $\overline{CP}_1$. Connect LED monitors to Q_0, Q_1, Q_2, and Q_3 (Q_0 = MSB; Q_1 = LSB).

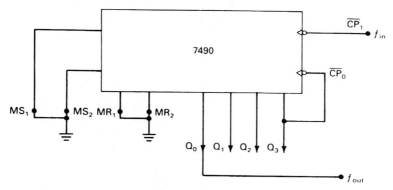

Figure 22-1

c) Pulse $\overline{CP}_1$ repeatedly, and observe the count sequence displayed on the LEDs. Record your observations in Table 22-1. Note that the counter does have ten different states, but the order in which they occur is not the normal binary sequence.

Table 22-1

Input Pulse Applied	Output States				Decimal Number
	Q_3	Q_2	Q_1	Q_0	
None	0	0	0	0	0
1					
2					
3					
4					
5					
6					
7					
8					
9					
10					

d) Disconnect the pushbutton switch, and apply a 10 kHz square wave to $\overline{CP}_1$. Observe the output at Q_0 on the oscilloscope. You should observe that the waveform is a 1 kHz square wave. The square wave signal was obtained by altering the counting sequence while maintaining 10 states.

e) *BCD MOD-10 configuration:* The second way the 7490 can be configured as a MOD-10 counter is the BCD configuration. Rearrange the wiring of the 7490 so that the circuit is like that of Figure 22-2. Connect a normally HIGH pushbutton switch to $\overline{CP}_0$. Connect LED monitors to outputs Q_0, Q_1, Q_2, and Q_3. This time Q_0 = LSB and Q_3 = MSB.

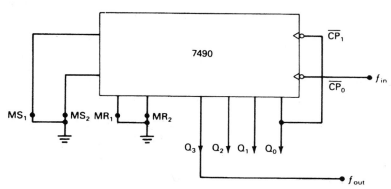

Figure 22-2

f) Pulse $\overline{CP}_0$ repeatedly and observe the count sequence displayed on the LEDs. Record your observations in Table 22-2. You should observe that the sequence is now normal binary and that there are still 10 different states.

Table 22-2

Input Pulse Applied	Output States				Decimal Number
	Q_3	Q_2	Q_1	Q_0	
None	0	0	0	0	0
1					
2					
3					
4					
5					
6					
7					
8					
9					
10					

g) Now disconnect the pushbutton switch from the counter input, and apply a 10 kHz square wave in its place. Observe the signal at Q_3, and draw it in Timing Diagram 22-1. Note that the signal is 1 kHz but not a square wave.

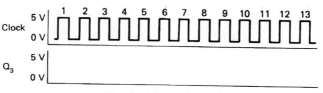

Timing Diagram 22-1

h) *Displaying BCD counters:* The count of the BCD counter can be more conveniently displayed in decimal. One of the most common devices used to display BCD counters is the seven-segment LED driven by a BCD-to-seven-segment decoder/driver, such as a 7446 IC. The seven segments that make up the display device each consist of one or two LEDs, and all are connected in a common cathode or common anode arrangement. The decimal digits are formed by turning on the appropriate segments (see Figure 22-3). The decoder/driver unit decodes a BCD number and supplies the correct levels at its outputs that will cause a seven-segment display unit to display the correct decimal digit.

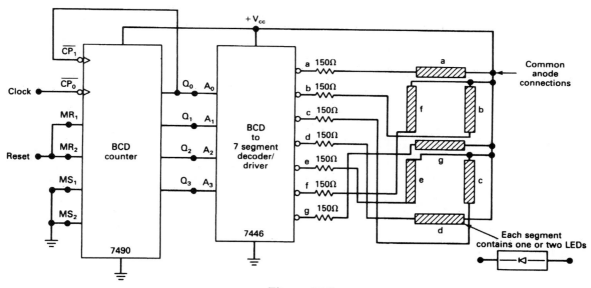

Figure 22-3

Refer to the data sheet for a 7446 IC, and draw its pin layout diagram:

Now examine the circuit of Figure 22-3, and then construct it. Connect a normally LOW pushbutton switch to the reset-to-zero pins. Connect a square wave generator set to a low frequency, and observe that the seven-segment unit is counting in decimal. Pulse the reset pushbutton switch, and note that the counter resets to 0, then continues counting.

Demonstrate the counter for your instructor.

i) *Cascading BCD counters:* BCD counters may be cascaded to count in decimal fashion. For example, two BCD counters may be cascaded to count from 00 to 99. The input counter of such an arrangement will count units, while the output counter will count tens. Refer to Figure 22-4, and cascade two 7490 ICs together to perform this function. Use seven-segment display units to display the counters' outputs. Demonstrate the counter to your instructor when it is operating correctly.

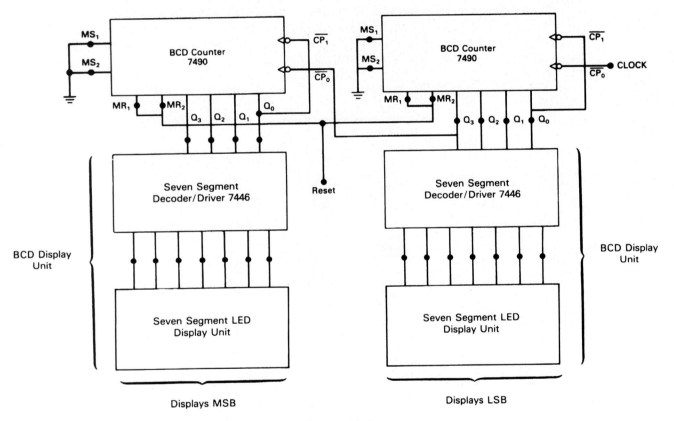

Figure 22-4

j) *Review:* This completes the exercises on BCD counters. To test your understanding of the principles covered in this experiment, answer the following questions:

1. Based on your observations, does the count sequence of a counter determine the MOD-number of a counter? _____.

2. Four 7490 IC counters are all configured to count BCD and are cascaded together. What is the MOD-number of the resulting counter? _____. What is the highest decimal number that can be displayed by the counter? _____.

3. Draw a diagram showing how you would convert a 7490 BCD counter into a MOD-6 counter. HINT: use the reset-to-zero inputs.

Experiment 23

Name_____

SYNCHRONOUS IC COUNTERS

OBJECTIVES

1. To investigate the operation of the 74193 IC counter as an UP counter.
2. To investigate the parallel load function of the 74193 IC.
3. To investigate the operation of the 74193 IC as a DOWN counter.
4. To investigate the cascading of 74193 IC counters.

TEXT REFERENCES

Read sections 7.7 through 7.9.

EQUIPMENT NEEDED

Components
7404 IC;
7493 IC;
74193 IC;
normally HIGH pushbutton switch and two normally LOW pushbutton switches (all debounced);
4 toggle switches;
8 LED monitors.

Instruments
0–5 volt DC power supply;
pulse or square wave generator;
dual trace oscilloscope.

DISCUSSION

In Experiments 21 and 22, you investigated some of the characteristics of asynchronous counters. One undesirable characteristic is the accumulation of propagation delays from clock input to clock output. Another undesirable characteristic that is directly related to propagation delay is the production of unwanted "glitches" at the outputs of decoders that are used to decode the counter. This type of glitch will be investigated in Experiment 25.

Recall that in asynchronous counters, each flip-flop receives its clock input from the output of the previous flip-flop. In another type of counter, each flip-flop clock input is connected to a common clock. This virtually eliminates the propagation delay problem and reduces the number of glitches appearing at the output of decoders significantly. This type of counter is referred to as a synchronous counter.

Flip-Flop Synchronous Counters

Examine Figure 23-1 closely. This figure gives the basic logic diagram for a four-bit synchronous counter. Note that all flip-flops have their J and K inputs tied together as in the asynchronous counter, but, except for the LSB flip-flop, these common connections are not tied to V_{cc}. They are instead connected to the outputs of the previous flip-flop. This means that these flip-flops are in the toggle mode part of the time and in the no-change mode the rest of the time.

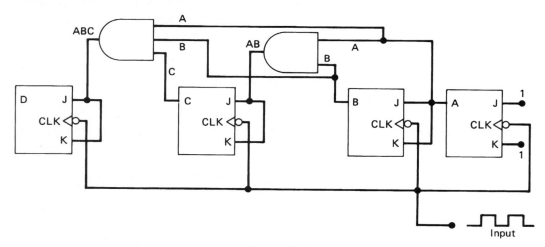

Figure 23-1

Two other differences are outstanding. One is the identifiable characteristic of synchronous counters that the flip-flop clock inputs are tied in parallel. Recall that a weakness of an asynchronous counter is that the individual flip-flop clock inputs are not connected together and that each flip-flop must wait on the output of the previous flip-flop to be clocked. If these inputs are tied together, then they are clocked simultaneously. The other difference is the presence of gates, which force the flip-flops to count in sequence. You should convince yourself that they are necessary by eliminating them. Simply connect the J and K inputs to the normal output of the previous flip-flop and derive a state table for such a counter (refer to Figure 23-2). You should observe that whenever a flip-flop's output is HIGH, the next flip-flop will toggle on the next clock pulse. Thus the counter will "skip" certain counts, such as 3 and 4, as well as others.

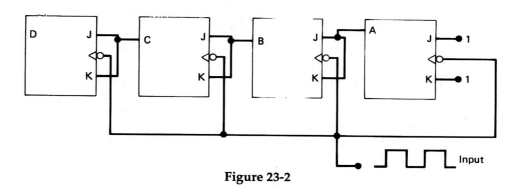

Figure 23-2

74193 IC Synchronous Up/Down Counter

The 74193 IC is representative of the trend toward versatility in the manufacture of ICs. It can count either up or down and can be preset. These features make the chip *programmable*, since they may be selected automatically, even while the circuit is operating. You will investigate other such ICs in future experiments.

The 74193's up/down feature is selected by applying the clock signal to the up or down clock inputs. For example, if it is desired that the counter count up, the clock is sent to the CP_U input. The preset feature is selected by setting the $\overline{PL}$ input LOW. Whatever is currently at the parallel inputs (P_0–P_3) will be loaded into the counter flip-flops.

Other features of the 74193 are the terminal count outputs, $\overline{TC_U}$ and $\overline{TC_D}$. These outputs go LOW when the counter reaches 1111 and 0000, respectively. Thus, they may be used in clocking another 74193 whenever cascading is desired.

PROCEDURE

a) Refer to the data sheet for the 74193 IC. This IC is a synchronous, four-bit, presettable UP/DOWN counter. The MOD-number may be changed by making the appropriate external connections. Draw the pin layout diagram for the 74193:

b) *74193 IC operation as a MOD-16 UP counter:* Construct the circuit of Figure 23-3. Make the following connections to the 74193 IC:

1) Connect toggle switches to P₃ through P₀.
2) Connect normally LOW pushbutton switches to CP$_U$ and MR inputs. (NOTE: if necessary, you may use a toggle switch for MR.)
3) Connect LED monitors to Q₃ through Q₀ and also at $\overline{TC_U}$.
4) Connect a toggle switch to CP$_D$.
5) Connect a normally HIGH pushbutton switch to $\overline{PL}$.

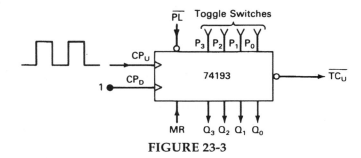

FIGURE 23-3

c) Set the toggle switches to the parallel inputs so that P₀ = P₁= P₂ = P₃ = 0. Set CP$_D$ HIGH. Clear the counter to 0000 by pulsing MR HIGH. Note that $\overline{TC_U}$ (terminal count-up mode) is HIGH.

d) Pulse CP$_U$ HIGH a couple of times, and note that the counter counts UP. Pulse the counter until a count of 1111 is displayed. Record the state of $\overline{TC_U}$: _____. Now pulse the counter one more time. Now record the value of $\overline{TC_U}$: _____. Record the observations you have made in Table 23-1.

Table 23-1

Input Pulse Applied	Output States Q₃ Q₂ Q₁ Q₀				Decimal Number	$\overline{TC_U}$
None	0	0	0	0	0	1
1						
2						
3						
4						
5						
6						
7						
8						
9						
10						
11						
12						
13						
14						
15						
16						

e) Set CP$_D$ LOW. Pulse the CP$_U$ input several times. What happens? _____. Return CP$_D$ to HIGH and pulse CP$_U$ a few more times. You should observe that the counter does not count as long as CP$_D$ is LOW.

f) Using the parallel inputs to preset the counter, set the toggle switches at the parallel inputs so the P$_3$ = P$_1$= 1 and P$_2$ = P$_0$ = 0 and pulse $\overline{PL}$ LOW. The LEDs should now indicate 1010. Pulse the counter until the $\overline{TC_U}$ output LED indicates 0, observing the output LEDs as you do so. What sequence of numbers does the counter count? _____.
Pulse the counter one more time. What is the count now? _____.

g) *74193 IC operation as a MOD-16 DOWN counter:* Disconnect the toggle switch from CP$_D$ and exchange it for the pushbutton switch at CP$_U$ and vice versa. Disconnect the LED from $\overline{TC_U}$ and reconnect it at $\overline{TC_D}$. Clear the counter by pulsing MR HIGH momentarily. Pulse the counter through its count sequence, and record your observations in Table 23-2.

Table 23-2

Input Pulse Applied	Output States				Decimal Number	$\overline{TC_D}$
	Q$_3$	Q$_2$	Q$_1$	Q$_0$		
None	0	0	0	0	0	0
1						
2						
3						
4						
5						
6						
7						
8						
9						
10						
11						
12						
13						
14						
15						
16						

h) Set the parallel input toggle switches to 1010 and pulse $\overline{PL}$ LOW. Note that $\overline{TC_D}$ is now at 1. Pulse the counter until $\overline{TC_D}$ indicates 0, observing the output LEDs as you do so. What sequence of numbers does the counter count? _____. Pulse the counter one more time. What is the count now? _____.

i) *Cascading 74193 IC counters:* Two or more MOD-16 counters may be cascaded to form a MOD-256 counter. In this step, you will cascade a 7493 MOD-16 counter with a 74193 MOD-16 (UP) counter. Use the 74193 to count the lower four bits of the count and the 7493 to count the upper four bits. Pass $\overline{TC_U}$ through an inverter, and connect the output of the inverter to the clock input of the 7493. Connect a square wave generator to the CP$_U$ input of the 74193. Use LED monitors to observe the count sequence of the counter. Draw a circuit diagram for the counter below.

j) Set the generator to a frequency low enough to easily observe the LEDs. Verify that the counter is a MOD-256 counter. Demonstrate the counter for your instructor.

k) *Review:* This concludes the exercises on synchronous IC counters. To test your understanding of the principles covered in this experiment, answer the following questions:

1. Draw a diagram showing how a 74193 IC might be used as a MOD-10 UP counter.

2. Draw a diagram showing how two 74193 ICs might be cascaded to form a MOD-100 DOWN counter.

3. What conditions must be satisfied in order for the 74193 to count DOWN?

4. If a six-bit synchronous counter is to be built, what type of gate is required to feed the J and K inputs of the counter's MSB flip-flop? _____

5. Repeat question 4 for a ten-bit synchronous counter. _____

6. The three-input AND gate in Figure 23-1 can be replaced by a two-input AND gate. How?

7. Does the circuit suggested by question 6 have an advantage over the circuit in Figure 23-1? Explain why (or why not).

Experiment 24

Name_____

IC COUNTER APPLICATION: FREQUENCY COUNTER

OBJECTIVE

To investigate the use of IC counters in a frequency counter.

TEXT REFERENCE

Read section 7.15.

EQUIPMENT NEEDED

Components
74LS13 IC;
7446 IC (2);
7476 IC;
7490 IC (2);
7493 IC (2);
74273 IC;
74121 IC;
seven-segment LED display units (2);
1N457 diode;
1 k-ohm resistor;
2.2 k-ohm resistors (2);
560 pF capacitor (value not critical).

Instruments

0–5 volt DC power supply;

6.3 VAC, 60 Hz power source;

pulse or square wave generator;

dual trace oscilloscope.

DISCUSSION

In previous experiments, frequency measurements have been made using an oscilloscope. Although accurate enough for many types of measurements, the procedure is time-consuming. In this experiment you will construct a model for another instrument capable of measuring frequency directly, without the operator having to make time-frequency conversions. This instrument is a *frequency counter*.

The frequency counter you will construct is composed of three major units:

1) Sampling unit
2) Counter unit
3) Decoder/display unit

The counter will be able to display a frequency count of 00–99 Hz. Of course, the frequency counter can be modified to extend this range considerably. The accuracy of the counter depends on the accuracy of the sampling unit. This unit is driven by an extremely accurate 60 Hz signal. After being divided down to 0.5 Hz by the MOD-120 counter, the pulse produced by the sampling unit controls the amount of time an unknown frequency is sampled. The amount of sampling time is very close to one second. Therefore, the counter unit (MOD-100 BCD) counts the unknown frequency for one second, displays the number of pulses counted during this period, then recycles and counts another sample. The BCD display will indicate the frequency of the unknown signal.

PROCEDURE

a) Examine Figure 24-1 very carefully. Put IC pin numbers for each connection on the diagram, including those not shown. In the latter case, pencil in these connections. Show your completed diagram to your instructor for approval.

b) Wire the circuit of Figure 24-1. Since the circuit is complex, cross off each connection you make with a yellow pencil or marker.

c) *Testing the frequency counter:* Apply a 50 Hz signal to the input of the frequency counter. Observe the displays. The displays should count up to a final value of between 48 and 52. This may change by + or – 1 count with each reading, since the sample pulses and the input signal are not synchronized. The start or end of a sample interval may sometimes catch the falling edge or rising edge of an input pulse, and sometimes it will not.

If the displays do not give the expected results, turn the power off and cross-validate your circuit wiring against the logic diagram. Visually inspect for unconnected V_{CC} and GND pins on each IC. Also check the reset-to-zero pins on the BCD counters—at least one on each IC should be grounded.

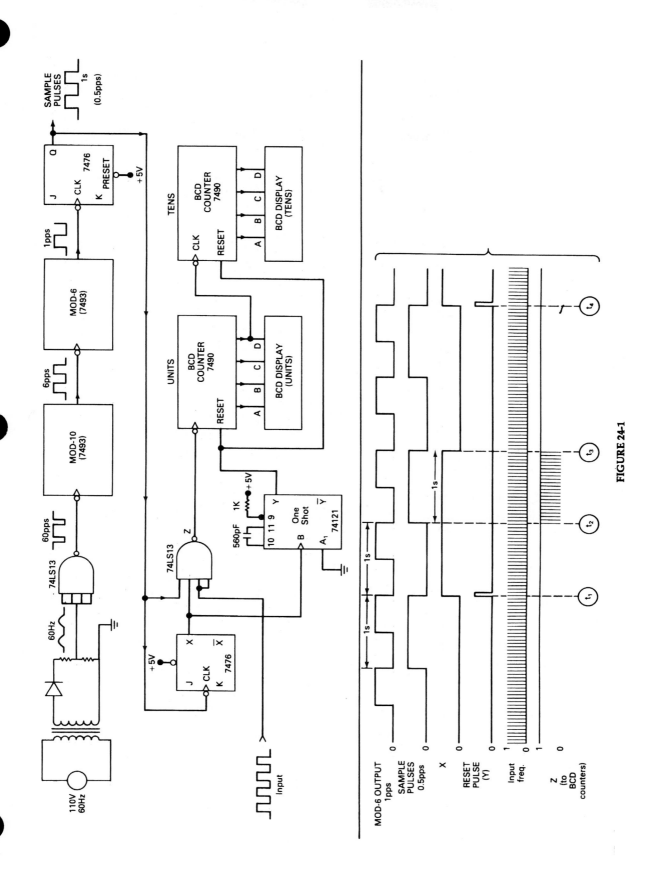

FIGURE 24-1

If the wiring checks out all right, you will have to continue troubleshooting with the power applied.

d) If the results in step c were successful, try some other frequencies between 0 and 100 Hz. Verify that the displays indicate the correct frequency in each case.

e) *Changing the sample time:* The counter you have constructed will measure frequencies ranging from 0 to 99 Hz. To measure higher frequencies, you could add another BCD counting unit. Another way would be to *decrease* the sample interval. For example, decreasing the sample interval to 0.1 second will permit your counter to count up to 999. However, you will still have a two-digit display. Thus the counter will display frequencies from 100–999 as 10–99. You would interpret the display as 100–990. This results in some inaccuracy since you have lost the units digit.

Modify the counter so that the sample interval is 0.1 second. When the modification is installed, test the counter by applying a 250 Hz signal at the counter input. Demonstrate your modified counter to your instructor.

f) *Eliminating the blinking display:* You should have observed that when you decreased the sample interval in step e, you experienced a reduction in the amount of time the final count was displayed. In fact, the entire sequence of counting, displaying, and then recycling was speeded up. Further decreases in the length of a sample interval will result in even less display time. At some point, the sample time would be so small that the displays will be constantly changing.

The only display of concern is the final count. In this step, you will modify the frequency counter so that it changes only whenever there is a change in the final count. To do this, you will use a 74273 IC, which is an eight-bit latch with CLEAR,

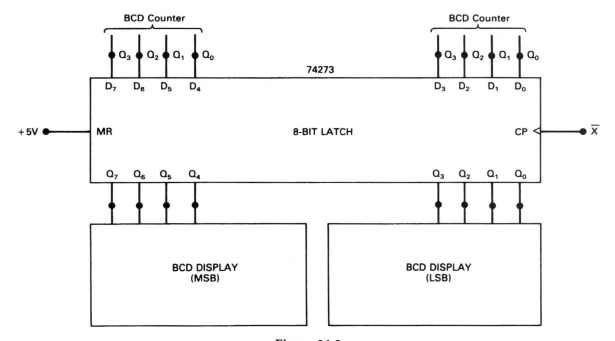

Figure 24-2

to latch the output of the counter when it reaches the end of a sample interval. The latched output will then be displayed. Figure 24-2 shows the circuit modification you are to make to the frequency counter.

Refer to the data sheet for a 74273 IC and draw its pin layout diagram:

Incorporate this modification into the frequency counter. Check the modified counter out for various input frequencies, and demonstrate it for your instructor.

g) *Review:* This concludes the exercises on applications of IC counters. To test your understanding of the principles covered in this experiment, answer the following questions:

1. Assume that the unknown frequency input to the counter is 50 Hz. Study the waveforms shown in Figure 24.1. Describe what the BCD counters and display units are doing during each of the following time intervals:

    a) $t_1 - t_2$:

    b) $t_2 - t_3$:

    c) $t_3 - t_4$:

2. Why is $\overline{X}$ used in Figure 24-2?

TROUBLESHOOTING COUNTERS: CONTROL WAVEFORM GENERATION

OBJECTIVES

1. To investigate the application of counter decoding in generating control waveforms.
2. To compare asynchronous and synchronous counters used in control circuits.
3. To practice troubleshooting counter circuits.

TEXT REFERENCES

Read sections 7.11 through 7.13.

EQUIPMENT NEEDED

Components
7400 IC;
7476 IC;
7493 IC;
74193 IC;
normally HIGH pushbutton switch (debounced).
Instruments
0–5 volt DC power supply;
pulse or square wave generator;
dual trace oscilloscope;
logic pulser;
logic probe;
ohmmeter or DMM.

DISCUSSION

In Experiment 22, we investigated a way to display the count of a BCD counter. The use of the seven-segment LED display unit was found to be superior to the usual single LED, because the former shows us the count in decimal. In the current experiment, you will investigate another reason for decoding counters. Often counters are used in controlling the sequence of steps in a process. For example, if a process consists of five steps, a MOD-5 counter could be used to count the steps and decoders could be used to detect the presence of the current count. The outputs of the decoders could then be used to initiate each step of the process.

We have already used this type of counter decoding in controlling the MOD-number of flip-flop counters in Experiment 18. A NAND gate was used to detect the presence of the MOD-number, and the resulting LOW output was applied to the flip-flop CLEAR inputs, thus causing the counter to recycle. The NAND gate decoder is called an active-LOW (or one-LOW) decoder, since it outputs a LOW when it detects the "right" number and outputs a HIGH otherwise (normal output). Other circuits may require an active-HIGH (one-HIGH) or AND gate decoder.

In the current experiment, you will construct a simple waveform-generating device that produces two control signals. These signals could be used to control two other devices by turning them on and off at regular intervals. You will then use the circuit to practice troubleshooting counter and counter decoder circuits.

Troubleshooting IC Counters

IC counters can have the same faults as gates and flip-flops. For example, they may have open (externally and internally) inputs and outputs, shorted (externally and internally) inputs and outputs, and other internal faults. A logic probe and pulser can be used to isolate many of the IC faults, and an ohmmeter (or DMM) can be used to pinpoint shorts.

As in previous troubleshooting exercises, you should know the operation of the circuit before attempting troubleshooting. Next, you should record your observations on how the circuit operates with a bug in it. Once this is accomplished, you should list as many possible faults as you can. You will use this list and your troubleshooting tools to isolate the fault.

A simple 7493 fault is open master reset inputs. Suppose the outputs of your counter do not respond to the input clock and appear to be stuck at 0000. The possible faults include an open clock input to the counter, counter outputs shorted to ground, and open master reset inputs. If the resets are supposed to be grounded to V_{ss}, place the tip of your logic probe on the master reset input pins. If it indicates a floating condition on both, you have an external open in the reset circuit. If the probe indicates ground, then it is possible that the IC has an internal open. If you have eliminated the other possible faults, replace the IC and retest the circuit.

Another counter problem is glitches. Glitches commonly occur in asynchronous counter decoder outputs. However, any binary counter whose MOD-number has been changed to a number that is not a power of two produces glitches. The current experiment will provide an opportunity for you to investigate this problem.

PROCEDURE

a) *Basic control circuit:* Figure 25-1 shows the circuit for a simple control waveform circuit that produces two control signals. It consists of a counter and two counter decoders that control the two flip-flops, from which the output waveforms are taken. Draw a diagram showing how you would implement this circuit, using a 7493 IC counter for the four-bit counter.

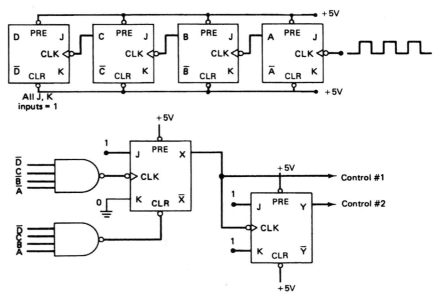

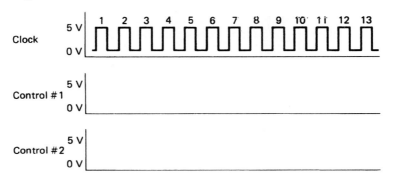

Figure 25-1

b) Draw all circuit output waveforms you expect to observe on an oscilloscope, assuming an input square wave at 10 kHz and no glitches. Use Timing Diagram 25-1.

Timing Diagram 25-1

Show the waveforms and the circuit you drew in step a to your instructor for approval. Then construct the circuit on the circuit board.

c) Apply a 10 kHz square wave to the counter clock input, and monitor both control outputs on the oscilloscope Trigger the oscilloscope on either control output signal. Draw the waveforms you *observe* on the oscilloscope. Do this even if the waveforms are not as expected. Use Timing Diagram 25-2.

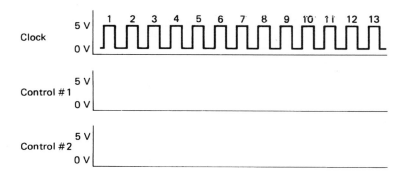

Timing Diagram 25-2

d) *Decoding glitches:* If your circuit failed to operate as expected, it could be because the circuit is decoding glitches. Since the output of the decoders controls the flip-flops, glitches could trigger the flip-flops erroneously. Examine the output of the NAND decoders with the oscilloscope, and check for the presence of glitches. If no glitches are found, then check your circuit wiring for possible errors, and also check for a possible faulty IC.

If glitches are found, disconnect the square wave generator from the counter clock input, and replace the square wave generator with a normally HIGH pushbutton switch. Pulse the counter clock input until a malfunction occurs. Record the count at the point where the malfunction occurs: _____.

Glitches are commonly found at the output of decoders that are driven by asynchronous counter outputs. One way to eliminate the glitches, although not foolproof, is to use synchronous counters instead of asynchronous counters. In the next step, you will reconstruct the control waveform generator using a 74193 IC, a synchronous counter.

e) Redraw the circuit of Figure 25-1, this time using a 74193 IC wired as a MOD-16 UP counter.

Show your circuit to your instructor before proceeding.

f) Repeat step c, using Timing Diagram 25-3 to record your observations.

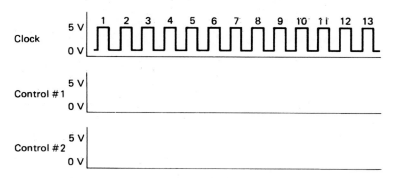

Timing Diagram 25-3

g) Check the outputs of the decoders for glitches. If the decoder outputs are free of glitches but the waveforms are not what is expected, check for faulty circuit wiring and ICs.

h) Now that you have your circuit operating normally, have your instructor or lab assistant put a bug into your circuit. Remember, if you see the bug, ignore it. Also, after you have drawn the observed waveforms (using Timing Diagram 25-4), list all the possible faults you can think of, in the space provided below, before beginning the fault isolation process.

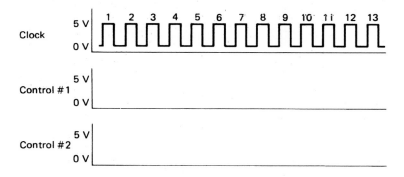

Timing Diagram 25-4

i) *Review:* This concludes the exercises on troubleshooting counters. To test your understanding of the principles covered in this experiment, answer the following questions:

1. Explain how a glitch is produced, and why it may cause faulty circuit operation.

2. Why is the use of synchronous counters to eliminate glitches not foolproof?

3. What other method of glitch elimination are you familiar with?

4. Describe how the control circuit you constructed in this experiment operates.

Experiment 26

Name _____

SHIFT REGISTER COUNTERS

OBJECTIVES

1. To investigate the operation of a ring counter.
2. To investigate the operation of a Johnson counter.

TEXT REFERENCE

Read section 7.14.

EQUIPMENT NEEDED

Components
7476 IC (2);
normally HIGH pushbutton switch, debounced (3);
4 LED monitors.

Instruments
0–5 volt DC power supply;
pulse or square wave generator;
dual trace oscilloscope.

DISCUSSION

Recall that flip-flops are circuits with cross-coupled feedback. Also J-K flip-flops are two-stage flip-flops with feedback from output to input. Shift-register counters are flip-flop devices with feedback, in some manner, from the counter's last flip-flop output to the counter's first flip-flop input.

There are two shift-register counters that are commonly found in digital systems: ring counters and Johnson counters. These two counters are covered in the current experiment. The normal output of a ring counter's last flip-flop is connected to the input of the first flip-flop, thus permitting the current contents of the counter to be continually circulated. On the other hand, the inverted output of a Johnson counter's last flip-flop is connected to the input of the first flip-flop. Thus, the Johnson counter also circulates the inverse of the counter's current contents.

In the current experiment, you will investigate both of these counters. You will study the basic characteristics of each counter. You should become familiar with the waveforms associated with each. While you will not be asked to construct decoders for the counters, you will be queried about the decoding requirements.

PROCEDURE

a) *Ring counter:* Construct the circuit of Figure 26-1. Connect all clear inputs to a single normally HIGH pushbutton switch. Connect the other two pushbutton switches to the DC SET and the clock input of flip-flop 3. Connect LED monitors to each flip-flop output.

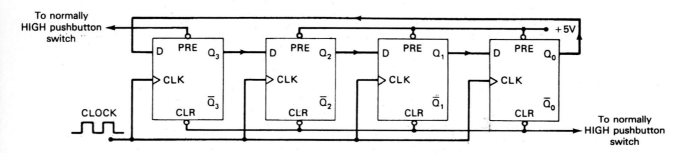

Figure 26-1

b) Clear the counter by pulsing the clear line LOW momentarily. Pulse the clock input LOW several times, and note that the counter outputs do not change. Now preset flip-flop 3 to 1 by pulsing its DC SET input HIGH momentarily. The LEDs should now indicate a count of 1000. Pulse the clock input LOW momentarily. The counter output is now _____. Pulse the clock input two more times. Observe that the 1 now occupies the rightmost position of the counter display. Now pulse the clock input once more. Where is the 1 positioned now? _____.

c) Verify that it does not matter which flip-flop is preset in order to get the counter started. Do this by reconnecting the DC SET pushbutton switch to any of the other flip-flops and repeating step b.

d) Disconnect the clock input from the pushbutton switch, and replace it with the output of a square wave generator set at 1 kHz. Display the generator output and Q_3 on the oscilloscope and observe the time relationship between the two signals. Draw the waveforms on Timing Diagram 26-1. Repeat this procedure for each of the other outputs of the counter.

The MOD-number of this counter is _____. The outputs of the counter [are, are not] square waves. The frequency of each output is _____.

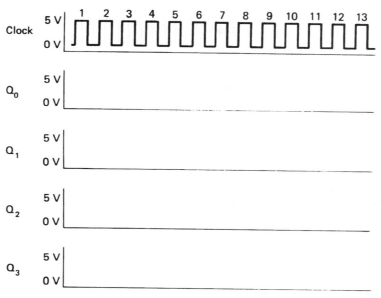

Timing Diagram 26-1

e) *Johnson counter:* Rewire the ring counter so that it is a Johnson counter. Disconnect the square wave generator, and reconnect the pushbutton switch to the clock input of the counter. Clear the counter. Verify the operation of the Johnson counter by pulsing the counter LOW eight times while observing the output. Record your observations in Table 26-1.

Table 26-1

Shift	Output State			
Pulse	Q3	Q2	Q1	Q0
0	0	0	0	0
1				
2				
3				
4				
5				
6				
7				
8				

f) Repeat step d, using Timing Diagram 26-2.

The MOD-number of this counter is _____. The outputs of the counter [are, are not] square waves. The frequency of each output is _____.

g) *Review:* This concludes the exercises on shift register counters. To test your understanding of the principles covered in this experiment, answer the following questions:

1. To start a ring counter, _____ flip-flop must be _____.
2. The MOD-number of a ring counter is equal to _____.
3. The MOD-number of a Johnson counter is equal to _____.
4. Compare the waveforms of the ring and Johnson counters. Which counter
   needs decoding gates in order to decode its outputs? _____.

asynchronously to the clock pulses, the two flip-flops are used to synchronize the loading and shifting of the 74194A.

Assume that the START pulse has been inactive and that clock pulses have been continuously applied for a long time before t_0 (see the waveforms in Figure 27-2). Draw the waveforms you might expect to appear at Q_x, $\overline{Q}_x$, Q_y, and Q_D in response to the START pulse shown in the figure. Use Timing Diagram 27-1.

TIMING DIAGRAM 27-1

i) Wire the circuit in Figure 27-2. Use a normally HIGH pushbutton switch for the START pulse. Connect a square wave generator set at 100 Hz to input CLK of the 74194A. Connect toggle switches to A through D, and set these switches to 1101. Connect one vertical input of the oscilloscope to the output of the generator. Use the other vertical input to monitor first Q_x, $\overline{Q}_x$, Q_y, and Q_D, in that order. Do this by pulsing the START pushbutton several times while connected to each output. You may have to slow the clock down or speed it up so that the outputs are easily observed. Verify that output waveform Q_D is the serial representation for the parallel data.

Demonstrate the circuit for your instructor.

j) *Review:* This concludes the exercises on IC registers. To test your understanding of the principles covered in this experiment, answer the following questions:

1. Why is it necessary to synchronize the load and shift operations of the 74194A?

2. Explain how the flip-flops accomplish this synchronization in the circuit of Figure 27-2.

3. The number of clock pulses necessary to transfer data in parallel is _____, while the number of clock pulses necessary to transfer data serially depends on _____.

4. Show how you would modify the circuit of Figure 27-2 to change it into an eight-bit converter.

5. Show how you would wire the 74194A as a ring counter that shifts left instead of right.

Name_____

DESIGNING WITH COUNTERS AND REGISTERS

OBJECTIVES

1. To practice designing systems using IC counters.
2. To practice designing systems using IC registers.

TEXT REFERENCE

Read Chapter 7.

EQUIPMENT NEEDED

Components and instruments are selected by the student according to her or his design needs.

DISCUSSION

The exercises below will give you an opportunity to practice designing devices using flip-flops, counters, and registers. Before constructing any of these projects, you should check with your instructor as to which exercises are to be completed from design through construction and testing. You should also be sure you know what documentation is required to be turned in.

For your own personal records, you should keep a notebook containing all draft schematics and text from each project as well as a copy of the final schematic and text. When a proposed solution does not work, make a notation on the back of its schematic about what is wrong and why. If you practice this technique, you will seldom repeat the same mistakes on other design projects. You will appreciate your efforts when you are assigned large projects.

PROCEDURE

a) *System clock :* Design a clock with a 100 kHz master oscillator and a 6.667 kHz symmetrical TTL compatible clock signal as its output.

b) *Variable timer:* Design a circuit that, when started, will produce a HIGH output for *N* milliseconds and then a LOW output for 1 second, where *N* is a number that can vary from 0 to 65,535 and that can be loaded into the circuit using toggle switches. Include in the design a clock oscillator to drive the circuit.

c) *Serial input with handshake:* An interface is a circuit that connects a computer to an external device. An input interface is usually capable of receiving a data word from the device—even if the computer is tied up doing something else—and store it until the computer takes it. Computers are not always ready to receive data from an interface. Similarly, interface circuits are not always ready to send data to the computer, interface units are not always ready to receive data from input devices, and finally, input devices do not always have data to send when the interface circuit is ready to receive. In order that all three units can communicate with each other, a single data line and several control lines, called *handshaking lines,* are used to interconnect them. These control lines help to minimize data loss.

A computer has a serial interface circuit that receives 10 bits of information from an input device and a (HIGH) INPUT DEVICE READY signal, and passes all bits, except the first and last bit, on to the computer in parallel when the computer is ready for it. Figure 28-1 shows the relationship among input device, interface, and computer and the format that the input device uses to send data to the interface. The following is a description of these lines:

- The input data line from the device to the interface is normally HIGH. When data is to be transmitted from the device, the device causes the input line to go LOW for one *bit time* (called the START bit), signalling that the next 10 bits are 8 bits of data followed by 2 (HIGH) STOP bits. Bit time is 100 microseconds in duration. See Figure 28-1.

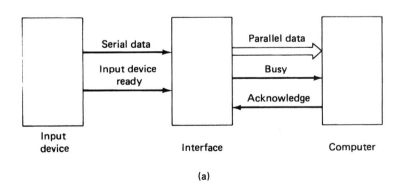

(a)

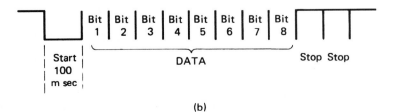

(b)

Figure 28-1

- The BUSY line is a control line from the interface to the computer. When this line is HIGH, the interface is not ready for the computer to take the data. When the line is LOW, the interface is ready.
- The ACKNOWLEDGE line is a control line from the computer to the interface. Whenever the computer has transferred the data from the interface, it drives this line LOW momentarily. The interface responds by forcing the BUSY line HIGH.
- The INPUT DEVICE READY line is a control line from the input device to the interface. As long as this line is LOW, the interface will not shift data serially. On the leading (NGT) edge of the START bit, the device drives this line HIGH, causing the interface to shift data from the input data line. At the end of the STOP bit, the input device forces the INPUT DEVICE READY line LOW, causing the interface to quit shifting data from the input data line. (You can assume that the device will not send data as long as the BUSY line is LOW.)

Design the interface unit.

Experiment 29

TTL AND CMOS IC FAMILIES – PART I

OBJECTIVE

To investigate some of the important characteristics of TTL and CMOS IC families.

TEXT REFERENCES

Read sections 8.1 through 8.5 and sections 8.14 and 8.15.

EQUIPMENT NEEDED

Components
4023 IC;
7410 IC;
74F10 IC (optional);
74LS10 IC;
4 toggle switches;
4 LED monitors.

Instruments
0–5 volt DC power supply;
pulse or square wave generator;
dual trace oscilloscope;
logic probe;
VOM.

DISCUSSION

This experiment is the first of two in which you will investigate some family characteristics of TTL and CMOS ICs. In this experiment, you will learn how to measure average current drawn by an IC, propagation delay, and input/output characteristics of both families.

A typical small scale integration (SSI) IC has 1 to 13 logic gates (or their equivalent). Each gate on a single chip is designed to operate independently of the other gates. However, each receives its power from a single V_{CC} (or V_{DD}) connection to the IC. Measuring the current into this connection will help you to establish a relationship between the power consumption of the chip and the number of the chip's gates that have a LOW output.

Propagation delay is a measure of a gate's speed. It is necessary to have propagation delay for some digital circuits to work properly. It is important for you to understand how propagation delay "accumulates" in circuits, and how individual components like gates contribute to this accumulation, even though you will rarely make such measurements in the field. This accumulated propagation delay is often the cause of incorrect circuit operation.

Most important in the current experiment are the input/output (I/O) characteristics of gates. Knowledge of these parameters is necessary in design work and troubleshooting, for the parameters tell how gates (and other devices) behave under given conditions. For example, the maximum fan-out rating for a gate tells a designer how many loads its output can handle, while the value V_{IH} tells a technician that if a HIGH digital signal on a gate's input goes below this value, the gate's output will be unpredictable.

When you finish these exercises, you should be able to transfer this knowledge to flip-flops and other types of TTL and CMOS devices.

NOTE 1: In this experiment and also in Experiment 30, you will be using CMOS ICs. It is important that you handle CMOS ICs carefully, since they are easily destroyed by static electricity. The ICs are shipped in a special conductive foam that keeps all pins at the same potential. Before removing the IC from the foam, be sure to discharge any potential that may exist among you, the chip, and the circuit board. Once on the board, make sure that all pins are connected (don't leave any disconnected) before applying power. When you are finished with the CMOS IC, remove it and return it to its protective foam.

NOTE 2: Unless specified otherwise, $V_{DD} = V_{CC} = +5$ V and $V_{SS} = GND = 0$ V.

NOTE 3: Some of these exercises may not be required by the instructor.

PROCEDURE

a) Refer to the data sheets for a 4023 IC and a 7410 IC, and draw their pin layout diagrams:

b) *Measuring $I_{CC}(avg)$:* Connect each of the 4023, 7410, 74LS10, and 74F10 ICs using the diagram of Figure 29-1. Do not connect V_{CC} (V_{DD} on 4023) until instructed to do so. Connect GND on each IC to power ground (V_{SS} on 4023). Connect toggle switches to one input of each 4023 gate. Tie all other 4023 gate inputs to V_{DD}. Do not connect any toggle switches to the 7410, 74LS10, and 74F10 inputs, but tie all but one input per gate to V_{CC}. Use a logic probe to check the toggle switches connected to the 4023 to make sure that they can switch between HIGH and LOW.

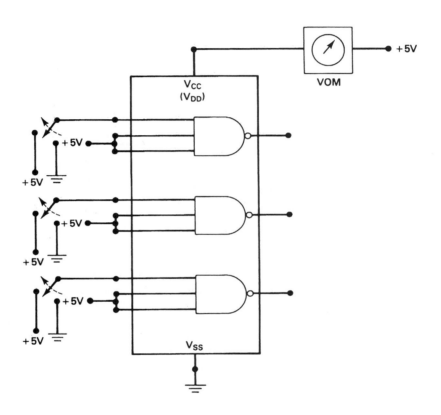

Figure 29-1

To measure the average current that an IC draws from its power supply, connect a VOM set-up to read DC milliamps between V_{CC} and +5 V. Set all three toggle switches to HIGH, and verify that each gate is operating properly with the logic probe. When all gate outputs are LOW, record the value of I_{CCL} indicated by the VOM: _____. Now set all three toggle switches to LOW. Verify that each gate output is now HIGH with the logic probe. Record the value of I_{CCH} indicated by the VOM: _____. Compute the average value for I_{CC} using the formula

$$I_{CC}(avg) = (I_{CCL} + I_{CCH})/2$$

and record this value in the "Static" column for the appropriate IC in Table 29-1.

c) Turn the power supply off. Disconnect the three toggle switches and V_{CC} connections from the inputs of the IC under test. Connect all inputs together on all three gates of the IC, and connect the square wave generator at their common

Table 29-1

Family	Static	10 Hz	100 kHz	1 MHz	Data Sheet
			I_{CC}(avg)		
CMOS					
TTL					
LSTTL					
FTTL					

junction. Turn the power supply and square wave generator on, and set the generator to 10 Hz. Observe the value of I_{CC}(avg) on the VOM, and record this value under "10 Hz" for the appropriate IC in Table 29-1. Repeat this step for square wave frequencies of 100 kHz and 1 MHz.

d) Refer to the data sheet for the 4023 IC, and locate the values given for I_{CCL} and I_{CCH} and record them in Table 29-2.

Table 29-2

	I_{CCL}	I_{CCH}
4023		
7410		
74LS10		
74F10		

Now compute I_{cc}(avg) using the formula given in step b. Record this value in Table 29-1 under "Data Sheet." Since I_{CCH} and I_{CCL} values given by the data sheet are maximums, I_{CC}(avg) should be greater than the observed values.

e) Repeat steps a-d for the 7410, 74LS10, and 74F10 ICs.

f) *Operating speed measurements:* Connect the circuit of Figure 29-2 for each IC that is to be tested. Connect a pulse generator set at 100 kHz signal to the circuit input and monitor both the generator output and the circuit output y on the dual trace oscilloscope. Measure the delay between the leading edge of a positive-going pulse of the generator and the leading edge of the circuit response at y as shown in the waveforms in Figure 29-2. You should note that this is the TOTAL propagation delay, t_{PD}, of the circuit and is the sum of t_{PHL} of the first gate and t_{PLH} of the second gate. An average value for one of the gates can be obtained by dividing t_{PD} by 2. Compute the average value, and record it in Table 29-3.

g) Refer to the data sheet for the IC being tested, and compute the average delay using the maximum values that are given for t_{PHL} and t_{PLH}. Record this value

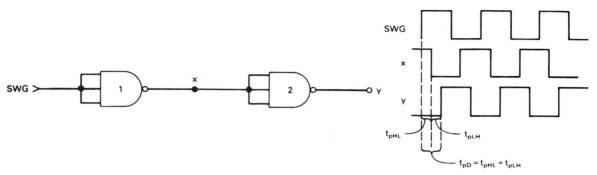

Figure 29-2

Table 29-3

Family	tPD	
	Observed	Data Sheet
CMOS		
TTL		
LSTTL		
FTTL		

in Table 29-3 also. This computed value should be greater than the observed value, since you used maximum values.

h) Repeat steps f and g for the 7410, 74LS10, AND 74F10 ICs.

i) *I/O Characteristics:* For one CMOS gate, remove the connection between its inputs and the inputs of the other gates. Make sure that the gate has nothing tied to its output. Refer to Figure 29-3a and connect a toggle switch to the inputs of the gate you just disconnected. Set the toggle switch to HIGH and measure V_{OL}, then set the switch to LOW, and measure the value of V_{OH}. Record these values in Table 29-4, line 1.

Table 29-4

	No Load	
	V_{OL}	V_{OH}
4023		
7410		
74LS10		
74F10		

j) Refer to Figure 29-3b and connect the output of the gate tested in step i to the inputs of one of the remaining gates. This represents three loads. Measure V_{OL} and V_{OH} of the driver gate, and record your measurements in Table 29-5, line 1.

184

Exper. 29

Table 29-5

	Under Load	
	V_{OL}	V_{OH}
4023		
7410		
74LS10		
74F10		

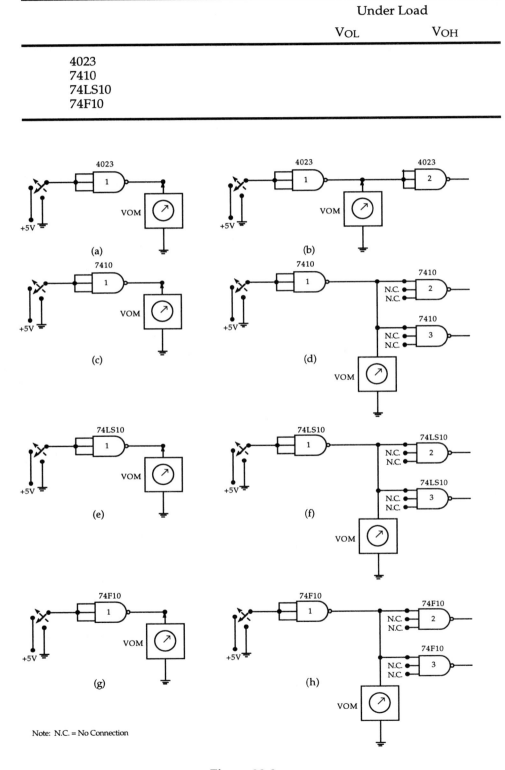

Note: N.C. = No Connection

Figure 29-3

These readings should not differ appreciably from those recorded in step i. This is due to the extremely high input resistance at a CMOS input.

k) Wire the circuit of Figure 29-3c. Make sure that you do not connect anything to the output of gate 1 except the VOM. Set the toggle switch to HIGH and measure V_{OL}. Record this value on line 2 of Table 29-4 under V_{OL}. Now set the toggle switch to LOW and measure V_{OH}. Record this value on line 2 of Table 29-4 under V_{OH}.

l) Wire the circuit of Figure 29-3d. Note that only one input to each of gates 2 and 3 is connected to the output of gate 1. These two inputs combine for a total of two TTL loads. The remaining two inputs to gates 2 and 3 are left disconnected. Also, make sure that nothing is tied to the outputs of gates 2 and 3. Set the toggle switch to HIGH and measure V_{OL} of gate 1. Record this value on line 2 of Table 29-5 under V_{OL}. Now set the toggle switch to LOW and measure V_{OH} of gate 1. Record this value on line 2 of Table 29-5 under V_{OH}.

m) Wire the circuit of Figure 29-3e. Make sure that you do not connect anything to the output of gate 1 except the VOM. Set the toggle switch to HIGH and measure V_{OL}. Record this value on line 3 of Table 29-4 under V_{OL}. Now set the toggle switch to LOW and measure V_{OH}. Record this value on line 3 of Table 29-4 under V_{OH}.

n) Wire the circuit of Figure 29-3f. Note that only one input to each of gates 2 and 3 is connected to the output of gate 1. These two inputs combine for a total of two LS-TTL loads. The remaining two inputs to gates 2 and 3 are left disconnected. Also, make sure that nothing is tied to the outputs of gates 2 and 3. Set the toggle switch to HIGH and measure V_{OL} of gate 1. Record this value on line 3 of Table 29-5 under V_{OL}. Now set the toggle switch to LOW and measure V_{OH} of gate 1. Record this value on line 3 of Table 29-5 under V_{OH}.

o) Wire the circuit of Figure 29-3g. Make sure that you do not connect anything to the output of gate 1 except the VOM. Set the toggle switch to HIGH and measure V_{OL}. Record this value on line 4 of Table 29-4 under V_{OL}. Now set the toggle switch to LOW and measure V_{OH}. Record this value on line 4 of Table 29-4 under V_{OH}.

p) Wire the circuit of Figure 29-3h. Note that only one input to each of gates 2 and 3 is connected to the output of gate 1. These two inputs combine for a total of two F-TTL loads. The remaining two inputs to gates 2 and 3 are left disconnected. Also, make sure that nothing is tied to the outputs of gates 2 and 3. Set the toggle switch to HIGH and measure V_{OL} of gate 1. Record this value on line 4 of Table 29-5 under V_{OL}. Now set the toggle switch to LOW and measure V_{OH} of gate 1. Record this value on line 4 of Table 29-5 under V_{OH}.

q) For the 7410, compare the no-load measurements (line 2 of Table 29-4) with the measurements made under two loads (line 2 of Table 29-5). You should have observed an appreciable difference. This is due to the fact that TTL input resistances are not extremely high. You should have observed a larger variation between the two V_{OL} readings. This is because of the current that is sunk from a 7410 gate input back through the driver output transistor. Increasing the number of loads will increase this sink current and therefore cause V_{OL} to increase, even though the output resistance is relatively low (< 50 ohms). This is true for all TTL devices.

r) Compare the 74LS10 no-load measurements (line 3 of Table 29-4) with the measurements made under two loads (line 3 of Table 29-5). As in step q above, you should have noted an appreciable difference between the two measurements.

s) Connect the circuit of Figure 29-4a. This circuit connects one unit load to the output of gate 1, a 7410 gate. Set the toggle switch to HIGH, then measure and record I_{OL}. Compare this reading to the one-unit load factor of 1.6 mA.

$$I_{OL} = \text{_____} \text{ mA (1 TTL load)}$$

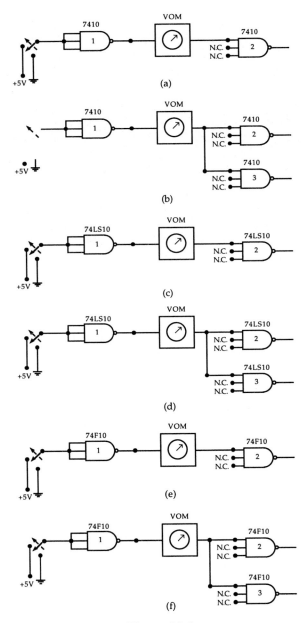

Figure 29-4

t) Connect the circuit of Figure 29-4b. This circuit connects two unit loads to gate 1. Set the toggle switch to HIGH, then measure and record I_{OL}.

$$I_{OL} = \underline{\hspace{2cm}} \text{ mA (2 TTL loads)}$$

u) Connect the circuit of Figure 29-4c. This circuit connects one LS-TTL load to the output of gate 1, a 74LS10 gate. Set the toggle switch to HIGH, then measure and record I_{OL}. Compare this reading to the one unit load factor of 1.6 mA.

$$I_{OL} = \underline{\hspace{2cm}} \text{ mA (1 LS-TTL load)}$$

v) Connect the circuit of Figure 29-4d. This circuit connects two LS-TTL loads to gate 1. Set the toggle switch to HIGH, then measure and record I_{OL}.

$$I_{OL} = \underline{\hspace{2cm}} \text{ mA (2 LS-TTL loads)}$$

w) (Optional) Connect the circuit of Figure 29-4e. This circuit connects one F-TTL load to the output of gate 1, a 74F10 gate. Set the toggle switch to HIGH, then measure and record I_{OL}. Compare this reading to the one-unit load factor of 1.6 mA.

$$I_{OL} = \underline{\hspace{2cm}} \text{ mA (1F-TTL load)}$$

x) (Optional) Connect the circuit of Figure 29-4f. This circuit connects two F-TTL loads to the output of gate 1. Set the toggle switch to HIGH, then measure and record I_{OL}.

$$I_{OL} = \underline{\hspace{2cm}} \text{ mA (2 F-TTL loads)}$$

y) *Review:* This concludes the first part of the investigation of TTL and CMOS families. To test your understanding of the principles covered in this experiment, answer the following questions:

1. The total propagation delay, t_{PD}, in a circuit like that of Figure 29-2 is computed by summing _____ of gate 1 and _____ of gate 2. The average value of one of the gates is _____.
2. The reason why V_{OL} increased with increasing loads for the TTL gate was
_____.
3. One unit load for standard TTL when output is low is _____.
4. The fan-out for LS-TTL when the output is LOW is _____ unit loads.
5. Compare standard TTL with CMOS in terms of the measurements you made on both in this experiment.
6. The fan-out for F-TTL when the output is LOW is _____ unit loads.

Experiment 30

TTL AND CMOS IC FAMILIES — PART II

OBJECTIVES

1. To investigate CMOS and TTL interfacing.
2. To investigate the operation of a TTL open collector IC, the 7405.
3. To investigate the operation of a TTL tristate IC, the 74125.
4. To investigate the operation of a CMOS transmission gate, the 4016.

TEXT REFERENCES

Read sections 8.7 through 8.8 and sections 8.18 through 8.20.

EQUIPMENT NEEDED

Components
4023 IC;
7405 IC;
7410 IC;
74LS10 IC;
74125 IC;
4 toggle switches;
1 LED monitor.

Instruments
0–5 volt DC power supply;
pulse or square wave generator;
dual trace oscilloscope;
logic probe;
VOM.

DISCUSSION

TTL-CMOS Interfacing

Interfacing two gates or circuits is not always straightforward. For example, you cannot drive the inputs of some CMOS gates (4000 and 74HC series) with a TTL output the way you drove TTL inputs with TTL outputs. One reason for this, as you discovered in Experiment 29, is that the lower limit for a HIGH (V_{IH}) at a CMOS input is 70% of V_{DD}, or about 3.5 volts if V_{DD} = 5 volts. Since V_{OH} for TTL outputs can be as low as 2.4 volts, the CMOS gate may not respond properly all the time. A solution to this problem is to use 74HCT series ICs, which are directly compatible with TTL. In the current experiment, you will investigate TTL-CMOS interfacing.

Open Collector TTL

Other interface devices are also investigated in this experiment: the open collector TTL and tristate TTL. The open collector is a common device for connecting TTL outputs to a device which operates at a slightly higher voltage or current than TTL can handle directly. Open collector devices can also be used to connect two or more TTL outputs together directly.

Tristate TTL

Tristate TTL devices have an enable input that can switch the output of the gate from a TTL HIGH or LOW to a third logic state, which is called high impedance (Hi-Z) or floating. These devices act like their standard TTL counterparts when enabled but like an open output when disabled. In fact, when the device is disabled, an ohmmeter will indicate an extremely high resistance between output and ground and output and V_{CC}. Tristate devices are primarily used to switch TTL outputs onto a bus when enabled and disconnect the outputs when disabled. Registers and other large ICs often have tristate devices built into their output circuits so that the devices may be used in bus systems.

CMOS Transmission Gates

The transmission gate is called by various other names, such as bilateral switch and analog switch. It is a circuit which switches analog or digital signals (as long as the signals are within the limits of 0 to V_{DD}), much like an electromechanical relay. The switching function is controlled by digital input logic. The gate's input and output are interchangeable.

> NOTE: See the note in Experiment 29 concerning the handling of CMOS ICs. Also, unless specified otherwise, $V_{DD} = V_{CC}$ = +5 V and V_{SS} = GND = 0 V.

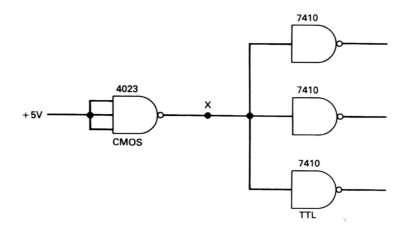

Figure 30-1

PROCEDURE

a) *CMOS driving TTL:* Connect the circuit of Figure 30-1.

Measure and record V_{OL} at point x.

$$V_{OL} = \text{_____} \text{ (3 TTL loads)}$$

You should observe that $V_{OL} > 0.8$ V, which is V_{IL}(max) for TTL. When V_{IL} exceeds 0.8 V, a TTL gate cannot be guaranteed to respond as if its input is LOW.

b) Disconnect two of the 7410 inputs from the 4023 output and observe that V_{OL} of the 4023 decreases, probably well below 0.8 V. Record this value.

$$V_{OL} = \text{_____} \text{ (1 TTL load)}$$

You should deduce that the 4023 can reliably drive <u>one</u> 7410 input.

c) *CMOS driving LSTTL:* Repeat step a, this time using three 74LS10 loads. You should observe that V_{OL} is well below 0.8 V, even though the 4023 is driving three loads. Why? _____.

d) *TTL driving CMOS:* Since CMOS gates draw virtually no current, you should expect no current problems when TTL gates drive CMOS gates. However, CMOS gate inputs require V_{IH} to be at least 3.5 V when $V_{DD} = 5$ V, while TTL HIGH outputs can go as low as 2.4 V under extreme conditions.

Connect the circuit of Figure 30-2, measure the voltage at x, and record it.

$$V_x = \text{_____} \text{ (no pull-up)}$$

While V_x is probably greater than 3.5 V and still sufficient for driving a CMOS input, the *safety noise margin* for the CMOS gate is greatly reduced. For this reason, a pull-up resistor would be advisable to raise the voltage at x. Use a 1 k-ohm pull-up resistor at x and measure V_x again. Record this value.

$$V_x = \text{_____} \text{ (1 k-ohm pull-up)}$$

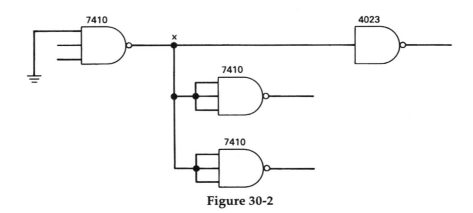

Figure 30-2

e) *TTL open collector—7405 IC operation:* Refer to the data sheet for a 7405 IC. Note that the pin layout is like the 7404 totem-pole hex-inverter. However, the 7405 inverter requires an external pull-up resistor to operate. Install a 7405 IC on the circuit board. Connect V_{CC} to +5 V and GND to power ground. Connect a toggle switch to each inverter input. Do not connect the pull-up resistor yet.

f) Toggle the input switch to one of the inverters, and use a VOM to measure V_{OL} and V_{OH} at the output of this gate. Record these values.

$$V_{OL} = \text{_____} \text{ (no pull-up)}$$

$$V_{OH} = \text{_____} \text{ (no pull-up)}$$

You should observe that there is no voltage in the HIGH state because there is no pull-up resistor.

g) Add a 1 k-ohm pull-up resistor, and repeat step f.

$$V_{OL} = \text{_____} \text{ (1 k-ohm pull-up)}$$

$$V_{OH} = \text{_____} \text{ (1 k-ohm pull-up)}$$

h) The value of the pull-up resistor used above was arbitrary. When determining the pull-up value for a particular load situation, you would compute the value using the outline given in the text. Assume three TTL loads, and compute R_C for a 7405 gate. Record your value below.

$$R_C = \text{_____} \text{ ohms}$$

i) *Open collector application—WIRED-AND:* Connect the circuit of Figure 30-3. Use a standard resistor slightly larger than the one computed for R_C in step h.

This circuit configuration is called the WIRED-AND. Connect one input from each gate of the 7410 IC to act as the three TTL loads. Connect inputs D, E, and F to ground and toggle switches to inputs A, B, and C. Connect an LED monitor to output x of the WIRED-AND circuit. The circuit is now a three-input logic gate. Test the operation of the circuit by setting toggle switches A, B, and C to each input combination listed in Table 30-1 and observing the effect of these inputs on output x. Record your observations in the table.

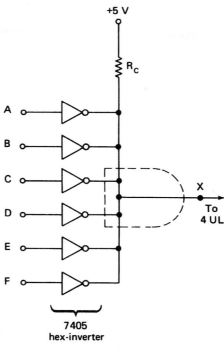

Figure 30-3

Table 30-1

Inputs			Output
A	B	C	x
0	0	0	
0	0	1	
0	1	0	
0	1	1	
1	0	0	
1	0	1	
1	1	0	
1	1	1	

j) Based on your observations in step i, the logic operation this circuit performs is the _____ operation.

k) *TTL Tristate—74125 IC operation:* Refer to the data sheet for a 74125 IC, and draw its pin layout diagram:

Study the various operating modes of the IC before continuing.

l) Install a 74125 IC on the circuit board, and connect V_{CC} to +5 V and GND to power ground. Connect toggle switches to one of the buffer inputs and to its enabling input, $\overline{E}$. Set $\overline{E}$ LOW to enable the buffer. Verify that the buffer is enabled by toggling the input and observing the output with a logic probe.

m) Now disable the buffer by setting $\overline{E}$ HIGH. Connect the common lead of a VOM, set up to measure resistance, to ground and the "+" lead to the buffer output. You should observe a very large resistance, typically several M-ohms. Disconnect the VOM, and monitor the output of the buffer with the logic probe while toggling the input switch. You should observe that the input has no effect on the output of the buffer. This is because the output is essentially disconnected from the rest of the circuit.

n) *TTL tristate application—busses:* A typical use of tristate buffers is in connecting two or more signals to a common output, typically a data bus. Examine the circuit of Figure 30-4. Note that the buffer enabling inputs are always at complementary levels. Data from input A_0 is allowed to enter bus B when buffer 1 is enabled. Data at input A_1 is prevented from entering the bus at this time because buffer 2 is disabled. The reverse situation occurs when buffer 2 is enabled. Therefore the two sets of data cannot be placed onto the bus at the same time.

Construct the circuit of Figure 30-4. Connect toggle switches to the buffer inputs A_0 and A_1 and to the enabling input, E. Test the circuit by setting E to LOW, and observe the effect of toggling the data input switches on bus B with a logic probe. Repeat this for E set to HIGH. Record your observations in Table 30-2. Under "Bus," put A_0 or A_1, depending on which one has an effect on the bus.

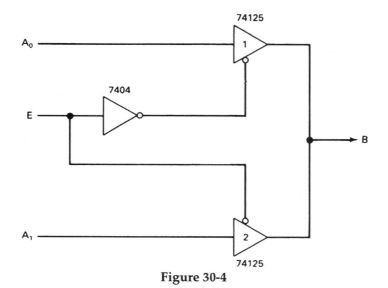

Figure 30-4

Table 30-2

E	Bus
0	
1	

o) *4016 IC operation:* Refer to the data sheet for a 4016 IC, and draw its pin layout diagram:

p) Install a 4016 IC on the circuit board, and make the connections as shown in Figure 30-5. Connect a toggle switch to pin 13 and a pulse generator set to 10 kHz and with an output that ranges from 0 V to 4 V to pin 1. Connect an oscilloscope set up to measure DC to pin 2. Set the control switch to 0, and turn the power on. What do you observe on the oscilloscope display? _____.

Now set the control switch to 1. What do you observe?_____.

q) Turn the power off, and reverse the connections at pins 2 and 1. Turn the power on. What do you observe on the oscilloscope display?

_____

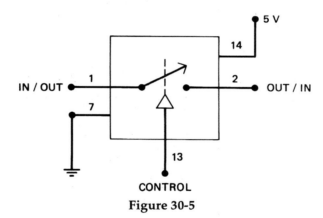

Figure 30-5

r) In step p, you should have observed that the output of the gate was about 0 V when the control switch was set to 0 and was essentially the output of the generator when the control switch was set to 1. In step q, you demonstrated that the switch is bidirectional.

s) *Review:* This concludes the second set of exercises on TTL and CMOS families. To test your understanding of the principles covered in this exercise, answer the following questions:

1. When a TTL gate is used to drive a CMOS input, a pull-up resistor is used at the CMOS input because

_____.

2. When a CMOS gate is used to drive several TTL inputs, the TTL gates may not respond correctly if _____.

3. Why are buffers necessary when tying LEDs to TTL outputs?

4. TTL totem-pole outputs cannot be connected together because

_____

5. Use Boolean algebra to prove that the WIRED-AND circuit you constructed performs the function you specified in step j.

6. Explain why it is necessary to use tristate buffers when connecting two or more data sources to a bus.

7. Compare a CMOS transmission gate to a TTL tristate buffer.

Experiment 31

USING A LOGIC ANALYZER

OBJECTIVES

1. To learn how to display and interpret digital waveforms using a 7D01 logic analyzer.
2. To practice using the various trigger modes and sources available on the 7D01.

TEXT REFERENCE

Read Appendix B in the back of this manual.

EQUIPMENT NEEDED

Components
7493 IC (2)

Instruments
7D01 logic analyzer;
0–5 volt DC power supply;
pulse or square wave generator;
logic probe.

DISCUSSION

Before attempting this experiment, read and be sure you understand Appendix B in the back of this manual. If your lab uses a logic analyzer other than the one this experiment features, your instructor will explain the differences and/or modify the experiment to fit the lab model.

PROCEDURE

PART 1—INITIAL CHECKOUT

a) 1. Do not connect the data probes to any signals.

2. Set the 7D01 panel controls as follows:

Vertical

POS. (position)..	MIDRANGE
MAG. (magnifier)	X1
RECORD DISPLAY TIME............................	∞ (fully clockwise detent)
CLOCK QUALIFIER	OFF

Horizontal

POS.	MIDRANGE
MAG..	X1
THRESHOLD VOLTAGE	TTL (+1.4 V)
EXT CLOCK POLARITY	↑
SAMPLE INTERVAL	1 ms
DATA CHANNELS	0–3
DATA POSITION	POST-TRIGGER
TRIG SOURCE	CH. 0 (channel 0)
EXT TRIGGER POLARITY...........................	↑

Word Recognizer (W.R.)

W.R. MODE	ASYNCH
FILTER..	MIN
CH. 0 through 15..	X (center)
EXTERNAL QUALIFIER.............................	X (center)
PROBE QUALIFIER	X (center)

b) Turn on the power to the 7D01.

c) Press the MANUAL RESET button (right above the SAMPLE INTERVAL selector). This initiates a new STORE mode. The analyzer is now sampling the various channel inputs every 1 μs.

d) To terminate the STORE mode and begin the DISPLAY mode, a TRIGGER EVENT must occur. With the TRIGGER SOURCE set to CH. 0, the logic analyzer is waiting for a positive transition on the channel 0 probe. Since this will not occur (with the probes not connected) we can use the MANUAL TRIGGER to generate a TRIGGER EVENT. Depress the MANUAL TRIGGER pushbutton.

e) Four waveform traces should appear on the CRT. They will have random logic levels, because the probes are not connected.

f) Verify that the VERT POS and VERT MAG controls can be used to vary the vertical position and spacing of the four traces. The HORIZ POS control should vary the horizontal position of the traces.

g) Change the DATA CHANNELS switch to 0–7. Eight traces should now appear. You may have to vary the VERT POS and MAG controls to get a reasonable display of the eight traces.

h) Change the DATA CHANNELS switch to 0–15 and repeat step g for 16 traces.

i) Set the DATA CHANNELS switch back to 0–3.

j) The four traces should have an intensified zone on the left end, which indicates the TRIGGER EVENT point. If you can't see this, gradually reduce the CRT intensity.

k) You should also see another intensified zone, which indicates the CURSOR point. It will be at some random point on the screen. Verify that it can be horizontally positioned on the screen using the CURSOR COARSE and FINE controls. The readout at the top of the screen will continually indicate the CURSOR position relative to the TRIGGER points in the units of one SAMPLE INTERVAL.

l) Set the CURSOR position to TRIG +45, and answer the following.

1. What is the time duration between the CURSOR and the TRIGGER point?
_____.

2. What are the logic levels on the four channels at the CURSOR point?
_____.

3. What is the total time duration from the beginning to the end of the trace?
_____.

m) Change the DATA POSITION switch to CENTER, and note that the intensified trigger point has moved to the approximate center of the display. Verify that the CURSOR can be positioned before or after the TRIGGER point.

n) Change to PRE-TRIGGER and verify that the trigger point is moved to the right end of the screen.

o) Set the DATA POSITION switch back to POST-TRIGGER.

p) The current display will stay on the screen indefinitely because the DISPLAY TIME has been set to ∞. A new STORE mode can be initiated by depressing the MANUAL RESET pushbutton. Then, a new DISPLAY mode can be initiated by pressing MANUAL TRIGGER. Do this several times.

q) Repeat step q for a shorter display time.

r) Set the DISPLAY TIME back to ∞. Hit MANUAL TRIGGER to obtain the four channel traces.

s) The SAMPLE INTERVAL that is used during the STORE mode can be varied between 10 n sec and 5 m sec. However, there are certain limitations when 8 or 16 channels are being used. When 8 channels are being used, the selected SAMPLE INTERVAL must be 20 ns or greater. For 16-channel operation, the

SAMPLE INTERVAL must be 50 ns or greater. If you try to use a smaller SAMPLE INTERVAL than allowed, a light will blink on the SAMPLE INTERVAL dial. Verify this by changing the DATA CHANNELS switch and the SAMPLE INTERVAL selector switch.

t) If the SAMPLE INTERVAL is set to EXT, the SAMPLE INTERVAL is determined by an external clock signal connected to the appropriate probe.

NOTE: In this experiment, we will not be using the external SAMPLE CLOCK. Instead, we will use the 7D01's internally-generated, switch-selected SAMPLE INTERVAL.

u) Set the SAMPLE INTERVAL back to 1.0 ms.

PART 2—DISPLAYING COUNTER WAVEFORMS

a) We will now use the logic analyzer to display the waveforms from a 7493 IC counter. Connect a 7493 IC as a MOD-16 counter. Be sure that the master reset inputs are grounded. Connect the power supply to the 7493 IC. Now connect the clock A input of the counter to a pulse generator that is set to 10 kHz. Turn on the pulse generator, and use your logic probe to verify that all of the counter outputs are pulsing.

b) Connect the 7D01's upper data probes to the counter outputs as follows:

Ch. 0 (black wire) .... Output Q_A
Ch. 1 (brown wire) .... Output Q_B
Ch. 2 (red wire)... Output Q_C
Ch. 3 (orange wire) .... Output Q_D

Also, connect the ground probe (white wire) to the ground of your circuit.

c) The logic analyzer can now be commanded to sample and store these waveforms by pressing the MANUAL RESET button. Do this, and note that a display of the counter waveforms appears almost immediately. This is because the signal connected to channel 0 has produced a positive transition for the TRIGGER EVENT (remember, our TRIG SOURCE is selected as Ch. 0).

NOTE: If the counter waveforms do not appear, notify your instructor immediately.

d) Check to see that the intensified TRIGGER point occurs when the channel 0 waveform has gone from LOW to HIGH. Also, note the logic levels on the other waveforms at the TRIGGER point. Record them as a four-bit number in the following order:

Ch. 3 _____, Ch. 2 _____, Ch. 1 _____, Ch. 0 _____.

e) Now position the CURSOR so that it coincides with the TRIGGER point. The 4-bit number on the bottom of the display will now indicate the waveform levels at the TRIGGER point. The results should be the same as you recorded in step d.

f) As you move the CURSOR to various other points on the waveforms, the 4-bit number should change to reflect the waveform levels at the CURSOR point. Verify this.

g) The CURSOR can be used to measure approximate time intervals between two points on a waveform. To demonstrate this, position the CURSOR just before one of the positive transitions of the Ch. 0 waveform. Note the CURSOR position relative to the TRIGGER point. Then move the CURSOR to the next Ch. 0's positive transition and note how many SAMPLE INTERVALS the CURSOR has moved. Record this number:

Number of SAMPLE INTERVALS = _____.

Record the measured value of one period of the Ch. 0 waveform. _____.

Compare this to the expected value (remember that the counter is being driven by a 10 kHz clock signal).

h) Use the same method to measure the pulse duration of the waveform on Ch. 2.

Pulse duration of Ch. 2 = _____.

i) The HORIZ MAG control can be used to horizontally magnify the waveforms by a factor of up to 10. Verify its operation.

j) When the waveforms are magnified horizontally, the HORIZ POS control can be used to find any part of the original unmagnified waveforms. Verify this.

k) Return the HORIZ MAG to ×1, and position the CURSOR at the TRIGGER point (TRIG + 0).

l) Press the MANUAL RESET button to initiate a new STORE mode and DISPLAY mode. Find the TRIGGER point on the waveforms; the CURSOR should still be at the TRIGGER point.

m) What are the waveform levels at the TRIGGER point this time? Are they the same as in steps d and e? If they are, then repeat step l until they change.

n) Why has the TRIGGER point changed? (Hint: what is our TRIGGER source?) _____.

o) With four channels, the duration of the waveform display is 1016 SAMPLE INTERVALS, or 1016 μs, since our SAMPLE INTERVAL is 1 μs. If we chose to use eight channels, the duration would be 508 SAMPLE INTERVALS, and the display would not show as many cycles of the counter waveforms. Check this out by switching the DATA CHANNELS to 0–7. Then press MANUAL RESET. You may have to use the VERT POS and VERT MAG controls to get all eight traces on the screen at the same time.

Note that the Ch. 0–Ch. 3 waveform displays are now spread out by a factor of 2 from what they were before, since the total time duration is 508 ms. This is similar to changing the time scale on a conventional scope.

p) Repeat step o for 16 channels, and observe what happens. What is the total time duration of the waveform now? _____.

q) Return to the 4-channel display mode.

r) We can also change the total time duration of the display by changing the SAMPLE INTERVAL. Change it to 2 μs and press MANUAL RESET. The resultant display now represents 1016 × 2.0 μs = 2032 μs time duration. Thus, there should be twice as many cycles of the various counter waveforms.

s) Change the SAMPLE INTERVAL to 0.5 μs and press MANUAL RESET. The display now represents 1016 × 0.5 μs = 508 μs. Thus, there are fewer cycles of the waveform being displayed.

t) The SAMPLE INTERVAL is usually made very small whenever we want to take a close look at a specific portion of the waveforms. For example, suppose we want to take a close look at the positive transition of the Ch. 0 waveform. The TRIG SOURCE is already set to Ch. 0, and we are using POST-TRIGGER so that the start of the display will show the positive-going edge of Ch. 0. Set SAMPLE INTERVAL to 10 n sec, and press MANUAL RESET. The display should now show the waveforms spread way out. The rising edge of Ch. 0 can now be examined with a resolution of 10 n sec. The total time duration of the display is only 1016 × 10 n sec = 10.16 μs. The other channel waveforms are not changing during this time.

u) A large SAMPLE INTERVAL is usually used when we want to see a larger portion of the waveforms. Set SAMPLE INTERVAL to 20 μs, and press MANUAL RESET. The display now represents 1016 × 20 μs = 20.32 m sec. Thus, there are many cycles of the waveforms crowded into the display. The HORIZ MAG can be used to spread out the display to make it easier to examine the various waveforms.

v) There are two important considerations that limit the maximum size of the SAMPLE INTERVAL:

1. If the interval chosen is too large, glitches or narrow pulses on the waveforms may be missed by the logic analyzer if they happen to occur in the interval between edges of the SAMPLE CLOCK. See Figure 31-1.

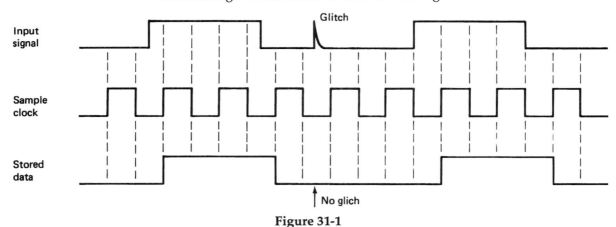

Figure 31-1

2. If the chosen SAMPLE INTERVAL is greater than the narrowest pulse width on the data waveform, the logic analyzer will not produce an accurate display of the waveform. For our waveforms, the narrowest pulse is about 100 μs on Ch. 0, 200 μs on Ch. 1, 400 μs on Ch. 2, and 800 μs on Ch. 3. Try various

SAMPLE INTERVALs greater than 100 µs and observe what happens to the displayed waveforms. Use the HORIZ MAG to spread the waveforms out. *In general, you should never use a SAMPLE INTERVAL greater than 1/2 the width of the narrowest data pulse.*

w) Set SAMPLE INTERVAL back to 1 µs and get a new display.

PART 3—USING AN EXTERNAL TRIGGER SOURCE

a) We have used MANUAL TRIGGER and Ch. 0 as the source for the TRIGGER EVENT. Another possible trigger source is EXT (external). Switch the TRIGGER SOURCE selector to EXT.

b) Press MANUAL RESET to initiate a new STORE mode. Note that the display does not appear. This is because no TRIGGER EVENT has occurred, since there is no signal connected to the EXT TRIG input jack.

c) Connect a 1× or BNC-to-alligator probe (*do NOT use a 10×probe*) from the EXT TRIG jack to a normally LOW pushbutton.

d) Press the pushbutton switch. The logic analyzer should now display the various waveforms, because the positive transition from the pushbutton output has produced the TRIGGER EVENT.

e) Change the EXT TRIG POLARITY switch to negative-going transition, and then press MANUAL RESET. Again, there is no display, because a TRIGGER EVENT hasn't occurred yet.

f) Press the pushbutton and hold it down. Why doesn't the display appear? Release the pushbutton. The display should now appear.

PART 4—USING THE WORD RECOGNIZER AS THE TRIGGER SOURCE

a) The WORD RECOGNIZER is used to generate a TRIGGER EVENT when a specific word (pattern of 0s and 1s) is present on the input data channels. For example, you might want to generate a TRIGGER when the 16 data inputs are at 1001101100101111. This binary pattern is called the TRIGGER WORD.

There are 16 three-position switches (one for each channel) that select the state of each data channel for the desired TRIGGER WORD. For example, if the desired TRIGGER WORD is 1010111000010110, the switches for channels 15, 13, 11, 10, 9, 4, 2, and 1 should be set HIGH, and the switches for the other channels should be set LOW.

Whenever a data channel is not being used, the WORD RECOGNIZER switch should be set to the middle position (X) so that it is not part of the TRIGGER WORD. Even when a data channel is being used, you can set its WR switch to X if you don't want that particular data channel to be part of the TRIGGER WORD.

b) Set the 16 WR channel switches to XXXXXXXXXXXX0101. The TRIGGER WORD is thus 0101 for the four channels we are using.

c) Set the TRIG SOURCE to WR. Then press the MANUAL RESET button.

d) Position the CURSOR at the TRIGGER point (TRIG + 0). The TRIGGER should occur when the waveform levels are 0101.

e) Display the four waveforms with a TRIGGER point at 1011. Demonstrate this to your instructor or lab assistant.

f) The WR MODE switch is currently in the ASYNC position. In this position, the WR generates a TRIGGER EVENT as soon as the conditions on the WR channel switches are met. *It does not wait for a clock signal.*

If this switch is placed in the SYNC position, the WR will generate a TRIGGER EVENT when the WR conditions are met *and* the active edge of the EXTERNAL SAMPLE CLOCK occurs. This position is used *only* when the SAMPLE INTERVAL switch is set to EXT and the external system clock is connected to the "C" probe on the Ch. 0–7 connector.

Since we are using the logic analyzer's internal SAMPLE CLOCK, the WR MODE has to be set to ASYNC or the WR will not produce a trigger. Verify this by switching to SYNC and hitting MANUAL RESET. Note that there is no display.

Return to the ASYNC mode. The display should appear.

g) There are two other switches that are part of the WR operation. One is the EXTERNAL QUALIFIER switch. It can be used to add one more condition to those needed to produce a WR TRIGGER. The other switch is the PROBE QUALIFIER. Let's examine the EXT QUALIFIER switch first.

1) Set the EXT QUALIFIER switch to HIGH.
2) Connect a toggle switch to the EXT TRIG/QUALIFIER INPUT jack (this is a dual purpose jack). Set the toggle switch to LOW.
3) Press MANUAL RESET. Note that there is no display, even though the data inputs satisfy the WR channel switch settings, because the level at the QUALIFIER INPUT does not match the EXTERNAL QUALIFIER switch setting.
4) Set the toggle switch HIGH, and note that the display appears, since the EXTERNAL QUALIFIER condition is now satisfied. The TRIGGER point on the waveform should still be 1011 (the settings on the WR channel switches).
5) Set EXT QUALIFIER back to X, and disconnect the QUALIFIER INPUT.

h) The PROBE QUALIFIER switch operates the same as the EXT QUALIFIER switch, except that it specifies the logic level required at the PROBE QUALIFIER input that is connected to the "Q" probe on the Ch. 8–15 connector.

1) Set the PROBE QUALIFIER switch to HIGH, and connect the Q probe to a toggle switch that is in the LOW state.
2) Press MANUAL RESET, and note that no display appears because the Q input is not HIGH.
3) Set the toggle switch connected to the Q probe to HIGH, and the display should appear. The TRIGGER point should still be at 1011.
4) Set the PROBE QUALIFIER switch back to X, and disconnect the Q probe.

i) The WR FILTER control (lower right-hand corner) is used to control the amount of time that the WR conditions have to be satisfied for the WR to generate a TRIGGER. This time requirement can be varied from 10 n sec to around 300 n sec. For example, if the WR FILTER setting is 100 n sec, then the WR will not generate a TRIGGER EVENT unless the WR conditions (WR channel switches and qualifiers) are met for 100 n sec or longer.

The WR FILTER can be used to prevent erratic triggering of the WR in situations where glitches or "race" conditions cause the WR conditions to be satisfied. This is demonstrated in the next step.

j) Make sure that the CURSOR is still positioned at the TRIGGER point.

k) Set the WR for a TRIGGER WORD of 0000.

l) 1) Set the DISPLAY TIME for a few seconds. The logic analyzer will now automatically perform a new STORE and DISPLAY mode every few seconds.

2) Examine each new display, and note the readout of the waveform levels at the TRIGGER point. Since the WR is set for a TRIGGER WORD of 0000, you expect the levels at the TRIGGER point to be 0000. However, you will see the levels at the TRIGGER point varying randomly (e.g., 0000, 1000, 0100, 0010). How can this happen if we selected 0000 for the WR TRIGGER WORD?

The answer is that the 0000 condition can occur momentarily at various points on the counter waveforms as the flip-flops are in transition from one state to another. An example is shown in Figure 31-2. Examine the waveforms where the transition is being made from 0111 to 1000. Because of its propagation delay, flip-flop D doesn't go HIGH until after C has gone LOW. Thus, for a few nanoseconds, the 0000 condition is present. This can be recognized by the WR, which will then generate a TRIGGER.

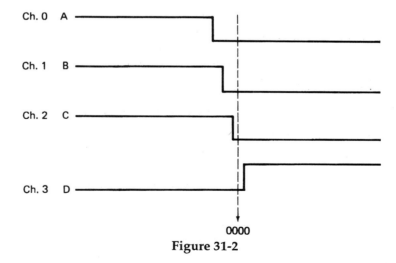

0000

Figure 31-2

m) We can prevent this erratic operation by setting the WR FILTER high enough so that the momentary occurrences of the 0000 TRIGGER WORD will be ignored by the WR, and it will respond only to the stable 0000 condition that occurs on the waveform.

Gradually increase the WR FILTER setting until the display always shows 0000 at the TRIGGER point.

Demonstrate this to the instructor or lab assistant.

n) We can use the logic analyzer to display the race condition depicted in Figure 31-2. To do so, however, we will have to use a much smaller SAMPLE INTERVAL, since the propagation delays between flip-flops is very small.

1) Set the WR for a TRIGGER WORD of 1000.
2) Change SAMPLE INTERVAL to 10 n sec.
3) Set DISPLAY TIME to ∞ and examine the waveforms. They should appear as in Figure 31-2. You can spread them out with the HORIZ MAG control.
4) Move the CURSOR to the point on the waveforms where the temporary 0000 condition occurs. Measure and record the duration of this 0000 condition.

PART 5—DETECTING GLITCHES WITH THE LOGIC ANALYZER

a) Very narrow glitches can be detected and displayed by using a very small SAMPLE INTERVAL. To demonstrate this, we have to somehow generate a glitch. One way to do this is to change our MOD-16 counter to a MOD-10 counter by connecting the outputs of flip-flops D and B back to the counter RESET inputs. This will produce a glitch at the B output as the counter reaches 1010 and immediately gets cleared back to 0000. See the waveform in Figure 31-3.

Ch. 1   B

Figure 31-3

b) Wire the 7493 IC counter as a MOD-10 counter.

c) Try to figure out a way to display the glitch. If you want to use the WR to trigger on the glitch, remember to reduce the WR FILTER to minimum because the glitch is very narrow. Demonstrate this to your instructor or lab assistant.

d) Measure and record the duration of the glitch: _____.

PART 6—EIGHT-CHANNEL OPERATION

a) Set SAMPLE INTERVAL to 1 ms.

b) Connect the channel 4–7 probes to the same counter waveforms as channels 0–3, in the same order.

c) Set the DATA CHANNELS switch for eight-channel operation.

d) Set WR for a TRIGGER WORD of 00010001.

e) Press MANUAL RESET.

f) Find the TRIGGER point on the waveforms. It should occur at 00010001.

g) Repeat for a TRIGGER WORD of 01010101.

h) Repeat for a TRIGGER WORD of 01010001. Why is there no display?

Experiment 32

Name_____

IC DECODERS

OBJECTIVES

1. To investigate the operation of a 1-of-8 decoder IC, the 74LS138.
2. To investigate the operation of a BCD-to-decimal decoder IC, the 7442.
3. To examine the outputs of a decoder with a logic analyzer.
4. To investigate a method of eliminating glitches from decoder outputs.

TEXT REFERENCES

Read sections 9.1 and 9.2.

EQUIPMENT NEEDED

Components
7402 IC;
7408 IC;
7442 IC;
7493 IC;
74121 IC;
74LS138 IC;
4 toggle switches;
normally HIGH pushbutton switch, debounced;
4 LED monitors;
1 k-ohm potentiometer;
270 and 330 pF capacitors.

Instruments
0–5 volt DC power supply;
pulse or square wave generator;
dual trace oscilloscope;
logic probe;
logic analyzer (optional).

DISCUSSION

You are already familiar with decoders, having investigated counter decoding in previous experiments. You are now ready to investigate representative examples of IC decoders. In this experiment you will study the behavior of two popular IC decoders, the 74LS138 and 7442.

74LS138 Decoder

The 74LS138 is an octal (1-of-8) decoder. It is frequently used to decode special binary codes called addresses in small computer systems. Its eight outputs are active LOW and it has three enable inputs and three data inputs. For a given octal code, one—and only one—of the eight outputs will go LOW if the chip is enabled. If the chip is not enabled, all of the outputs will remain HIGH no matter what data is present at the inputs.

7442 BCD-to-Decimal Decoder

In an earlier experiment, you investigated a special IC called a BCD-to-seven-segment decoder/driver. You found that it decoded a BCD counter and provided the necessary translation and power to drive a seven-segment LED display unit. The 7442 is a BCD-to-decimal (1-of-10) decoder, but, like the 74LS138, only one of its outputs will go LOW when a *valid* BCD code is at the data inputs. Unlike the 74LS138, the 7442 has no enables.

PROCEDURE

a) Refer to the data sheet for a 74LS138 IC and draw its pin layout diagram:

The 74LS138 can operate as a 1-of-8 decoder or a 3-line-to-8-line demultiplexer. In this experiment you will investigate the decoder function. The demultiplexer function will be covered in Experiment 34. Study the data sheet and familiarize yourself with the IC's functions.

   b) *74LS138 decoder operation:* Install a 74LS138 on the circuit board. Connect the IC as follows:

1) Connect V_{CC} to +5 V, GND to power ground.
2) Connect toggle switches to select inputs A_2, A_1, and A_0, and enable inputs $\overline{E}_1$, $\overline{E}_2$, and E_3. The select inputs will be used to input data.

   You will use a logic probe to monitor the ouputs, $\overline{O}_7$ through $\overline{O}_0$.

   c) Set E_3 to 1 and $\overline{E}_1 = \overline{E}_2 = 0$. Verify the decoder operating mode by setting inputs A_2, A_1, and A_0 to each input combination listed in Table 32-1 and checking the decoder outputs with the logic probe.

   d) Now set $\overline{E}_1$ to 1. You should observe that the decoder is now disabled (all outputs are HIGH) and that the select inputs have no effect. Repeat this for $\overline{E}_2$ = 1 and then E_3 = 0.

Table 32-1

Select Inputs			Outputs							
A_2	A_1	A_0	$\overline{O}_0$	$\overline{O}_1$	$\overline{O}_2$	$\overline{O}_3$	$\overline{O}_4$	$\overline{O}_5$	$\overline{O}_6$	$\overline{O}_7$
0	0	0								
0	0	1								
0	1	0								
0	1	1								
1	0	0								
1	0	1								
1	1	0								
1	1	1								

   e) *Decoder used as a device enabler:* Decoders are often used to select or enable other devices such as memory ICs and peripheral interface adapters. Each device is assigned a device number such as 0, 1, or 2. The device enable input is connected to the corresponding output of a decoder, and whenever the decoder receives the binary code for the device at its inputs, the decoder will activate the device. Let the four NOR gates of a 7402 IC simulate four devices numbered 0, 1, 2, and 3. One input of each NOR gate is connected to a toggle switch to represent data. Draw a diagram showing how a 74LS138 can be used to selectively enable the four gates.

Show your diagram to your instructor for approval. Then construct the circuit and test it, using a logic probe to monitor the outputs of the NOR gates.

f) *BCD decoder operation—7442 IC:* Refer to the data sheet for a 7442 IC and draw its pin layout diagram:

You should note that the 7442 has four inputs, A_3 through A_0, and ten outputs, $\overline{O}_9$ through $\overline{O}_0$. You should also note that this decoder has no enable inputs.

g) Install a 7442 IC on the circuit board and also a 7493 IC counter. You will use the counter to supply the binary data to the 7442. Connect V_{cc} to +5 V and GND to power ground on each IC. Wire the 7493 as a MOD-16 counter and connect its outputs to the corresponding inputs of the 7442 (A_0 to Q_0, A_1 to Q_1, A_2 to Q_2, and A_3 to Q_3). Use a pushbutton switch to clock the counter. You will monitor the output of the decoder with a logic probe.

Clear the counter outputs. Verify that $\overline{O}_0$ is now LOW and the rest of the outputs are HIGH. Single-step the counter through its count sequence, and verify that the appropriate decoder output is LOW for each count, and that the rest of the outputs are HIGH. You should observe that any count greater than 1001 is not decoded. In other words, all outputs should be HIGH for any invalid BCD code.

h) *Observing decoder outputs with a logic analyzer:* If a logic analyzer is not available, go on to step i. Otherwise, connect the decoder outputs $\overline{O}_7$ through $\overline{O}_0$ to logic analyzer channels 0–7, respectively. Set the analyzer controls as follows (consult with your instructor to learn the exact settings for your particular model):

MODE .... Timing Diagram

CLOCK QUALIFIER .... Off

THRESHOLD .... TTL

EXTERNAL CLOCK POLARITY .... Positive Edge

SAMPLE INTERVAL .... 20 n sec

DATA POSITION .... Post-Trigger

TRIGGER SOURCE .... Word Recognizer (WR)

WR FILTER .... MAX

WR DATA 11111110

Apply a 1 MHz square wave to the counter. Start the logic analyzer so that it begins a new store mode. You should observe that the analyzer displays the decoder output waveforms almost immediately. If the screen remains blank, check the WR data switch setting (on some models this is displayed at the top of the screen) to make sure you set it correctly. If you persist in having difficulty getting a display, consult with your instructor.

Observe the waveforms, and note that they go LOW one at a time as the counter goes through its count sequence. You may see glitches on some of the waveforms.

Repeat this procedure several times. You may note that any glitches that appear may vary as to position on the screen. This is because they are very narrow, and even with a 20 n sec sample interval, the logic analyzer does not always pick them up.

Use the cursor to measure the approximate duration of one of the decoder output pulses. Record your value: _____.

The WR FILTER was set to MAX so that the WR would not be triggered by a glitch on the $\overline{O}_0$ waveform. If possible, set the WR FILTER to MIN, and repeat the measurement several times. You should see that the logic analyzer occasionally triggers on one of these glitches.

i) *Eliminating decoder glitches:* If you did not have access to a logic analyzer to do the last step, you should first apply a 1 MHz square wave to the counter input (or highest frequency obtainable) and observe decoder output $\overline{O}_0$ for glitches. Depending on the quality of your oscilloscope, you should be able to spot a few that occur randomly.

Glitches can cause serious problems, as you are already aware. You have seen one way to possibly eliminate glitches by using synchronous counters instead of asynchronous. Since that method is not always satisfactory, you will now employ another method, strobing the decoder. Strobing requires the decoder to have an enable input, like the 74LS138. The 7442 does not have an enable input. However, you can convert the 7442 into a 1-of-8 decoder WITH an enable. To do this, you simply use data inputs A_0, A_1, and A_2 as usual, and use the A_3 input as an enable. Since outputs $\overline{O}_8$ and $\overline{O}_9$ will not be needed, they will not be connected. When A_3 is set LOW, the 7442 outputs $\overline{O}_0$–$\overline{O}_7$ will respond to the correct data input. With A_3 HIGH, they cannot respond.

Disconnect input A_3 from the counter, and connect it to a toggle switch. Set the toggle switch HIGH. Set the square wave generator to a low frequency and verify with the logic probe that none of the decoder outputs $\overline{O}_0$–$\overline{O}_7$ are activated at any time. Set the toggle switch LOW, and verify that the decoder now acts like a 1-of-8 decoder.

j) Set up the circuitry shown in Figure 32-1. Note that the enable input (A_3) of the 7442 is to be driven by a pulse delay circuit consisting of a 74121 IC one shot. Note also the values of R_t and C_t. R_t is selected to be variable, since you will have to adjust t_p slightly in order to achieve a delay of slightly more than 0.5 microseconds.

Assuming that the count is 111 prior to the first clock pulse, draw the predicted signals at the enable input and decoder output $\overline{O}_0$.

k) With the dual trace oscilloscope, display the OS output and the output of the square wave generator. Adjust R_t so that t_p is slightly more than 0.5 microsecond. If this is not possible, change the value of C_t to 330 pF.

l) If a logic analyzer is available, get a display of the decoder waveforms $\overline{O}_7$ through $\overline{O}_0$ on the analyzer. You should observe no more glitches. If there are still some, try increasing t_p slightly. If this doesn't work, check your OS connections.

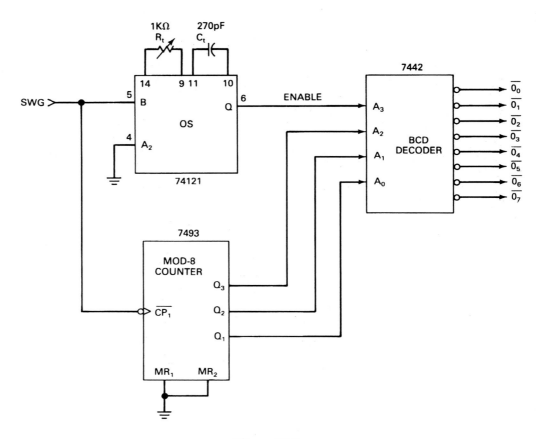

Figure 32-1

m) Once you have no glitches, reduce t_p gradually while observing the outputs of the decoder. You should, at some point, see the glitches return. This is because t_p is too narrow and the decoder is enabled during counter flip-flop transitions.

Demonstrate your circuit to your instructor.

n) *Review:* This concludes the exercises on decoders. To test your understanding of the principles covered in this experiment, answer the following questions:

1. Give a few examples of decoder applications.

2. Give the conditions necessary for the 74LS138 to decode input data.

3. In using the logic analyzer, if the WR data word is set to 11101111 when observing the 7442 outputs $\overline{O_7}$–$\overline{O_0}$, on what output will the logic analyzer be triggered?

_____ .

4. Can you think of other devices you have tested where the logic analyzer might have been useful?

5. If the clock signal used in steps j–m had been 2 MHz, what value of OS t_p would have been necessary? _____.

Experiment 33

Name_____

IC ENCODERS

OBJECTIVES

1. To investigate the operation of a decimal-to-BCD encoder, the 74147 IC.
2. To investigate the application of the 74147 IC in key encoding.

TEXT REFERENCE

Read section 9.4.

EQUIPMENT NEEDED

Components
7404 IC;
7408 IC;
7476 IC;
74121 IC;
74147 IC;
74192 IC;
4 toggle switches;
normally HIGH pushbutton switch, debounced;
4 LED monitors;
33 k-ohm resistor;
1 µF capacitor;
decimal or hex keyboard with normally open contacts (recommended).

Instruments

0–5 volt DC power supply;

accurate 1 Hz square wave source;

storage oscilloscope (recommended), time interval counter, or nonstorage oscilloscope set at very low sweep speed.

DISCUSSION

In Experiment 32, you investigated IC decoders. Recall that for a given N-bit code received by the decoder, one and only one output became active. In this experiment, you will investigate the opposite of decoding: encoding. An encoder takes a single input and produces an N-bit code. For example, an octal encoder gives a three-bit code for a given octal input (digits 0–7) and a BCD encoder gives a four-bit code for a given decimal input (digits 0–9).

In the current experiment, you will investigate a 74147 IC decimal-to-BCD encoder. You were introduced to this IC in Experiment 1. You will use this encoder to interface a keypad with a programmable timer circuit, so that you can input (preset) the amount of time desired by pushing a single key.

PROCEDURE

a) Refer to the data sheet for the 74147. Note that the inputs are active LOW. Grounding one (and only one) input will result in a binary code being produced at

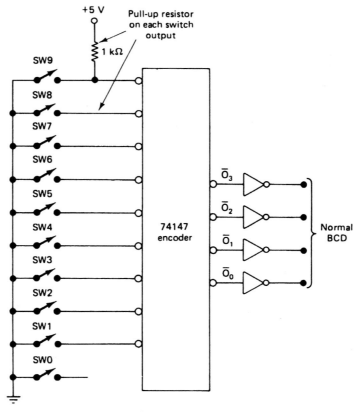

Figure 33-1

the encoder outputs, which represent the number of the input activated. Note also that the outputs are active LOW. Therefore the output code will be *inverted* BCD.

b) Install 74147 and 7404 ICs on the circuit board. Connect them as shown in Figure 33-1. Connect V_{CC} to +5 V and GND to power ground for both ICs. Connect LED monitors to the output of the inverters. If a keyboard is available, connect it to the inputs of the 74147. If not, simply touch a small length of wire to ground, and use this wire to activate the inputs. Verify that the 74147 operates as a decimal-to-BCD encoder.

c) Study the programmable timer circuit in Figure 33-2. You will construct and test this circuit using toggle switches to provide the binary inputs to the counter. Once the circuit operates satisfactorily, you will then replace the toggle switches with the encoder unit you currently have on the board.

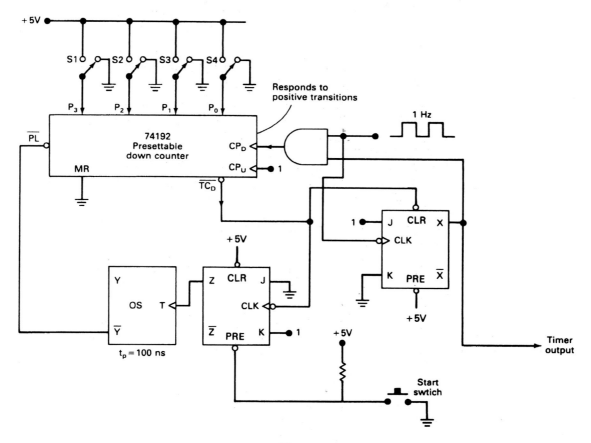

Figure 33-2

The timer output is normally LOW, and then it goes HIGH for 1–9 seconds, depending on the counter's preset conditions. The counter will be a 74192 BCD presettable UP/DOWN counter operated in the DOWN mode. The accuracy of the circuit depends on the accuracy of the 1 Hz square wave.

Refer to the data sheet for the 74192 IC counter. Note that its pin layout is the same as the 74193 and that it is functionally equivalent to a 74193 that is wired to operate as a MOD-10 counter.

Now complete the following circuit description:

1) Assume $S_1 = S_2 = 0$ and $S_3 = S_4 = 1$. Initially the counter is at 000 and $\overline{TC_D} = 0$.

2) Pressing the START switch produces a [positive-, negative-] going transition at Z.

3) This causes the OS, whose $\overline{Y}$ output goes _____, to activate the 74192 $\overline{PL}$ input. This loads the counter with _____, and as a result, $\overline{TC_D}$ goes _____.

4) Flip-flop X now goes to ____ on the next [positive-, negative-] going transition of the 1 Hz timing signal, causing the AND gate to allow the _____ to pass through into the counter.

5) The counter begins counting at _____. When the count reaches zero and CP_D is LOW, $\overline{TC_D}$ goes ____ and clears _____ to 0. This disables (inhibits) the _____ from getting through the AND gate to the counter.

6) The counter stays at 0000 until _____.

____**d)** Draw the expected waveforms for the 1 Hz clock, START, Z, Y, X, CP_D, and $\overline{TC_D}$. Assume that switches S1–S4 are set as above. Use Timing Diagram 33-1.

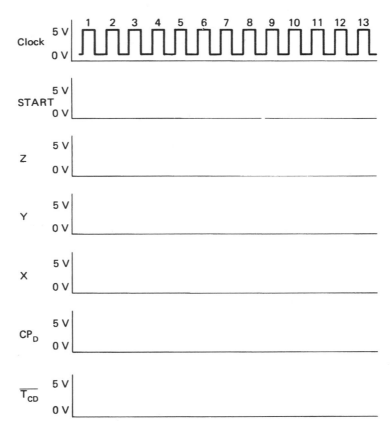

Timing Diagram 33-1

e) Show the results of steps c and d to the instructor before continuing.

f) Construct the programmable timer. Check its operation for several settings of switches S_1–S_4. Use either the storage oscilloscope or the time interval counter to measure the timer output. A nonstorage oscilloscope set at a very slow sweep can be used if necessary.

g) When the circuit is working as expected, press the START switch, and keep it depressed until after the output returns LOW. What happens when the START switch is pressed again? _____.

Draw a circuit that, when added to the programmable timer, will prevent this from happening. Obtain approval from your instructor or laboratory assistant and then install the modification before continuing.

h) Now remove switches S_1–S_4 and replace them with the outputs of the encoder circuit. Test the operation of the circuit by pressing and holding a key (or activating a 74147 input) and pressing the START switch. The timer output should be a pulse whose duration, in seconds, corresponds to the key pressed (or input of the 74147 activated).

i) Demonstrate the programmable timer for your instructor.

j) *Review:* This concludes the exercises on encoders. To test your understanding of the principles covered in this experiment, answer the following questions:

1. Why can't the START switch be connected directly to the OS?

2. Why can't the output of the timer be taken directly from $\overline{TC}_D$?

3. Explain the results you obtained in step g.

Name_____

IC MULTIPLEXERS AND DEMULTIPLEXERS

OBJECTIVES

1. To investigate the operation of a 1-of-8 multiplexer, the 74151 IC.
2. To investigate the operation of a frequency selector.
3. To investigate the operation of a 3-line-to-8-line demultiplexer, the 74LS138 IC.
4. To investigate the application of multiplexers and demultiplexers in a synchronous data transmission system.

TEXT REFERENCES

Read sections 9.7 through 9.9.

EQUIPMENT NEEDED

Components
7404 IC;
7408 IC;
7474 IC (2);
74LS76 IC (4);
74121 IC (2);
74LS138 IC;
74151 IC;
74194A IC (4);
8 toggle switches;
normally HIGH pushbutton switch, debounced;
student selected capacitors and resistors.

Instruments
0–5 volt DC power supply;
pulse or square wave generator;
dual trace oscilloscope;
logic analyzer (optional).

DISCUSSION

Switches used to select data from several input sources are common in electronic systems. Digital systems use electronic circuits to simulate data selector switches called multiplexers. The multiplexer consists of several inputs, one output, and a number of SELECT inputs. When a binary code is applied to the SELECT inputs, the data with the input number represented by the code will be routed to the output. In the current experiment, you will investigate the operation of a 74151 IC, an 8-line-to-1-line multiplexer with a complementary output, and an enable. You will then use the multiplexer in a frequency selector.

The opposite of multiplexing is demultiplexing. A demultiplexer receives a single data line and distributes it over several outputs. Each output is selected by SELECT inputs, and each gets a "slice" of the data present on the input line. In this experiment, you will discover that the 74LS138 IC, whose decoder function was investigated in Experiment 32, can also be used as 1-line-to-8-line demultiplexer.

Finally, an elaborate, but not too complex, synchronous data transmission system is investigated. This system makes use of both the multiplexer and demultiplexer and is representative of serial communication on a small scale. You will use this system in Experiment 35, which is a troubleshooting exercise.

Note: The completed transmission system may be used in Experiment 35. Verify this with your instructor before disassembling the circuit.

PROCEDURE

a) Refer to the data sheet for a 74151 IC and draw its pin layout diagram:

Note that the 74151 has two complementary outputs and an enable input.

b) *74151 IC operation*: Install a 74151 IC and a 7493 IC. Connect V_{CC} to +5 V and GND to ground for each IC. Wire the 7493 as a MOD-8 counter. Wire the remaining pins on the 74151 as follows:

1) Connect toggle switches to each of its eight inputs.
2) Connect select inputs S_2 through S_0 to outputs Q_2 through Q_0, respectively, of the counter.
3) Connect the enable input, $\overline{E}$, to ground.

Set the toggle switches so that $I_0 = I_2 = I_4 = I_6 = I_7 = 0$ and $I_1 = I_3 = I_5 = 1$. Set the clock counter to 1 kHz, and observe the output at Z and the counter clock with the dual trace oscilloscope. Trigger the oscilloscope sweep on Q_2 to get a stable display of the Z waveform. Draw the waveforms displayed on the oscilloscope. Use Timing Diagram 34-1.

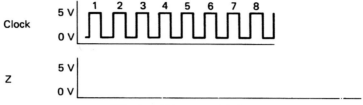

Timing Diagram 34-1

You should observe that the output at Z is the serial representation of the data at the multiplexer input. Toggle the I_2 data switch and observe the effect on the output. You should be able to locate the position of the input channel's data by observing the change in the output.

c) Lift the enable input momentarily. What happens?

_____

d) *Frequency selector*: Figure 34-1 shows a circuit for a frequency selector. The 74151 IC multiplexer is fed various square wave frequencies with I_3 the highest and I_0 the lowest. Inputs I_4–I_7 are kept LOW. The data select inputs of the 74151, S_1–S_0, are used to select any of the square waves to be output at Z.

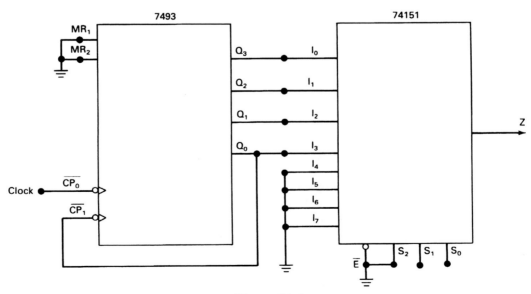

Figure 34-1

e) Wire the circuit of Figure 34-1. Use the SWG set at 5 kHz for the counter clock. Connect toggle switches to select inputs S_1 and S_0, and set them both to HIGH. If you are using an oscilloscope to monitor the circuit waveforms, use one vertical input to monitor Z and the other input to monitor the 74151 data inputs I_0–I_3. If you are using a logic analyzer, connect the logic analyzer to display I_1 through I_4 on channels 0–3 and the multiplexer output, Z, on channel 4. Use a sample interval that allows you to observe several cycles of the lowest frequency waveform to be displayed. Draw the waveforms that you observe on the logic analyzer, using Timing Diagram 34-2.

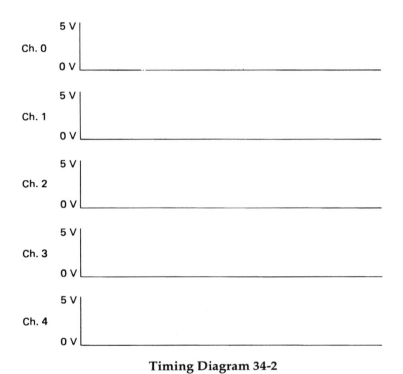

Timing Diagram 34-2

f) Vary the select inputs to produce other frequencies at output Z. Demonstrate the frequency selector for your instructor or laboratory assistant.

g) *Demultiplexer operation of the 74LS138 IC:* You are already familiar with the decoder operation of the 74LS138 (Experiment 32). You will now investigate its demultiplexer operation. Install the 74LS138 IC on the circuit board. Connect V_{cc} to +5 V and GND to power ground. Then wire the circuit of Figure 34-2. Connect the output of the 74151 multiplexer, Z, to the E_1 input of the 74LS138. Connect the other two enable inputs as shown in Figure 34-2. Connect the select inputs of the 74LS138 to the corresponding select inputs of the 74151. You will monitor outputs O_0–O_3 of the 74LS138 and inputs I_0–I_3 of the 74151 with the logic analyzer, if available, or oscilloscope.

h) Set the select inputs to 011, and monitor input I_3 of the 74151 and output $\overline{O}_3$ of the 74LS138. Are the waveforms the same? _____. Verify that all other outputs of the demultiplexer are inactive.

Set the select switches to several other values and verify that the signal at the selected demultiplexer output is the same as the selected multiplexer input.

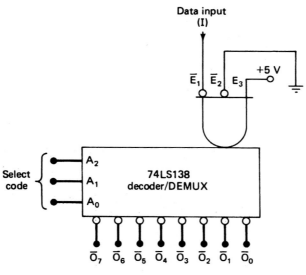

Figure 34-2

i) *Application of multiplexers and demultiplexers—synchronous data transmission system:* Now that you have verified the demultiplexer operation of the 74LS138 and have observed multiplexers and demultiplexers in the same circuit, you will build a synchronous data transmission system that makes use of these two operations. The operation of the data transmission system is described in the text, section 9.9. Review the operation of the system carefully, and then fill in the following statements:

Transmitter section operation:

Each register A, B, C, and D is configured as a _____ shift register. Each register will shift on the [PGT, NGT] of the shift pulse from AND gate 2. The *word counter* _____ the register data that will appear at Z. This counter counts from _____ to _____. The *bit counter* makes sure that _____ data bits from each register are transmitted through the _____ before advancing to the next register. This counter advances one count per _____ so that after _____ pulses, it recycles to 0. The word counter is incremented by _____. The Z signal contains _____ bits from each register for a total of _____ bits. The transmission system is controlled by

_____.

Receiver section operation:

The receiver _____ the Z signal into _____ sets of data and _____ them to their respective outputs.

j) Construct the circuit of Figure 34-3. Use the following ICs (or their equivalent):

1) Registers A, B, C, and D - 74194 (4)
2) Multiplexer - 74151.
3) Demultiplexer - 74LS138.
4) Flip-flops W, X, and Y - 7474 (2)
5) MOD-4 counters - 74LS76 (4).
6) One-shots ($t_p = 1 \mu S$) - 74121 (2).

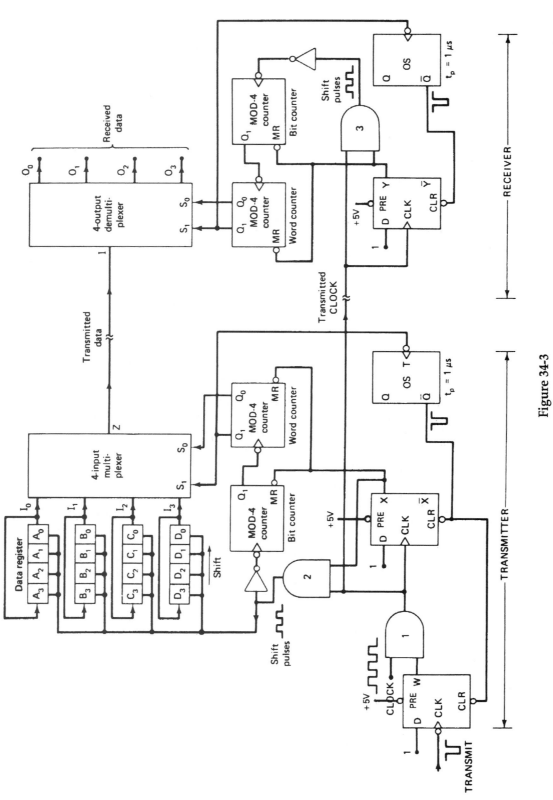

Figure 34-3

k) The 74194 ICs are to be wired as ring counters with parallel load capability. Connect a single toggle switch to all the register S_1 inputs. Connect all S_0 inputs to V_{cc}. The parallel data inputs will be permanently wired as follows:

Register A - [0110]
Register B - [1001]
Register C - [1011]
Register D - [0100]

The registers must be loaded manually before applying a TRANSMIT pulse. To accomplish this, set S_1 HIGH, and pulse the clock inputs LOW using a normally HIGH pushbutton switch. Then set S_1 LOW, and remove the pushbutton switch from the clock inputs.

Connect the output of AND gate 2 to the clock inputs of the registers. Output Q_D of each register should be connected to the appropriate multiplexer input and also to the right serial input SR SER. Connect the $\overline{Q}$ output of the flip-flop W to S_1 of each register.

Review Experiment 27 if necessary for the correct wiring of the 74194A as a ring counter.

l) Wire a normally HIGH pushbutton to the clock input of flip-flop W to provide the TRANSMIT pulse, and complete the rest of the circuit wiring according to the figure. Monitor the demultiplexer outputs with an oscilloscope or logic analyzer if one is available.

m) Test the circuit, and verify that the outputs of the demultiplexer are serial representations of the data stored in the corresponding register. Refer to Timing Diagram 34-3 for the waveforms that you should obtain.

If the system does not work properly, use a pushbutton switch for the clock input, and check out the operation of the circuit step-by-step.

___**n)** Once the circuit is operating successfully, temporarily lift the connection at $\overline{MR}$ of the receiver word counter. What happens?

Reconnect the wire you just lifted. Now temporarily lift the connections at S_0 and S_1 of the 74151 IC. What happens?

Reconnect the select inputs, and demonstrate the circuit for your instructor.

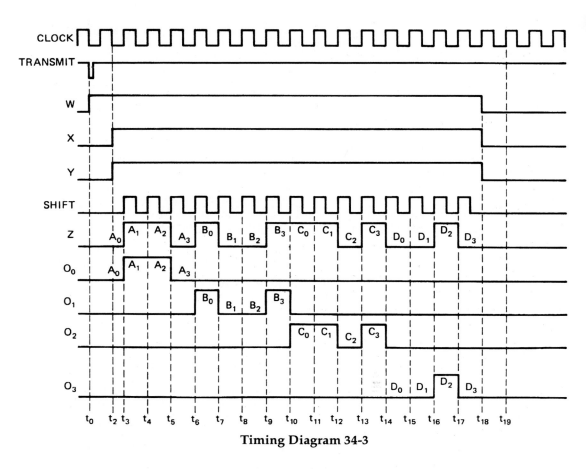

Timing Diagram 34-3

o) *Review*: This concludes the exercises on multiplexers and demultiplexers. To test your understanding of the principles covered in this experiment, answer the following questions:

1. In the data transmission system, what circuit modifications would be necessary to increase the number of channels to eight?

2. What would happen if register A's SR SER input became shorted to V_{cc}?

3. Draw a circuit diagram showing how three 74151 multiplexers can be arranged to form a 1-of-24 multiplexer.

Experiment 35

TROUBLESHOOTING SYSTEMS CONTAINING MSI LOGIC CIRCUITS

OBJECTIVE

To practice troubleshooting systems containing MSI logic circuits.

TEXT REFERENCES

Read sections 9.6 and 9.11.

EQUIPMENT NEEDED

Components
74151 IC;
74LS76 IC (2);
74LS138 IC;
7493 IC;
toggle switches (8);
LED monitors (11);
OR
functioning circuit from Experiment 34.

Instruments
0–5 volt DC power supply;
logic probe;
logic analyzer (optional);
oscilloscope;
pulse generator or SWG.

DISCUSSION

Before beginning this exercise, check with your instructor to determine which exercise you are to do. Also, reread the text assignment, and work through the examples in each section. This experiment will help you to gain confidence in your ability to reason out a troubleshooting problem using what the author of the text refers to as observation/analysis.

PROCEDURE

a) *Troubleshooting a parallel-to-serial converter*: Examine Figure 35-1 closely. It is the circuit for a parallel-to-serial converter using a multiplexer and a counter. Construct the circuit, and test it until you have it operational.

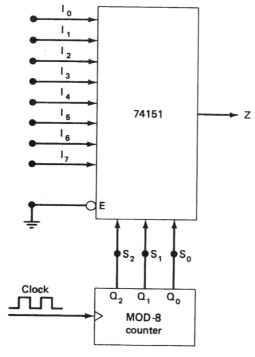

Figure 35-1

b) Have your lab partner or another student insert a fault into the circuit while you are not looking. Do not look for the bug yet. Now examine the circuit with a scope. Connect one vertical input to the clock and the other to the output of the converter. On a separate sheet of paper, draw the waveforms that you observe. Using your observations, narrow the location of the bug to a few possible faults. Then use this list and your test equipment to find the fault. Repeat this step as many times as possible.

c) Have your instructor place a bug in your circuit, and then repeat step b. Place your observations, list of possible faults, and your final solution on a separate sheet of paper.

d) *Troubleshooting a security monitoring system*: Examine Figure 35-2 closely. It is the circuit for a security monitoring system. Construct the circuit, using toggle switches for the door switches. Use a pulse generator set to a frequency sufficiently low (so that the LEDs can be monitored) to clock the counter. Test the system until you have it operational. Now review Example 9.6 in the text.

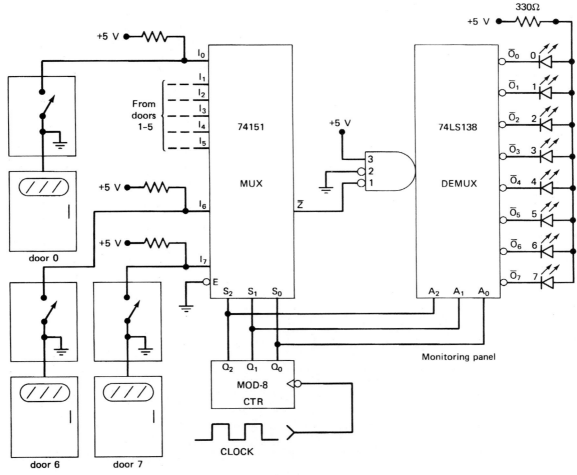

Figure 35-2

e) Have your lab partner or another student insert a fault into the circuit while you are not looking. Do not look for the bug yet. On a separate sheet of paper, draw a table that shows which LEDs are flashing (if any) for any door that opens. Also note the state of the LEDs when all doors are closed. Using your observations, narrow the location of the bug to a few possible faults. Use this list and your test equipment to find the fault. Repeat this step as many times as possible.

f) Have your instructor or laboratory assistant place a bug in your circuit, and then repeat step e. Place your observations, list of possible faults, and your final solution on a separate sheet of paper.

g) If you are to troubleshoot the synchronous data transmission system, make sure that it is functional before beginning the exercise; otherwise, you may be chasing down several bugs instead of just one. Also review Example 9.14 in the text. When you are ready, have your lab partner insert a bug into the circuit while you are not looking. Monitor the MUX and DEMUX outputs with the oscilloscope (or logic analyzer, if available) during one transmission cycle, and draw the waveforms on a separate sheet of paper. Now study the observations, and try to narrow the location of the fault to a small area in the system. List what you think are the possible faults on the same sheet of paper as your observations, then proceed to look for the fault with your troubleshooting tools. Write a description of the fault on the sheet of paper containing your other data. Repeat this step as often as time permits.

   h) When you are ready, ask your instructor or laboratory assistant to place a bug in your system. Repeat step g.

Name_____

IC MAGNITUDE COMPARATORS

OBJECTIVES

1. To investigate the operation of a 7485 IC four-bit magnitude comparator.
2. To investigate the cascading of 7485 ICs.
3. To investigate a word recognizer application of the 7485 IC.

TEXT REFERENCE

Read section 9.12.

EQUIPMENT NEEDED

Components
7485 IC (2);
student-selected ICs and other components;
8 toggle switches;
3 LED monitors.

Instruments
0–5 volt DC power supply;
logic probe;
pulse generator or SWG.

DISCUSSION

The magnitude of any pair of real numbers A and B can be compared. A law of mathematics (called the law of trichotomy) tells us that A can be less than, equal to, or greater than B. Many systems call for this type of comparison, especially programmed systems like computers.

The 7485 IC can compare two 4-bit numbers and give an indication of how the two numbers compare. The ICs can be cascaded so that larger numbers may be compared. The 7485 IC has four pairs of data inputs, three outputs (A = B_{out}, A > B_{out}, A < B_{out}), and three cascading inputs (A = B_{in}, A > B_{in}, A < B_{in}). When cascading 7485 ICs, A = B_{out} is connected to A = B_{in} of the next stage, handling more significant bits, and, similarly, A > B_{out} is connected to A > B_{in}, and A < B_{out} is connected to A < B_{in}. The comparator handling the least significant nybble (group of four bits) must have A = B_{in} tied HIGH and the other cascading inputs tied LOW for the cascaded comparators to work properly.

PROCEDURE

a) *7485 IC operation*: Refer to the data sheet for a 7485 IC, and draw its pin layout diagram:

b) Install a 7485 IC on a circuit board. It will be referred to as IC1. Connect V_{cc} to +5 V and GND to power ground. Connect toggle switches to inputs A_0–A_3 and B_0–B_3. Connect the cascading inputs as described above. Connect LED monitors to the outputs. You will not have to make all possible comparisons, so just use the number pairs in Table 36-1 and record which output is lighted for each pair.

Table 36-1

			Inputs						LED Monitors	
A_3	A_2	A_1	A_0	B_3	B_2	B_1	B_0	A > B_{out}	A < B_{out}	A = B_{out}
0	0	0	0	1	1	1	1			
0	0	1	0	0	1	1	1			
0	1	0	0	0	0	1	1			
1	0	0	0	0	0	0	1			
0	0	0	0	0	0	0	0			
1	1	1	1	0	0	0	0			

c) Now, connect another 7485 IC as shown in Figure 36-1. The new IC (IC2) will handle the least significant nybble. Connect all of its data inputs to V_{cc} with jumper wires. Now connect the outputs of this IC to the cascading inputs of IC1. Be sure to remove the jumpers to ground and V_{cc} from the cascading inputs that were connected in step a.

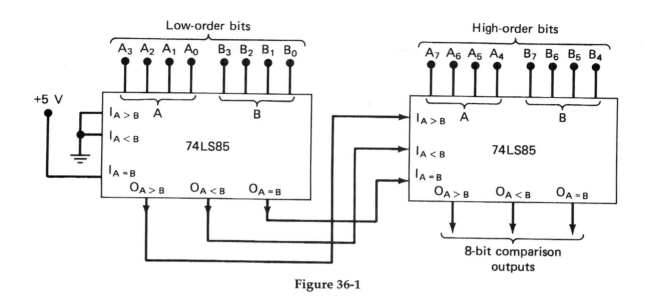

Figure 36-1

d) Set all toggle switches connected to IC1 to HIGH. Which LED is lighted? _____. Now disconnect B3 on IC2 from V_{cc} and connect to ground. Now which LED is lighted? _____. Reconnect B3 to V_{cc}. Remove A3 on IC2 from V_{cc} and connect to ground. Which LED is lighted? _____. Set the toggle switch connected to A3 on IC1 to LOW. Which LED is lighted? _____. Return the switch to HIGH, and set the toggle switch connected to B3 to LOW. Which LED is lighted? _____.

e) *Word recognizer application*: Design a circuit that compares the output of an eight-bit counter (MOD-256) with an eight-bit word supplied by eight toggle switches. Whenever the two eight-bit words are equal, the circuit produces a LOW pulse with a time duration of 10 μs.

f) *Review*: This concludes the exercises on data buses. To test your understanding of the principles covered in this experiment, answer the following questions:

1. Design a circuit for an eight-bit comparator that will give a HIGH output only when A > B, where A and B are any two eight-bit numbers.

2. Design a circuit for a 16-bit comparator.

Experiment 37

Name_____

DATA BUSING

OBJECTIVES

1. To investigate the operation of a tristate register, the 74173 IC.
2. To demonstrate the application of tristate devices in bus systems.
3. To investigate register-to-register data transfer in bus systems.

TEXT REFERENCES

Read sections 9.13 and 9.14.

EQUIPMENT NEEDED

Components
7406 IC;
74125 IC;
74LS139 IC;
74173 IC (3);
74174 IC;
10 toggle switches;
normally LOW pushbutton switch (2), and normally HIGH pushbutton switch, all debounced;
4 LED monitors;
SK-10 circuit board.

Instruments
0–5 volt DC power supply;
logic probe.

241

DISCUSSION

Most modern digital computers use data buses for data transfer. Data sources come from the outputs of different devices and cannot normally be tied together. We have already seen how tristate buffers can be employed to isolate the data source outputs from other outputs. Most devices that are connected together contain registers to hold their data, and since register outputs cannot be tied together either, they will need tristate buffers at their outputs so that the registers may be tied to the bus safely. Of course, an added benefit of tristate devices is that data on a bus may flow in either direction. This minimizes the number of bus lines in the system.

74173 IC Tristate Register

The 74173 IC is a four-bit register capable of parallel I/O. The inputs are fed to the D inputs of D flip-flops through an enable circuit. Two active-LOW input enables control the input modes, of which there are two: the LOAD and HOLD modes. If both input enables are LOW, the data from the bus reaches the register's flip-flop inputs. If one or both enables are HIGH, the output of each flip-flop is fed back to the flip-flop's input. Also, there are two output enables that control the two output modes. If both output enables are LOW, all of the internal tristate buffers are enabled, connecting the flip-flop outputs to the data bus. If one or both enables are HIGH, the tristate buffers are all disabled, disconnecting the flip-flop outputs from the data bus.

The register requires clocking in the LOAD mode in order that new data may be transferred to the flip-flops. The clock does not affect the flip-flop in the HOLD mode. Normally, if a register is outputting, its inputs should be in the HOLD mode.

Data Bus System

This exercise is one of the most important in the lab manual. That is because the exercise shows how data is transferred in a data bus environment and how the transfer is controlled. As remarked in an earlier exercise, much of what goes on in a digital computer is associated with data transfer.

The basic data bus, as shown in Figures 37-1, 37-3, and 37-4, consists of three tristate registers, an input unit (switches and tristate buffers), an output unit (LEDs and latches), and a control unit (the dual decoder). The decoder receives its instruction from its inputs and connects two devices together (either register to register, or input switches to register) via the bus. The system clock then causes the data transfer to take place. This data bus system could be expanded with a little design work, but it is highly instructional as it is.

PROCEDURE

a) *74173 IC operation*: Refer to the data sheet for a 74173 IC, and draw its pin layout diagram:

The 74173 is a four-bit tristate register with a pair of input enables, $\overline{IE}_1$ and $\overline{IE}_2$; a pair of output enables, $\overline{OE}_1$ and $\overline{OE}_2$; and a master reset input, MR. Since you will tie the input enables together in this experiment, they will be referred to, collectively, as $\overline{IE}$. The output enables will be referred to as $\overline{OE}$. When $\overline{IE}$ and $\overline{OE}$ are both HIGH, the inputs D_3 through D_0 and the outputs O_3 through O_0 are tristated. In other words, data can neither get in nor get out. When $\overline{IE}$ is LOW and $\overline{OE}$ is HIGH, data can be clocked in and latched on a positive-going transition at $\overline{CP}$. The output is tristated during this time. When both input AND output enables are LOW, both are enabled. There is no problem with this when both inputs and outputs are connected to the same bus, since the levels will be the same.

b) Install a 74173 on the circuit board. Connect V_{cc} to +5 V and GND to power ground. Connect normally LOW pushbutton switches to $\overline{CP}$ and MR. Connect toggle switches to $\overline{IE}$, $\overline{OE}$, and the data inputs. You will monitor the outputs with a logic probe. Set the data switches to LOW, the enable switches both HIGH, and pulse MR to clear the register if it is not cleared already. Now set the data switches to 1001. Verify that changing the data switches has no effect on the register by toggling $\overline{OE}$ LOW and monitoring the outputs. Now return $\overline{OE}$ to HIGH, and set $\overline{IE}$ LOW. Pulse $\overline{CP}$ momentarily HIGH, then enable the output and verify that the register is now storing the data present at the inputs. Toggle $\overline{IE}$ HIGH, and verify that the data is still present at the outputs. Change the data switches to 0110. Pulse $\overline{CP}$ HIGH. Enable the output, and verify that the data is still 1001. Now set $\overline{OE}$ HIGH and $\overline{IE}$ LOW, and pulse $\overline{CP}$ once again. Verify that the data at the output is now 0110.

c) *Operation of the data bus*: Connect the circuit of Figure 37-1 carefully. Note that all three registers have their inputs and outputs tied to the bus. You should be aware that it is undesirable to have no more than one register's *outputs* enabled at the same time. When this occurs, a condition known as *bus contention* exists. If each register is outputting different data, there is a tug-of-war between the two, which may result in chip damage. Having more than one register's inputs enabled at the same time does not present a problem. In fact, it will be desirable to do so, because it may be necessary to transfer data from one register to the other two, which is a common situation in digital systems.

Construct the circuit of Figure 37-1 on a separate SK-10 circuit board. Use its four common horizontal rows for the four bus lines. You will mount all circuit components on another board and connect them to the bus. Connect a normally LOW pushbutton switch to the common clock line. Connect toggle switches to all

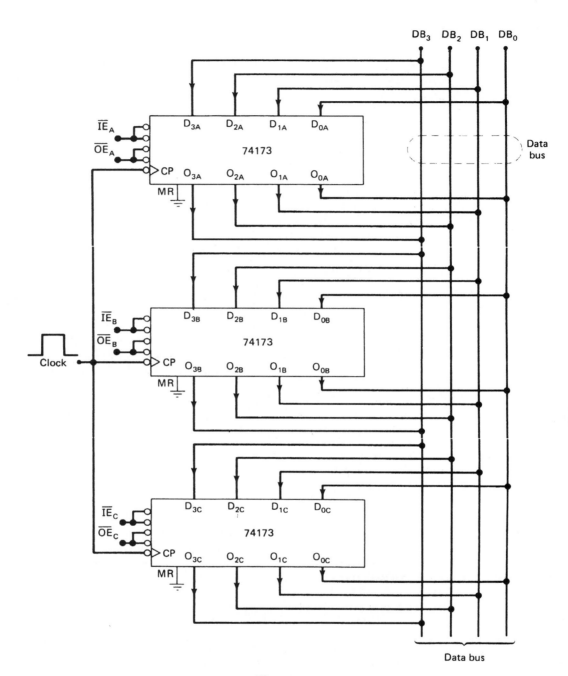

Figure 37-1

register input and output enables. Make sure that you wire all MR inputs to the normally LOW pushbutton switch connected to the register tested in step b. You will use this switch to clear all registers simultaneously.

Install a 74125 IC on the component board. Connect V_{cc} to +5 V and GND to power ground. Connect toggle switches to the inputs of the 74125 tristate buffers. Connect the outputs of the buffers to the data bus. Connect all buffer enables together to a single toggle switch. Figure 37-2 illustrates these connections. The purpose of the tristate buffers is to permit data to be loaded into the registers manually without having to connect and disconnect the toggle switches prior to and following data entry. To operate the buffered data switches, you will first toggle the data switches to the desired settings and then hold the enable switch LOW. After data is loaded into the registers, release the pushbutton.

Set the data switches on the bus to 1010, and enable the buffers. Set $\overline{IE}_A$ LOW. Then pulse $\overline{CP}$ HIGH momentarily. Return $\overline{IE}_A$ to HIGH, and disable the switch buffers. Verify that only register A contains the data from the data switches by enabling first $\overline{OE}_A$ and checking the bus. Repeat this for register C.

d) After disabling all register outputs and inputs, set the switches to 0110, and enable the buffers. Enable $\overline{IE}_B$ and $\overline{IE}_C$, and pulse $\overline{CP}$ HIGH momentarily. Disable the inputs of registers B and C. Verify that register A still contains 1010 and that B and C contain 0110. Remember, enable $\overline{OE}_B$ and $\overline{OE}_C$ one at a time, and check the data bus.

e) *Register-to-register data transfer*: Now that you are familiar with entering data into a register from an external source, you will observe that the registers themselves are sources of data. Therefore, it is likely that on occasion, data from one register might be moved to another. You should note that there is a particular sequence of steps involved in manipulating the registers and that each sequence can be repeated.

Enable $\overline{IE}_A$ and $\overline{OE}_C$. Make sure that all other enables are inactive. Pulse $\overline{CP}$ HIGH momentarily. Now disable $\overline{IE}_A$ and $\overline{OE}_C$. Enable $\overline{OE}_A$, and verify that the new contents of register A are the same as what is stored in register C.

From this point on, the convention [Z] = xxxx, where Z is any register and xxxx is a binary number, will be used to refer to the contents of register Z. Thus, [B] = 1001 means that register B contains 1001.

Assume that [A] = 1011, [B] = 1000, and [C] = 0111. Study the waveforms of Figure 37-3. Write a procedure for applying these waveforms to the bus system *manually*.

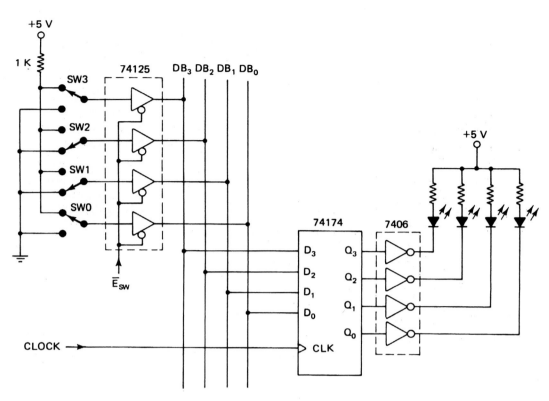

Figure 37-2

Predict [A], [B], and [C] at times t_1, t_2, and t_3, and record them in Table 37-1.

Table 37-1

Time	[A]	[B]	[C]
t_1			
t_2			
t_3			

Show the procedure and Table 37-1 to your instructor.

Now perform the procedure you wrote for this set of waveforms, and verify that Table 37-1 is correct.

f) *Latching data on the bus*: Examine Figure 37-2. You have already installed the buffered switches in step c. Now you will install the other IC, a 74174 register that will be used for latching any data that is on the bus during a data transfer, and display it on a set of LEDs.

Refer to the data sheet for a 74174 IC, and draw its pin layout diagram:

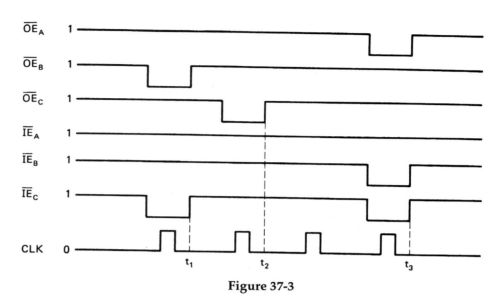

Figure 37-3

g) Add the new components to the data bus system. Make a connection between the clock pushbutton and the clock input on the 74174.

Write a procedure for loading the registers with the following data from the switches:

[A] = 1101, [B] = 1110, [C] = 0101.

What will be the state of the LEDs at the end of this sequence? _____.

Perform the procedure you wrote above, and verify that the state of the LEDs is as predicted.

h) *Enabling registers with decoders:* The last item to be added to the data bus is a 74LS139 decoder, which will generate the necessary enable pulses during data transfer operations. Refer to the data sheet for a 74LS139 IC, and draw its pin layout diagram:

The 74LS139 is a dual 1-of-4 decoder IC with an active LOW enable, $\overline{E}$.

Examine the circuit of Figure 37-4(a). The top decoder unit will be used to select the device that will put data onto the data bus (output select), and the bottom unit will be used to select the device that will take the data from the bus (input select). The actual devices selected are determined by the decoders' select input signals, OS_1, OS_0, IS_1, and IS_0.

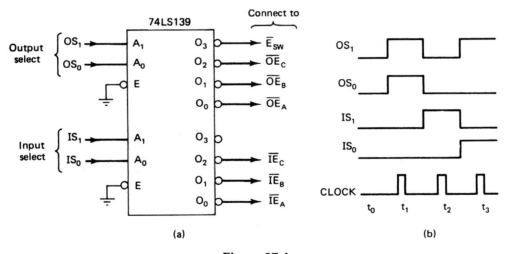

Figure 37-4

For each combination of select inputs, determine the transfer that is to take place, and record the registers affected by each transfer in Table 37-2.

Show Table 37-2 to your instructor or laboratory assistant.

Add the 74LS139 to the data bus system, and make the connections in the diagram and also the connections necessary to make the 74LS139 operate, which are not shown. Connect toggle switches to the decoder select inputs.

Clear all registers by pulsing the switch connected to the register MR inputs momentarily. Set the data switches to 1001. Set $OS_1 = OS_0 = 1$ and $IS_1 = IS_0 = 0$, and pulse the clock momentarily HIGH. What data transfer is taking place on the bus, and what is the value of the data being transferred?

Table 37-2

IS_1	IS_0	OS_1	OS_0	To Register	From Register
\-	\-	Selects	\-	Data Transfer	
0	0	0	0	A	A
0	0	0	1	A	B
0	0	1	0		
0	0	1	1		
0	1	0	0		
0	1	0	1		
0	1	1	0		
0	1	1	1		
1	0	0	0		
1	0	0	1		
1	0	1	0		
1	0	1	1		
1	1	0	0		
1	1	0	1		
1	1	1	0		
1	1	1	1		

Now set $OS_1 = OS_0 = IS_0 = 0$ and $IS_1 = 1$, and pulse the clock again. What data transfer is taking place and what is the value of the data being transferred?

_____

Set $OS_1 = OS_0 = IS_1 = 0$ and $IS_0 = 1$. Pulse the clock momentarily HIGH. What data transfer is taking place, and what is the value of the data being transferred?

_____

Finally, set $OS_1 = OS_0 = 1$ and $OS_0 = IS_1 = 0$. Pulse the clock HIGH momentarily. What data transfer is taking place, and what is the value of the data being transferred?

_____

What are the final conditions of the registers?

_____

_____

_____

Verify this by enabling the output of each register one at a time, pulsing the clock, and observing the state of the LEDs.

Try other sequences of data transfer. Predict the final condition for each register before executing any sequence. When you are familiar enough with this type of data transfer, ask your instructor or laboratory assistant for a sequence to execute. Execute the sequence for the instructor.

2. Apply power to the circuit and adjust the 0-5K potentiometer until the milliameter reads 2 mA.

3. Remove the power and disconnect the milliameter. Reconnect the potentiometer to the DAC and connect the DVM to point V_{out}. Connect a normally-LOW pushbutton switch to the clock input of the 7490 counter.

4. Set the counter to 9 and adjust the 0-1K potentiometer until the voltage at point V_{out} is -0.9V $\pm$ 0.001V, as measured with the DVM.

5. Pulse the counter through its counting range (0-9) and record the output at point V_{out} in Table 38-1 under First Unit V_{out} (observed).

6. Compare the results in steps c and 5 above. How close in agreement are they?

Table 38-1

BCD Input	V_{out} Expected	First Unit V_{out} Observed	Second Unit V_{out} Observed
0			
1			
2			
3			
4			
5			
6			
7			
8			
9			

e) Disconnect the pushbutton switch from the clock input to the counter and replace it with a TTL-compatible signal from the squarewave generator. Examine the signal at point Vout with an oscilloscope and draw the waveform observed using Timing Diagram 38-1.

Timing Diagram 38-1

f) Construct and calibrate a second unit as in steps b-e. Use Second Unit V_{out} of Table 38-1 to record your calibration results. This unit will also be used later in this experiment and in Experiment 39, so do not disconnect it until then.

g) Construct the summing amplifier of Figure 38-2(b) and connect each of the DAC units to one of its inputs.

h) Pulse the counter so that the BCD input is 09. Measure V_A' with the DVM. It should indicate a value close to +0.9 V. Adjust the 0-1 k-ohm potentiometer at the LSD output, if necessary, until V_A' is as close to +0.9V as possible.

i) Now set the BCD count to 90. The voltage at V_A' should now be close to +9.0 V. If necessary, adjust the 1 k-ohm potentiometer at the MSD output to bring this value as close as possible to +9.0 V. The BCD-to-analog converter is now calibrated.

j) Remove the toggle switches and install a MOD-100 BCD counter in their place as shown in Figure 38-2. Also connect BCD display units to display the counter. Clock the MOD-100 counter with a pushbutton.

k) Fill in the expected values of V_A' for each BCD number listed in Table 38-2.

Table 38-2

BCD Input	V_A' expected	V_A' observed
00		
05		
10		
15		
20		
25		
30		
35		
40		
45		
50		
55		
60		
65		
70		
75		
80		
85		
90		
95		
99		

l) Step the counter through its count sequence, stopping every five counts and reading V_A'. Record these values in the table. If any reading is off by more than 0.05 V from the expected value, notify your instructor or laboratory assistant.

m) Remove the pushbutton switch connected to the counter clock input, and replace it with the output of the square wave generator. Set the square wave generator to 1 kHz. Connect the oscilloscope to V_A', and draw the waveform displayed using Timing Diagram 38-2.

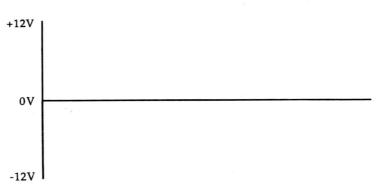

Timing Diagram 38-2

n) *Review*: This concludes the exercises on digital-to-analog converters. Do not disassemble the converter you have on the circuit board at this time. It will be used in Experiment 39.

To test your understanding of the principles covered in this experiment, answer the following questions:

1. What is the percent resolution of the BCD-to-analog converter you constructed? _____ %.

2. What problems would you have encountered had you not calibrated the DAC outputs before using them in the two-digit converter?

Experiment 39

Name_____

ANALOG-TO-DIGITAL CONVERTERS

OBJECTIVES

1. To investigate the operation of a TTL compatible comparator circuit.
2. To investigate the operation of a digital-ramp analog-to-digital converter in a 2-digit DVM circuit.

TEXT REFERENCES

Read sections 10.6 and 10.7.

EQUIPMENT NEEDED

Components
MC1408 (or DAC0808) (2);
LM324 op-amp;
7446 IC (2);
7490 IC (2);
seven-segment display unit (2);
4.7 V zener diode;
1.5 k-ohm potentiometer (two 10-turn potentiometers recommended);
5 k-ohm potentiometer;
18 k-ohm resistor;
180 k-ohm resistor (2);
student-selected resistors and capacitors;
8 toggle switches;
normally HIGH pushbutton switch, debounced.

257

Instruments

0–5 volt DC power supply;

+15 volt DC power supply;

-15 volt DC power supply;

DVM;

pulse or square wave generator.

DISCUSSION

In Experiment 38, you investigated the DAC. You used DACs to construct a two-digit BCD-to-analog converter. Analog-to-digital converters (ADCs) and digital computers work together to measure real world variables. Thus the ADCs extend a digital computer by acting as an interface to sensors that convert analog quantities into voltages or current. In this way, whenever the computer needs information on a variable, it acts like a digital voltmeter, measures the quantity, and then stores the measurement in memory for future use.

In the current experiment, you will first investigate a comparator circuit that is TTL compatible. This type of circuit is used quite frequently in hybrid systems. It is also a component in an analog-to-digital converter. You will then complete your two-digit DVM circuit by constructing a digital-ramp ADC.

PROCEDURE

a) *TTL compatible comparator*: To construct a counter-ramp ADC, you need to add only a comparator circuit to the output of a counter-driven DAC, like the one you constructed in Experiment 38. Since the comparator output will be used to control a TTL gate, it is desirable to have the output of this comparator TTL compatible.

Examine the circuit of Figure 39-1. The circuit has two inputs. One is V_A', the input from the DAC output, and the other is V_A, the analog input. Note the zener diode at the comparator output. Since the digital output is negative or 0, the analog input must also be negative. The purpose of this diode is to limit the output excursions to a range of about -0.7 V to 4.7 V, making the output of the comparator TTL compatible.

Suppose the analog input is -2 V. If $V_A' = -1.5$ V, then the op-amp input difference will be positive, causing the output to swing positive toward +15 V. The zener diode limits this swing to +4.7 V. On the other hand, if $V_A' = -2.5$ V, the input difference will be negative, causing the output to swing negative toward -15 V. The zener diode this time will be forward-biased, so the voltage at the output will be -0.7 V, the voltage drop across the zener.

Construct the comparator. Connect one end of the 5 k-ohm potentiometer to -15 volts and the other to ground. Connect a wire to the wiper of the potentiometer. This wire will be the analog source, V_A.

Connect V_A' from the DAC to the + input of the comparator and the analog source to the - input. Adjust V_A for approximately -5 V. Pulse the MOD-100 counter until a count of around 55 is reached. Measure V_A' and the comparator output voltage, and record the measurement in Table 39-1.

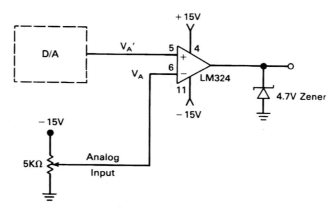

Figure 39-1

Table 39-1

V_A	Count	V_A'	Output
-5 V	55		
-5 V	45		

Now reset the counter, and pulse it until a count of around 45 is reached. Measure V_A' and the comparator output voltage, and record them in Table 39-1.

If the voltages measured above are correct, proceed to the next step. If not, check the calibration of the DACs and the connections between V_A' and the comparator.

b) *Analog-to-digital converter application—Digital voltmeter*: Now that the comparator is operating satisfactorily, you are ready to finish the DVM circuit. Figure 39-2 shows the complete wiring of the DVM. Make the necessary additions to the BCD-to-analog converter and the comparator, which are already on the board. One-shot OS1 controls the display time of the DVM. Its t_p should be made adjustable from about 1 second to 5 seconds or greater. One-shot OS2 provides a clear pulse for the BCD counters, and its t_p should be 10 microseconds. The AND gate is a transmission gate for the counter clock. As long as $V_A < V_A'$, the comparator output is HIGH and the AND gate is enabled, allowing the clock through to the counter. Whenever $V_A > V_A'$, the comparator switches to LOW, inhibiting the AND gate and freezing the counter at its current count.

When you have completed the circuit, disconnect the pushbutton switch from the BCD MOD-100 counter, and apply a 1 kHz square wave as clock input. Set the analog source to -5 V or slightly over. The DVM display should display 51, which represents -5.1 V. It could, however, be 50 or 52, depending on the accuracy of the calibration of the BCD-to-analog converters. Try several values of V_A between 0 and -10 V and record the results in the space provided below.

c) *Resolution of analog-to-digital converter*: With the lab DVM monitoring V_A, determine what change in V_A is needed to cause the counter display to change by one step. What is the resolution of the ADC? _____.

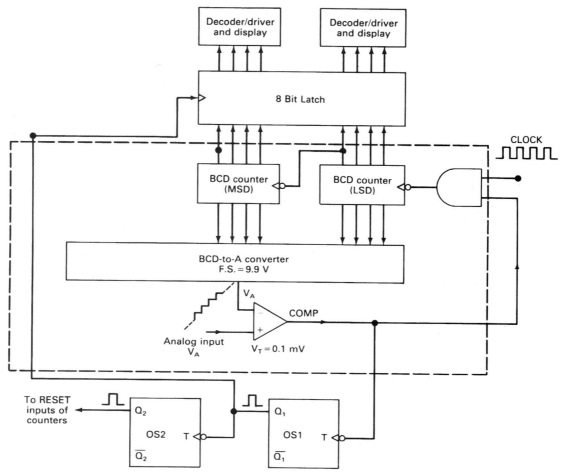

Figure 39-2

d) *Conversion time*: Change the display OS1 circuit so that t_p is 1 millisecond. Connect the dual trace oscilloscope to V_A' and the output of the comparator. Set V_A to -5 V. Observe the waveforms, and draw them, using Timing Diagram 39-1. Be sure to show proper levels. Label the conversion time and display time on the waveforms. Measure and record the conversion times for V_A = -1 V, -5 V, -9 V, and -11 V in Table 39-2.

Table 39-2

V_A	t_C
-1 V	
-5 V	
-9 V	
-11 V	

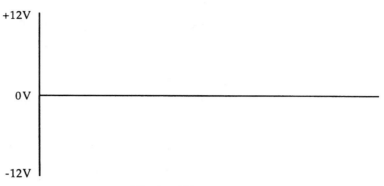

Timing Diagram 39-1

e) In step d, you observed the effect of applying an analog input that is overrange (-11 V). How would you modify the DVM circuit to indicate that V_A is overrange? Draw a circuit showing the modification:

Show the circuit to your instructor for approval, and then add the modification to the DVM. Test the modified DVM. When the DVM is working properly, demonstrate the DVM to your instructor.

f) *Review*: This concludes the exercises on analog-to-digital converters. To test your understanding of the principles covered in this experiment, answer the following questions:

1. Why were the (constructed) DVM readings always higher than the actual value of V_A?

2. Explain why V_A has to be a negative value.

Experiment 40

Name_____

SEMICONDUCTOR RANDOM ACCESS MEMORY (RAM)

OBJECTIVES

1. To investigate the operation of an N-MOS static RAM memory IC.
2. To demonstrate the use of a logic analyzer in examining memory.
3. To demonstrate memory-to-register data transfer.
4. To demonstrate register-to-memory data transfer.

TEXT REFERENCES

Read sections 11.1, 11.2, 11.4, 11.12, 11.13, and 11.14.

EQUIPMENT NEEDED

Components
2114A IC;
7486 IC;
7493 IC;
74125 IC;
74LS139 IC;
74174 IC;
SK-10 circuit board;
10 toggle switches;
normally HIGH pushbutton switch (2), normally LOW pushbutton switch, debounced;
4 LED monitors.

Instruments
0–5 volt DC power supply;

logic probe;
logic analyzer (optional).

DISCUSSION

We know that memory is a characteristic of all useful digital systems. Up to now, we have been using flip-flops and registers for storing data. In Experiment 37, you investigated the tristate register and connected three of them to a data bus system. You discovered that in order to use (access) a particular register, the register has to be enabled. If data is to be stored in (written to) a register, its input must be enabled. If data is to be transferred from (read from) it, its output must be enabled. Recall that a decoder was used to do the enabling (or controlling).

Digital systems normally need hundreds of registers, and the word size needed is usually more than four bits. Memory ICs are available in various sizes, ranging from a few registers to several thousand. Large decoders are needed to access any particular register. For example, selecting one register from a 1024-word (1K) memory requires a 1-of-1024 decoder. How would you like to wire one of those? Rest at ease, for these large devices are included on the memory chip. For the same 1024-word memory, there are 10 special enable lines called address lines, which are used to externally select any register inside the chip.

A memory system that can be written to and read from is generally called read/write memory. However, semiconductor read/write memories are usually referred to as random access memory (RAM). In the current experiment, you will investigate a popular 1K RAM chip, the 2114. The word size of the 2114 is four bits. The number of data lines is four, and the chip is classified as common I/O. The chip must be enabled at the CS (chip select) input for the memory system to function. A normally HIGH WE (write enable) input keeps the chip in the read mode most of the time. Reading does not destroy the data in the memory. Whenever a WRITE operation is necessary, the WE input is pulsed LOW long enough for storage to take place.

PROCEDURE

a) In this experiment, you are to connect a 2114A memory chip to a data bus. Refer to the data sheet for a 2114A IC, and draw its pin layout diagram:

The 2114A is an N-MOS static RAM chip organized as 1024 four-bit words (1024 × 4). Its ten address inputs permit access to any of the 1024 words by applying the correct binary number representing the address to these pins. The addresses range from 0000000000 to 1111111111. Since it is more efficient to express such large binary numbers in *hexadecimal*, we will do so from now on. The range of addresses in hexadecimal is 000_{16} to $3FF_{16}$.

The $\overline{WE}$ input is used to select the READ or WRITE operation. When the input is HIGH, the READ operation is selected; when it is LOW, the WRITE operation is selected.

The $\overline{CS}$ (chip select) input enables the chip, when LOW, so that either the READ or the WRITE can take place. When HIGH, $\overline{CS}$ disables the chip so that neither operation can take place.

The 2114A has four tristate I/O lines, I/O_3 through I/O_0. During a READ operation, the memory word selected by an address will be made available at these pins. During a WRITE operation, the word to be written must be on the lines connected to these pins.

Summarize the memory chip's operations using Table 40-1.

Table 40-1

WE	$\overline{CS}$	Operation
0	1	
1	1	
0	0	
1	0	

b) Examine the circuit of Figure 40-1. The circuit shows how the memory chip will be wired for initial testing. Later you will add other components to the bus. Read through the following steps, and make each connection as directed.

1) Mount a 2114A IC, a 7493 IC, and a 74125 IC on a circuit board. This board will be separate from the board to be used for the data bus. Connect V_{cc} to +5 V and GND to power ground for the three ICs.

2) Wire the 7493 as a MOD-16 counter. Connect the 7493 outputs, Q_3–Q_0 to address inputs A_3–A_0, respectively, of the 2114A memory chip. Make sure address inputs A_4–A_9 are grounded.

3) Connect a toggle switch to the write enable toggle input.

4) Connect a normally HIGH pushbutton switch to the device select clock input ($\overline{CS}$).

5) Connect a normally HIGH pushbutton switch to the address select clock input ($\overline{CP_0}$ input of the 7493).

6) Connect I/O outputs I/O_3–I/O_0 to data bus lines DB_3–DB_0, respectively.

7) Connect the outputs of the 74125 buffers to the data bus.

8) Connect a normally LOW pushbutton switch to the reset input (MR of the 7493). You will use this switch to reset the counter.

You are now ready to test the 2114A. Using the logic probe to monitor the counter outputs, clear the counter by pulsing it until its output is 0000. Set $\overline{WE}$ to HIGH and the data switches to 1001. Use the logic probe to check the data bus levels. The probe should indicate an indeterminate level. Why?

c) *2114 READ operation:* To read data from memory, $\overline{CS}$ must be made LOW while $\overline{WE}$ is HIGH. Press and hold the pushbutton connected to $\overline{CS}$, and check the data bus levels. Since the counter is at 00_{16}, the data stored at that address should

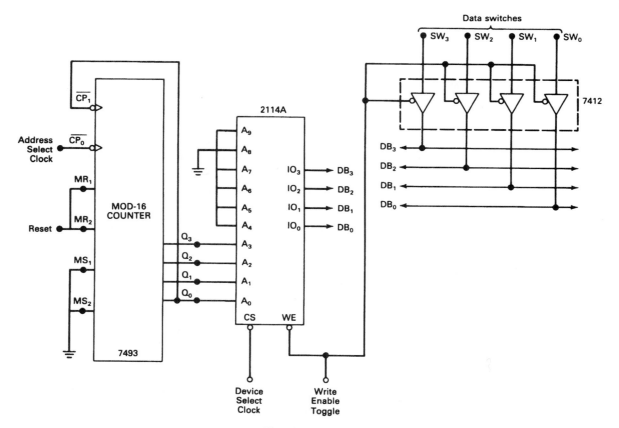

Figure 40-1

be on the data bus. Since nothing has been written into memory, whatever is on the data bus is random. Release the $\overline{CS}$ switch, and pulse the counter to 0001 (01_{16}). Press and hold the $\overline{CS}$ pushbutton switch, and check the bus levels. Again, the levels on the data bus are random. Read the data words in other memory locations in the same manner, and verify that the levels on the data bus are random.

    d) *2114A WRITE operation*: To write data to memory, $\overline{CS}$ must be made LOW while $\overline{WE}$ is LOW. Set the address counter to 00_{16}. Set $\overline{WE}$ to LOW. Check the levels on the data bus now. Since the data switch buffers are enabled, the data word on the bus should be 1001. However, the data has not been written yet, since $\overline{CS}$ = 1. Momentarily pulse $\overline{CS}$ LOW. Verify that 1001 has been written to memory location 00_{16} by performing a READ as done in step c.

    e) Momentarily disconnect V_{cc} from the 2114A. Then reconnect it, and READ the data word at memory location 00_{16}. It should be lost, since RAM memory is volatile.

    f) Store all of the words at the memory locations shown in Table 40-2. Have your instructor check the data.

    g) *Using a logic analyzer to examine memory*: If a logic analyzer is not available, go on to step h.

    The contents of your memory chip can be displayed in "state table format." In order to sample and display the data, the memory must be cycled continuously

Table 40-2

Address	Data	
	Binary	Hex
00	1111	F
01	1110	E
02	1101	D
03	1100	C
04	1011	B
05	1010	A
06	1001	9
07	1000	8
08	0111	7
09	0110	6
0A	0101	5
0B	0100	4
0C	0011	3
0D	0010	2
0E	0001	1
0F	0000	0

through each of the 16 addresses so that the contents of each memory location are placed on the data bus. Use the following procedure to set up and display memory on the logic analyzer. The instructions are very general, so you may have to consult your instructor for specific details on how to set up your particular logic analyzer.

1) Connect a 10 kHz square wave to the counter clock input.
2) Connect the logic analyzer probes as follows:

    Channels 0–3 to DB_0–DB_3
    Channels 4–7 to address lines A_0–A_3
    "C" probe to the 10 kHz clock

3) Set $\overline{WE}$ to 1 (READ mode).
4) Set the logic analyzer sample interval to EXT (positive edge).
5) Set the logic analyzer to trigger on address 0000.
6) Set the logic analyzer to state table mode. Display should be binary.
7) Have the logic analyzer start a sample cycle. Observe the tabular data displayed. Then position the cursor so that the trigger word is at the top of the table. This line should be either highlighted, blinking, or both. The table should show addresses 0000–1111 and their respective data contents. Since $\overline{CS}$ was HIGH, the data will not be correct.
8) Now hold $\overline{CS}$ LOW, and repeat step 7. The table should now display the correct memory data. This time store the sample.
9) Disconnect one of the memory's I/O lines from the data bus. Have the logic analyzer take another sample. Next, use the COMPARE mode to compare the new sample with the sample that you stored. You should observe that the missing I/O line's data position in the display is highlighted in some manner to indicate differences between old and new data.
10) Reconnect the I/O line you disconnected in step 9.

11) Disconnect the square wave generator from the counter, and replace the pushbutton switch there.

h) *Memory-to-register data transfer:* This type of transfer requires close attention to timing. During a READ operation, $\overline{WE}$ is HIGH and the $\overline{CS}$ line is pulsed LOW. After internal delays, the memory produces the data word at the I/O pins. This data can be clocked into the register at this time. For proper operation, the $\overline{CS}$ pulse has to stay LOW long enough to give the data a chance to stabilize on the data bus. If not, the register will latch erroneous data.

Refer to the data sheet for the 2114A, and determine how much time should be allowed for the memory outputs to stabilize before latching them into a register. Record this value: _____.

i) Examine the circuit in Figure 40-2. You are to add a 74LS139 IC and a 74174 IC to the data bus system. Install the 74174 IC onto the component board, and make the connections shown in Figure 40-2. Keep the 74174 $\overline{MR}$ input unconnected; it can be momentarily grounded to clear the register. Also make all other connections not shown that are required for the proper operation of the IC.

j) Make a table of transfer operations like you did in Experiment 37, this time for the new data bus system. Show the table to your instructor or laboratory assistant for approval.

k) Test the operation of the completed data bus system by setting the decoder select inputs to all possible combinations and verifying that the correct input and output devices are selected. What happens when the decoder select inputs are all

Table 40-3

Selects				Data Transfer	
IS_1	IS_0	OS_1	OS_0	To Register	From Register
0	0	0	0		
0	0	0	1	memory	data switches
0	1	0	0		
0	1	0	1		

LOW? _____. Check the memory READ/WRITE operations. Enter the data in Table 40-3 and then verify that the data was written.

l) *Register-to-memory data transfer:* The way the data bus is currently configured, you cannot transfer data from the 74174 to memory. Come up with a circuit modification that will permit this type of data transfer. Keep in mind the following considerations:

1) You cannot tie the register outputs directly to the data bus. Why?

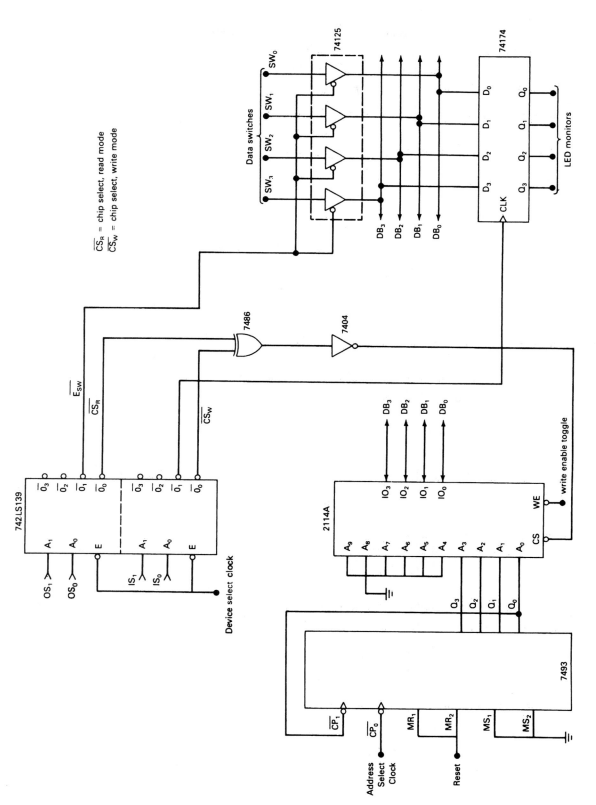

FIGURE 40-2

2) You still want to be able to write a word into memory from the switch inputs. Thus, you must have some way of selecting either the register or the switches as the source of data to be placed onto the data bus to be written into memory. Draw the circuit modification:

Show the circuit to your instructor for approval.

m) Construct your modification, and check it out using the following sequence of operations:

1) WRITE 1011 from the data switches to memory address 05.
2) READ the contents of address 05, and transfer it to the 74174 register.
3) Clear the register.
4) WRITE 0000 from the register into address 05.
5) READ address 05 to see if it is storing 0000.

Demonstrate this sequence to your instructor.

n) *Review*: This concludes the exercises on RAM memory. To test your understanding of the principles covered in this experiment, answer the following questions.

1. Explain the sequence of events illustrating how data is transferred from memory to the 74174 register.

2. Explain what might happen to memory if the enables to the 74LS139 were NOT pulsed LOW to enable the decoder operation, but rather tied permanently LOW.

3. Explain why timing during memory-to-register data transfer was not a critical factor in performing this experiment.

Experiment 41
(Optional)

Name _____

SYNCHRONOUS COUNTER DESIGN

OBJECTIVE

1. To learn how to design synchronous counters.

TEXT REFERENCES

Digital Systems , 6th edition, by **R.J. Tocci** - Read section 7.14.
Student's Study Guide, by **F.J. Ambrosio -** See Chapter 7.

EQUIPMENT NEEDED

Components
7400 IC (1);
7402 IC (1);
7404 IC (3);
7410 IC (1);
7474 IC (2);
7486 IC (1);
4 LED monitors.

Instruments
05 volt DC power supply;
pulse or square wave generator;
dual trace oscilloscope;
logic probe.

DISCUSSION

In this experiment, you will use the step-by-step procedure described in the text in order to design and build synchronous counters of any Mod number, and compare their operation and advantages over asynchronous counters.

PROBLEM

Design and build a synchronous counter that counts as follows:
0, 2, 4, 6, 8, 10, 11, 12, 14, 15, 0, 2, 4, ...(recycles).... The *undesired* states are 1, 3, 5, 7, 9, and 13. If any of the undesired states occur upon power-up or due to noise, on the next clock pulse the counter should go to count 15.

PROCEDURE

1) Complete the table of Figure 41-1 showing the desired counting sequence for

D	C	B	A

FIGURE 41-1

the counter.

2) Complete the state transition diagram of Figure 41-2 showing all possible states, including those that are not part of the desired counting sequence.

3) Use the state transition diagram of Figure 41-2 to set up the table of Figure 41-3, which lists all **PRESENT states** and their **NEXT states**.

4) Complete the column for the **J K** *Levels*. For each **PRESENT state**, indicate the levels required at each J and K input in order to produce the transition to the **NEXT state**.

5) Use the Karnaugh maps in Figure 41-4 to derive the simplified Boolean expressions for the variables Ja, Ka, Jb, Kb, Jc, Kc, Jd, and Kd. *(Hint: Use DON'T CARE conditions whenever possible.)*

6) Implement the circuits for the variables of step 5 and, in the space provided on page 277, draw the complete schematic for the counter described in the original problem. *Wire it and verify its operation.* **Show it to the instructor.**

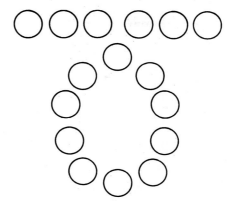

Figure 41-2

	PRESENT States D C B A		NEXT States D C B A		J K Levels			
					Jd Kd	Jc Kc	Jb Kb	Ja Ka
0								
1								
2								
3								
4								
5								
6								
7								
8								
9								
10								
11								
12								
13								
14								
15								

Figure 41-3

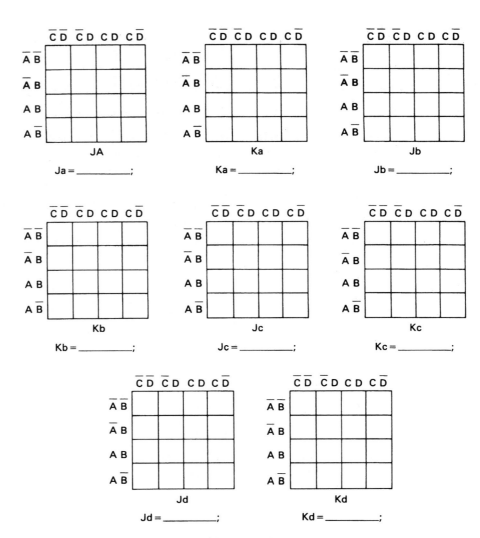

Figure 41-4

Schematic for the Synchronous Counter

QUESTIONS

1. State one advantage (a) and one disadvantage (b) that synchronous counters have over asynchronous counters.

   (a)

   (b)

2. What is the MOD number of the counter that you designed and built in this lab?

3. Verify the answer to question 2 by applying a 10 kHz TTL square wave (F_{in}) to the clock input of the counter and then by measuring the output frequency (F_{out}) at the output of the most significant flip-flop of your counter. The MOD number is then obtained by solving

   $$MOD = \frac{Fin}{Fout}.$$

4. Assume that the average propagation delay of each flip-flop is 15ns and that the average propagation delay of each gate and inverter is 10ns. Determine the approximate f_{max} for the counter.

Experiment 42
(Optional)

Name _____

PROGRAMMABLE FUNCTION SEQUENCER

OBJECTIVES

This experiment utilizes an EPROM to sequence through the hexadecimal number system, an up/down count as well as two different chase light sequence patterns. The results of each operation will be verified by a seven segment LED display. Tasks such as this can also be accomplished by using RAMs, ROMs or PLAs.

TEXT REFERENCES

Digital Systems, 6th edition, by **R.J. Tocci** - Read section 9.13.

EQUIPMENT NEEDED

Components
2716 EPROM (1);
7405 (2);
7493 (1);
7-segment LED, common anode. (1);
SPST switches (4);
1KΩ resistors (4);
220Ω resistors (7).

Instruments
0-5 volt DC power supply;
pulse or square wave generator;
dual trace oscilloscope;
logic probe;
PROM programmer;
UV PROM eraser.

DISCUSSION

Refer to the circuit of Figure 42-1. IC-1 is being used as a MOD-16 counter. As the clock input is applied, it will cycle through all 16 possible states. Each one of these states will address a certain memory location of the EPROM (IC-2). The contents of each memory location (pattern of 1s and 0s) will vary according to which switch SW0-SW3 is selected (grounded). The results will be displayed on a common anode LED such as that of Figure 42-2(b).

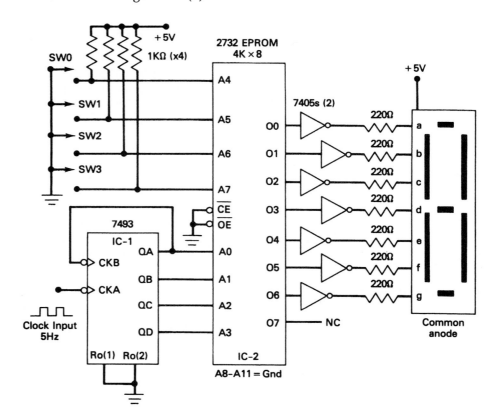

Figure 42-1

OPERATION

When SW0 is selected, the contents of the addressable locations of the EPROM should be the hexadecimal codes (0–F). Thus, the LED display should cycle through the hexadecimal number system. When SW1 is selected, the display should cycle through the up/down count sequence 1–8, 8–1 ...(up/down count sequence). SW2 selects the chase LED segment pattern sequence a,b,g,e,d,c,g,f,a...(figure-8 LED pattern). SW3 selects the LED chase segment pattern sequence a,b,g,f,g,e,d,c,a...(alternating circles LED pattern).

● **PROCEDURE**

I.   The first step is to make sure that you have a clean EPROM (unprogrammed). This can be done by using a W PROM eraser. In this experiment the EPROM must be programmed before being used. There are a couple of ways of programming the 2732 EPROM (either the 2716 or 2732 EPROM may be used). One way is to use one of the many commercially available programmers. Another way is to program the EPROM manually. (Refer to the EPROM's data sheet for programming instructions).

II. Refer to the memory map of Figure 42-2(a). Determine which four blocks of memory (16 bytes each) will be used to store the data necessary for the proper operation of the circuit of Figure 42-1, as it was described above.

III. Fill out the EPROM worksheets of Figure 42-3 with the hex codes necessary to execute the program in each of the four blocks of memory determined in step (II).

IV. Use the specification data sheets in appendix B and transfer the pin numbers to all ICs used in the circuit of Figure 42-1.

V.   Construct the circuit of Figure 42-1 and verify its operation. Demonstrate for the instructor.

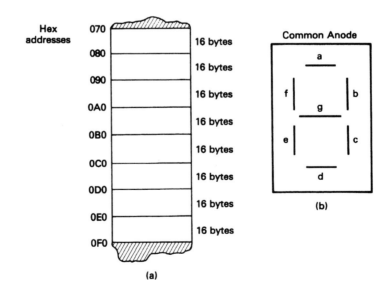

Figure 42-2

Figure–8 LED pattern

Hex Address	EPROM contents (hex)

Alternating circles LED pattern

Hed Address	EPROM contents (hex)

Hexadecimal number system

Hex Address	EPROM contents (hex)

Up/Down count sequence

Hex Address	EPROM contents (hex)

Figure 42-3

QUESTIONS

QUESTIONS

a) Switches SW0-SW3 select four different sets of programming instructions. By using three switches (SW0-SW2) and one more IC, show how you would modify the circuit of Figure 42-1 so that you could have access to 8 different sets of programming instructions?

b) In the circuit of Figure 42-1 SW0-SW3 are normally HIGH and become active when they go LOW. If they were to be normally LOW and became HIGH when active, what would be the range of selectable addresses?

c) How would you modify the circuit of Figure 42-1 if a common cathode 7-segment LED was used instead?

Appendix A

WIRING AND TROUBLESHOOTING DIGITAL CIRCUITS

OBJECTIVES

1. To discuss general wiring procedures for digital circuits.
2. To introduce the student to formalized troubleshooting procedures.
3. To list some of the common faults found in digital systems.

DISCUSSION

The experiments in this manual are designed to give you hands-on experience with digital circuits. More than that, they provide you with an opportunity to develop sound breadboarding and troubleshooting skills that will be invaluable to you whether you eventually become an engineer or a technician. This appendix will present some very basic information and suggestions concerning each area. It is not meant to replace any laboratory standards. However, much of the information given here can be used as reference material that can be, and should be, reviewed from time to time.

Most of the experiments contain operational testing of various ICs. At times, this may appear to be a tedious undertaking on your part. Don't fall into the trap of treating this sort of experimentation mechanically, taking for granted that an IC will operate just as it did in the classroom lecture. In the classroom, you are working with the ideal. In the lab, you will occasionally work with ICs that are less than ideal. In fact, they may not work at all, or at least not in the manner they were designed to work. If you keep in mind that lab experimentation is not only to verify principles but also to learn to recognize common problems associated with the circuits, you will get more out of the experiments. As you will learn, verification of a circuit's operation is one of the first steps taken in troubleshooting.

A.1 Prototype Circuit Wiring

It is assumed that you will be wiring circuits using a prototype circuit board. Such boards come in different sizes, but most have the following features:

a) Two horizontal rows of holes, one at the top and one at the bottom. The contacts underneath the holes on each of these rows are connected together to form a bus. They are not directly connected to the other holes on the board.

b) At least two sections of holes, with each section arranged so that the holes are in vertical groups called circuit blocks. Each circuit block is isolated from all others. This permits several wires to be joined at common junctions. The two sections are separated by a horizontal gap. This gap separates the sections electrically as well as physically. Thus, a vertical circuit block in the top section of the board is not connected to the block directly below it in the bottom section. ICs will straddle this gap so that each IC pin will be inserted into its own block. Connections to each pin will be brought to its block.

Installing ICs: ICs should be installed or mounted on the board to permit wires going from the top section of the board to the bottom to go between the ICs. It is not advisable to pass wires over ICs, although sometimes it is hard to avoid. Strapping ICs to the board in this manner will present problems if the IC has to be removed. The consequences of this are obvious.

As you mount an IC, check to make sure that none of its pins are being tucked beneath it. If it is necessary to remove an IC, always use an IC puller. *Never* remove an IC with your fingers or with a pair of pliers. The first causes a definite safety hazard, while the second will often result in eventual damage to the IC.

Wiring the circuit: Wires should be dressed so that 3/8" insulation is stripped from each end and the length of wire is no more than needed to make a neat connection between circuit blocks. If the wires are too long, some circuits will malfunction, especially flip-flops and flip-flop devices such as counters. You may have to rearrange the ICs on the board to solve this problem, if it occurs. Another way to solve the problem is by inserting a 2 k-ohm resistor in series with the wire at the input end of the wire.

Have a lab partner call out each connection to be made. Route the wires along the circuit board neatly, bending them smoothly wherever necessary. Avoid bending the wire sharply, since this will increase the likelihood of fracture beneath the insulation, resulting in an open circuit or an intermittent open. Minimize the number of crossovers, that is, wires routed over other wires.

The overall appearance should be neat, not like a bowl of spaghetti. If you have made all of your connections as outlined above, it may not be picture perfect, but the neatness will pay off in reduced troubleshooting time and easier IC replacement.

A.2 Testing the Circuit

Circuit testing is also known as troubleshooting. You are probably accustomed to discrete circuit (e.g., a transistor amplifier) troubleshooting methods. Since each circuit element of a discrete circuit is accessible to the troubleshooter, faulty circuit elements can be isolated by making basic measurements such as voltage, resistance, capacitance, and inductance, using conventional test equipment. Modern digital circuits and systems, on the other hand, consist mainly of digital ICs. The IC's components are not accessible to the troubleshooter, so the troubleshooter must rely on knowledge of the IC's operation(s) in order to isolate the IC as being faulty. The experiments in this manual are designed to give you the necessary experience to test for and recognize proper operation of ICs.

A digital IC is considered defective or faulty if its outputs do not respond correctly, according to its truth table, for each set of input conditions and for each of its various operating modes. A similar statement can be made for digital circuits and systems. Once it has been verified that a circuit or system is not responding correctly, a *fault is said to exist,* and further troubleshooting is indicated. The next troubleshooting step is to *isolate the cause of the fault,* which may be in one or more smaller circuits or subsystems. By progressively isolating smaller circuits, and perhaps smaller subsystems, the troubleshooter will eventually isolate the defective components, which may be one or more ICs and/or discrete components. After *replacing the defective components,* the circuit or system is tested for proper operation once more. Once proper operation is established for all operating modes, the troubleshooter's task is completed.

Now that the student is acquainted with the nature of digital troubleshooting, a procedure for fault isolation is presented. The student should, when applying the procedure in the lab, perform each step in the order given. After sufficient experience with digital circuits is attained, common sense and intuition may lead the student directly to the faulty device and thereby reduce the amount of troubleshooting time.

Step 1: Perform a visual inspection of the system or circuit. Look for loose or damaged connecting wires, cables, and printed circuit (PC) boards, evidence of burning or extreme overheating, missing components, and blown fuses. If the circuit or system is mounted on prototype boards, look for wiring errors, damaged boards, and digital ICs improperly inserted. Also check for incorrect circuit design.

Step 2: Check all power source levels, and confirm that power is actually being applied to the circuit or system.

Step 3: Study all relevant documentation on the circuit or system, such as block diagrams, schematics, and operating instructions. Learn how the circuit or system operates normally.

Step 4: Verify all operating modes of the circuit by running tests.

Step 5: Record results of the tests run in step 4. Test results often show patterns that may lead to the faulty device. Repeat steps 4 and 5 at least once before proceeding to step 6.

Step 6: If the circuit passes all tests, end the procedure. If the circuit fails at least one test, continue to the next step.

Step 7: Analyze the test results recorded above and select a possible location for the fault.

Step 8: Check all signals and static logic levels at this location, and record them. If nothing appears abnormal, return to step 7.

Step 9: Analyze the test results recorded above, and select a possible faulty device.

Step 10: Check the device for proper functioning. If it is a discrete component, take basic Ohm's Law measurements and/or use a device tester to determine if the device is faulty. If the device is an IC, check the IC for proper functioning. This includes checking inputs and outputs for stuck-HIGH and stuck-LOW conditions and other types of digital IC faults (see below, *Common Digital IC Faults*). If the device passes all tests, then return to step 9.

Step 11: Repair or replace the faulty device and return to step 4.

A.3 Common Causes of Faults
in Digital Systems

In this section, several common causes of faults in digital systems are listed along with symptoms given for each cause and steps that may be taken to correct or minimize its effects on the system.

Defective components: Components normally fail because of age, because the maximum voltage or current rating of the device was exceeded due to improper design or because of the breakdown of another component, improper connections, or excessive ambient temperature. In the case of digital ICs, overheating caused by improper connections (especially prototype circuits), overvoltage, or ambient temperature may result in the IC operating only sporadically. After cooling down, the IC will usually operate normally.

IC loading problems: Exceeding the fan-out of a TTL logic output may result in the output voltage dropping below $V_{OH}(min)$ or rising above $V_{OL}(max)$. To verify this condition, the output voltage should be checked for a level of 0 V–0.8 V for a LOW and 2 V–5 V for a HIGH. If not, the excessive fan-out is causing a problem.

CMOS and MOS logic outputs will not be affected significantly by exceeding the fan-out limits. However, any transitions at the output will show an increase in risetime and falltime. This is because each CMOS or MOS input loads the output capacitively (5 pf each input).

Some common symptoms to look for are flip-flops, counters, and flip-flop registers that do not respond to the signal at the clock input. Measure t_R and t_F of the clock signal, and compare the measurements to the minimum required by the flip-flop, counter, or register for proper triggering.

To correct the problem caused by excessive fan-out, a buffer should be used or the fan-out reduced by load splitting. Another solution is to insert a pulse-shaping circuit such as a Schmitt trigger between the overloaded output and the clock input.

Improper signal characteristics: A digital IC may function improperly if logic signals not meeting its requirements are applied to its inputs. Minimum requirements are given for amplitude, pulse duration, and transition times. A signal that fails to meet any one of these requirements can cause the IC to function incorrectly.

Common symptoms brought on by improper signal characteristics include flip-flops, counters, and flip-flop registers that respond incorrectly to signals at clock, clear, and preset inputs.

The characteristic(s) causing the problem must be determined and brought back into specification.

Power supply—Improper levels: Since all IC logic devices use voltage to represent logic levels, trouble with the output level of the supply can cause ICs to function improperly. A common cause of improper power supply levels is overload. This can be particularly true in prototype systems and circuits.

Symptoms of this type of trouble include the condition where logic HIGH at circuit outputs is less than V_{OH}. Disconnecting a few ICs from the power supply will usually cause the level of V_{CC} to rise if this is the case.

Using a larger power supply or redesigning the existing one for higher current output will solve the problem.

Power supply—Poor regulation. Poor regulation in a power supply will cause V_{CC} to fluctuate when large numbers of logic circuits are switching states. These fluctuations act like noise pulses and can cause false triggering of logic devices. This problem is especially significant in TTL circuits.

A symptom caused by this problem is flip-flops, counters, and registers triggering when they are not supposed to, and triggering instead at the time other devices in the system are changing states. To verify that poor regulation is the problem, V_{CC} should be examined with an oscilloscope. If spikes or pulses are riding on the V_{CC} level causing V_{CC} to drop by more than 0.2 V, then the power supply has poor regulation.

There are two ways to correct this problem: (1) improve the power supply regulation by either replacing or redesigning the current one, or (2) use RF decoupling capacitors (refer to text, Chapter 8).

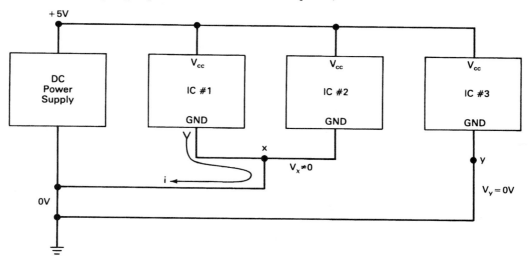

Figure A-1

Grounding problems: Poorly designed ground return circuits can cause the voltage at IC ground pins to be nonzero. This is because currents flowing through the ground system can cause resistive and inductive voltage drops (see Figure A-1). To avoid this problem, all ground wires should have low resistance and inductance, and each IC ground pin should be connected to the power supply separately. PC board ground returns should be large conductive traces.

Noise problems: Circuit noise can be externally or internally generated. Internally generated noise was discussed earlier. Externally generated noise can cause sporadic triggering of logic circuits. Common sources are electromechanical devices (e.g., motors and relays that produce electromagnetic radiation) and electronic power control circuitry using SCRs and TRIACs. This type of problem can be minimized by using special AC power line filtering devices to prevent noise from entering through the AC lines and grounded shields or conducting planes to short radiated noise signals to ground.

A.4 Common Digital IC Faults

Digital IC faults are classified as either internal or external faults. We begin our discussion with internal faults.

Internal digital IC faults: There are four types of internal failures:

1) inputs or outputs shorted to ground or V$_{CC}$
2) inputs or outputs open
3) shorts between pins (not to ground or V$_{CC}$)
4) internal circuitry failure

These failures are corrected by replacing the faulty IC. A discussion on each type of failure follows.

Short to ground or V$_{CC}$:   This failure causes the inputs or outputs to be either permanently HIGH or permanently LOW (referred to as stuck-HIGH or stuck-LOW). Figure A-2(a) shows a NAND gate with a stuck-LOW input and a stuck-HIGH output. The stuck-HIGH condition may be the result of an internal short in input A, an internal short at output X, or both.

Connections to output X are also forced HIGH; connections to input A are forced LOW. Shorts of this type in emitter-coupled logic (ECL) devices result in neither a HIGH nor a LOW.

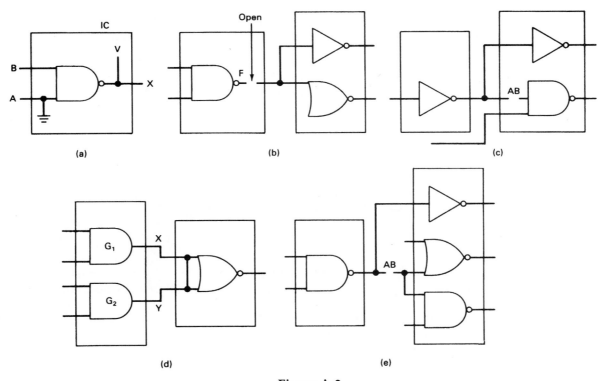

Figure A-2

In troubleshooting this type of failure, the student should be aware that signals may not change beyond the point where the short is located.

Open inputs or outputs: An open output will result in an open input for all inputs driven by the output. Open inputs in TTL logic devices generally act as HIGHs, causing inputs that are tied to open outputs to resemble a stuck-HIGH input, though not always. Open CMOS inputs do not generally act as a HIGH or a LOW. This being the case, inputs tied to an open TTL or CMOS output will resemble a stuck-LOW or stuck-HIGH input or may even oscillate between HIGH and LOW. Open inputs for ECL devices, with inputs pulled down by a resistor, are LOW.

Figure A-2(b) illustrates an open output in a NAND gate. Figure A-2(c) shows an open input. In the latter diagram, the student should note that all signals before point A are unaffected.

Short between two pins: Figure A-2(d) shows two input pins shorted together. This means that the outputs of the two driver gates are also shorted. This condition will cause a fault in TTL and CMOS devices only if the two driver outputs try to go to opposite levels, say, X to HIGH and Y to LOW. In this case, if the device is TTL, X will be stuck-LOW. In other words, if one output is LOW, both will be LOW. However, if the device is CMOS, this condition typically produces an intermediate level (see Figure A-3). There is obviously no fault which occurs when both outputs are supposed to be at the same level. ECL device outputs can normally be connected together, so no logic faults will occur unless the driver gates are damaged by excessive currents.

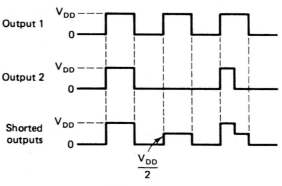

Figure A-3

Internal circuitry failure: Failure in the circuits within a digital IC can cause its inputs and outputs to be stuck-HIGH or stuck-LOW.

External digital IC faults: In addition to the four types of internal failure, there are four types of external failures that can occur:

1) line shorted to ground or power supply
2) open signal line
3) short between signal lines
4) failure of a discrete component

To discover these faults, look for poor soldering joints, solder bridges, open wires or traces, or test components such as capacitors and resistors for opens, shorts, and/or values that are out of tolerance.

Line shorted to ground or power supply: This type of failure will appear like an internal short and can't be distinguished from it. Perform a careful visual inspection to isolate this fault.

Open signal line: Figure A.2(e) shows an open signal line that results in an open input only for points beyond point B. All inputs before A are unaffected by the open line. Signal tracing and/or continuity checks are useful techniques for discovering this type of fault.

Short between two signal lines: This type of fault cannot be distinguished from an internal short. Often, poor soldering on PC boards results in solder bridges across the signal lines. On prototype boards, look for bare connecting wires (poorly dressed) too close together. In either case, a visual inspection is necessary to locate this fault.

Shorted signal lines in TTL will appear different from shorts in CMOS circuits. In TTL, if one signal is trying to go HIGH and the other is going LOW, the level at the short will be about 0 V. This is because resistance at TTL outputs is lower in the LOW state than in the HIGH state. For CMOS and MOS devices, the level at the short will be about midway between 0 V and 5 V for this same situation, because their output resistance is about the same in both states. See Figure A-3 for an example of how waveforms would look for shorted signal lines in CMOS and MOS circuits. Note the 2.5 V levels. These levels would not normally appear on the waveforms.

Failure of discrete components: While most digital components are ICs, there is still circuitry that requires discrete components such as resistors, capacitors, transistors, and diodes. These components can be tested either completely out of the circuit or by unsoldering one or more of their leads and checking them with an appropriate test instrument such as an ohmmeter, capacitance checker, or transistor checker. Faulty discrete components could mean another circuit caused the failure. Be sure and check around for other faults because, in the long run, this avoids repeated failures in the device replaced.

Common test equipment used in digital troubleshooting: Besides the usual analog test equipment, such as VOMs, oscilloscopes, and the like, digital troubleshooting requires some specialized equipment. A list of these specialized instruments would include the following:

1) logic probe
2) logic pulser
3) current tracer
4) logic analyzer

Of the four, the logic probe is the most useful in general troubleshooting. The pulser is useful when it is necessary to trigger gates, flip-flops, counters, or other types of circuits to check for proper operation. Both the logic probe and pulser are described in Experiment 3.

The current tracer is a more specialized test probe used in locating shorts in digital circuits. Whenever a short circuit is suspected, the current tracer can assist the troubleshooter in pinpointing the exact location of the short.

The logic analyzer is a complex instrument used to compare many different logic signals at one time. However, it is expensive and is used mostly in complex systems to solve the more difficult problems that occur in digital systems. The operation of a typical logic analyzer, the Tektronix Model 7D01, is discussed in Appendix B of this manual.

The experiments in this manual provide opportunities to gain experience with the logic probe, logic pulser, and the logic analyzer. It is recommended that you become acquainted with the logic probe you will be using by reading the user manual that should accompany the probe. If your laboratory has a logic analyzer, it would also be to your advantage to learn as much as possible about the instrument before you attempt to use it. If there is an operator's manual for the analyzer, get it and read it.

CONCLUDING REMARKS

The material in this appendix will be of more use to you if you review it from time to time. There is too much information relating to troubleshooting to include all of it in a short appendix. Your learning resource center or library may have some video tapes, journals, or books on the subject.

Appendix B

LOGIC ANALYZERS

A logic analyzer is a device that can store and display several channels of digital data. Although it resembles a multitrace oscilloscope, the logic analyzer differs from the oscilloscope in several ways:

- The logic analyzer displays only digital data; it cannot display both analog and digital signals like the oscilloscope can.

- The logic analyzer stores its data in memory first, then causes this data to be continually displayed on its CRT screen. Thus, the data that the analyzer displays has already occurred and is not real-time like that displayed by the oscilloscope.

- The logic analyzer is capable of displaying several channels of data simultaneously. A multitrace oscilloscope either chops or alternates between traces (channels) and thus cannot display the channels simultaneously.

- The logic analyzer can display its data in tabular format, using binary, octal, or hexadecimal characters, as well as in timing diagram format. The oscilloscope uses the timing diagram format only.

PART 1—LOGIC ANALYZER FUNDAMENTALS

In this section, we will describe the principles of operation of a typical logic analyzer. The model to be described is the Tektronix 7D01/7D01F. You should consult the operator's manual for your particular logic analyzer and/or ask your instructor for assistance in applying the information covered here to your analyzer.

B.1 Basic Block Diagram

Figure B-1 shows a block diagram for a simple logic analyzer. The probes are connected to a bus that carries the signals you wish to examine. The examination begins when the control block causes the trigger circuitry to issue a write enable to memory. The data on the bus is then clocked into memory, where it is stored. When enough data is stored, the write enable to memory is removed and replaced with a read enable. This permits the data that was stored to be read and displayed on the multitrace oscilloscope.

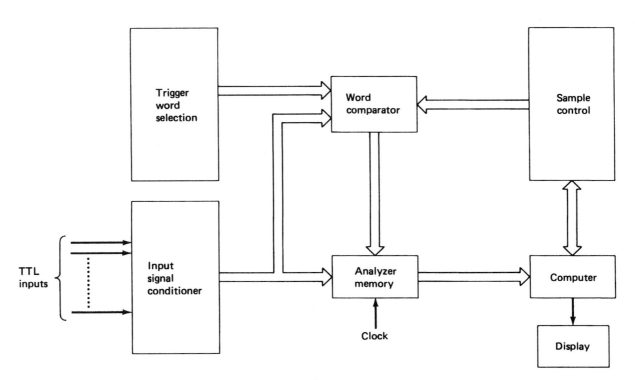

Figure B-1

The logic analyzer described here could be modified to display tabular data. What is needed is a computer to control the probes and display. The probes would be connected to the computer via a peripheral interface adapter (PIA), and the computer would be programmed to clock in the data, store it, and then display the data in the format desired.

B.2 Operating Principles

At the heart of the logic analyzer is its capability to store data in its memory. The memory is organized as serial shift registers, one per channel. Each channel's register size depends on the number of channels being used. For example, the Tektronix 7D01 has three possibilities:

No.data channels		No.bits/channel
4	(Ch. 0-3)	1024
8	(Ch. 0-7)	508
16	(Ch. 0-15)	254

In each case, the memory capacity is 4064 bits (about 4K).

Figure B-2 shows the basic structure for a single data channel. This structure is the same for all of the other channels (up to 16 channels). The input signal that is to be examined is connected to the probe for that channel and delivered to a comparator. Regardless of whether the signal is digital or analog, the comparator

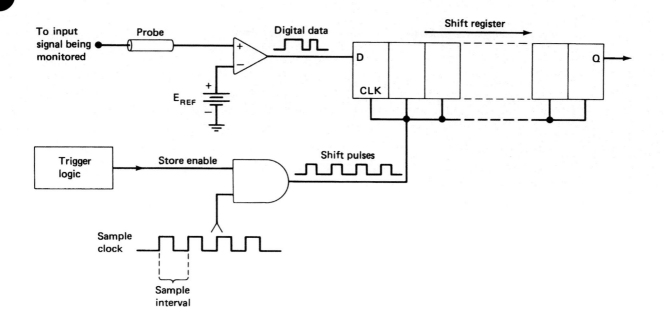

Figure B-2

compares the input to a reference (threshold) voltage, converting the input signal to a pure digital signal. For TTL logic, the threshold voltage is set to +1.4 volts.

Figures B-3 and B-4 show two cases of input signals. In Figure B-3, the input signal is digital, and the output of the comparator is the same as its input. Figure B-4 shows that in the case of a nondigital input, the comparator output will be a digitized version of the input.

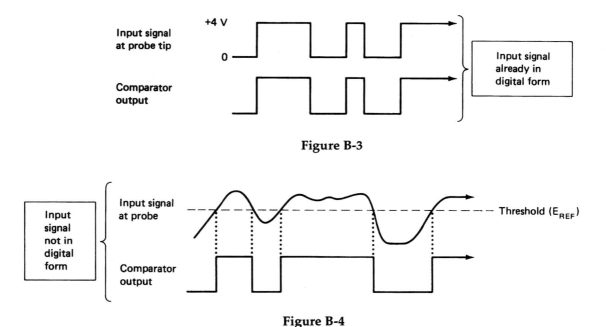

Figure B-3

Figure B-4

B.3 Storing Data (Store Mode)

After the comparator converts the input data to digital, the data is sent to the input of a shift register, where it is clocked into the shift register by the SAMPLE CLOCK for as long as the STORE ENABLE is HIGH. The shift register stores the data until it is needed for display. Figure B-5 shows the timing relationship between the output of the comparator, the STORE ENABLE signal, SAMPLE CLOCK, and the data shifted into the shift register. Note that while the STORE ENABLE is HIGH, the level of the comparator's output at each positive-going transition of the SAMPLE

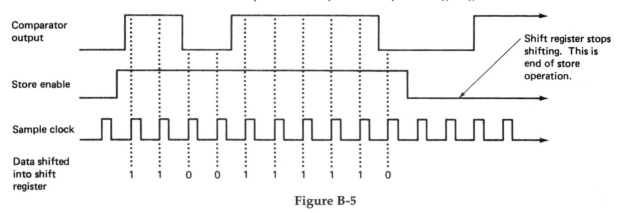

Figure B-5

CLOCK is shifted into the shift register from left to right, and that when the STORE ENABLE goes LOW, the shifting stops. Even though the data at the comparator output is changing, the data currently in the shift register does not change. In other words, the SAMPLE CLOCK periodically samples the data and shifts it into the register for storage. The period between samples is called the SAMPLE INTERVAL. As new data is shifted into the shift register, the old data is shifted out.

B.4 Displaying Data (Display Mode)

After the logic analyzer has completed the STORE operation, its memory contains a digital representation of the input signals that are connected to its inputs. As soon as the STORE ENABLE goes LOW, the logic analyzer goes into its DISPLAY mode of operation. In this mode, the logic analyzer displays the contents of each channel's shift register on the CRT as a serial digital waveform. It does this by applying clock pulses to each shift register to shift the stored data out of the last flip-flop of the register and to the vertical amplifier of the CRT to be displayed.

As mentioned earlier, the 7D01 can be used to display 4, 8, or 16 channels. It is possible that the actual number of channels being monitored is fewer than the number of channels being displayed. If this is the case, the unused channels are simply ignored.

Figure B-6 illustrates how the 7D01 can be used to display four channels of stored data on the CRT screen. Note that the channels are numbered from 0 to 3 starting at the top of the display. Each waveform represents the complete contents of the channel memory register. For the 7D01, this means that each waveform represents the 1016 bits that were shifted into the register during the STORE mode, one bit per SAMPLE INTERVAL.

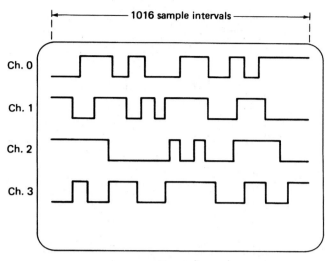

Figure B-6

If the logical analyzer were to be used in the 8-channel display mode, there would be eight channels, numbered 0 through 7, displayed on the screen. Each channel waveform would represent 508 bits of stored data on the screen. In the 16-channel display mode, there would be 16 waveforms displayed on the screen, each one representing 254 bits of data. Thus, as mentioned earlier, the total number of displayed bits is constant at about 4K, but the number per channel depends on how many channels are used.

EXAMPLE 1:

The data displayed in Figure B-6 was obtained using a SAMPLE INTERVAL of 5 microseconds during the STORE operation. What is the total time duration of each waveform?

SOLUTION:

Each waveform consists of 1016 bits, which were shifted into the memory register at the rate of one every 5 microseconds. Thus, the waveform duration is 1016 x 5 microseconds = 5080 microseconds.

EXAMPLE 2:

Repeat Example 1 for a 16-channel display.

SOLUTION:

For a 16-channel display, each waveform consists of 254 sample intervals or 254 x 5 microseconds = 1270 microseconds.

B.5 Types of Sampling

The 7D01 logic analyzer permits input signals to be sampled either *synchronously*, using the clock signal from the system under test, or *asynchronously*, using the 7D01's internal clock (refer to Figure B-7).

B.5.A Synchronous

Most digital systems, and all digital computers, operate from a master clock signal that synchronizes all of the system operations. The logic states of all the system

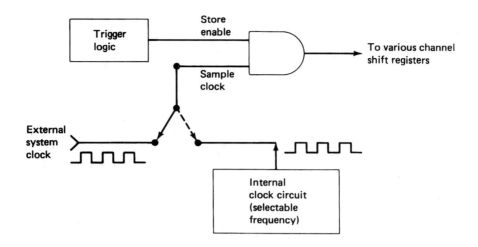

Figure B-7

signals can change only on the appropriate clock edge. The logic analyzer can use synchronous sampling to examine the system's data signals at the precise time that system clock edges occur. Figure B-8 illustrates the use of the negative-going edge of the system clock. The 7D01 permits either clock edge to be selected. Note that the stored data represents data on the input signal line when the negative clock edges occur. Any glitches that occur in the intervals between clock edges are ignored.

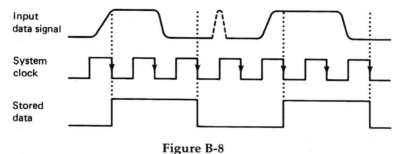

Figure B-8

B.5.B Asynchronous

Asynchronous sampling uses the 7D01's internal clock, which allows selectable sampling intervals from 10 nanoseconds to 5 milliseconds. The smaller sampling intervals permit you to acquire more information about the data signals over a shorter time duration. In other words, for a given number of samples, the use of a shorter sampling interval provides a more detailed look at the data signals. Figure B-9 shows the data signal used in Figure B-8 being sampled at a much higher rate (shorter interval between samples) using the 7D01's internal (asynchronous) clock.

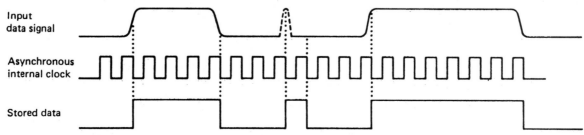

Figure B-9

Note that the shorter sample interval will store a more accurate picture of the input data signal, including glitches or erroneous pulses that occur in the intervals between system clock edges.

In troubleshooting, the synchronous sampling mode is often used to locate the general problem area; then, the asynchronous mode is used to take a closer look at the suspected signals for detection of glitches or erroneous pulses.

B.6 Triggering

In our previous discussion, we stated that the TRIGGER LOGIC circuit (see Figure B-2) generates the STORE ENABLE to control the store and display operations. If the STORE ENABLE is HIGH, the input data is sampled and stored; if the STORE ENABLE is LOW, the stored data is displayed on the CRT.

B.6.A Data Storage Relative to Trigger Event

The TRIGGER LOGIC controls STORE ENABLE in accordance with the occurrence of a selected TRIGGER EVENT. (We will describe the different TRIGGER EVENTS later.) When the TRIGGER EVENT occurs, the TRIGGER LOGIC decides when to make the STORE ENABLE go LOW to end the STORE operation and begin the DISPLAY operation. The 7D01 permits three different possibilities:

1) *Pre-trigger*: In this mode, STORE ENABLE will go LOW right after the TRIGGER EVENT occurs. Thus, the data that is stored in the different channel shift registers represents data that occurred prior to the TRIGGER EVENT. When the data is displayed on the CRT, the display will show those portions of the input waveforms that occurred before the TRIGGER EVENT.

Figure B-10 illustrates how the pre-trigger display appears for the 7D01 logic analyzer. The intensified dots on the display show when the TRIGGER EVENT occurred relative to the various channel waveforms. The greater part of the waveforms occurs prior to the TRIGGER EVENT. The 7D01 also displays a small portion of the waveforms that occur after the TRIGGER EVENT.

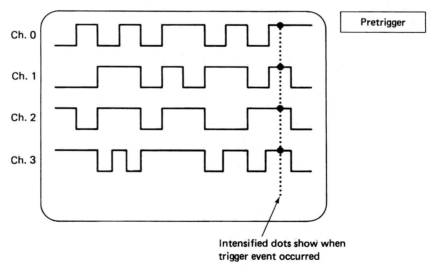

Intensified dots show when trigger event occurred

Figure B-10

2) *Post-trigger*: In this mode, the logic analyzer stores and displays data that occurs after the TRIGGER EVENT. Figure B-11 shows how the post-trigger appears for the 7D01 and shows that the greater part of the displayed waveforms occurs after the TRIGGER EVENT. The 7D01 also displays a small portion of the waveforms that occur before the TRIGGER EVENT.

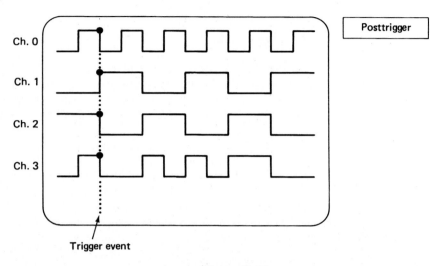

Figure B-11

3) *Center-trigger*: In this mode, the logic analyzer stores and displays data that occur both before and after the TRIGGER EVENT. This is illustrated in Figure B-12, which shows that the TRIGGER EVENT, indicated by the intensified dots, is in the center of the displayed waveforms.

Each of these three trigger modes is useful in different situations, depending on what portion of the waveforms you are interested in examining relative to a particular TRIGGER EVENT. We will now describe the possible TRIGGER EVENT sources that are used in the 7D01.

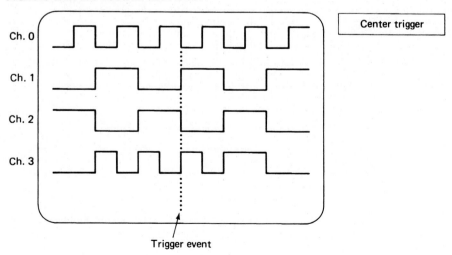

Figure B-12

B.6.B Sources of Trigger Events

The 7D01 allows you to select one of four different sources to produce the TRIGGER EVENT. They are described below:

1) *Manual.* The TRIGGER EVENT occurs when the operator presses the manual trigger button. This is used for the initial setting-up and positioning of the display or for getting a display of stored data when the expected TRIGGER EVENT has failed to occur.

2) *Channel 0 (Ch. 0).* The TRIGGER EVENT is the positive-going transition of the signal on Channel 0.

3) *External.* The TRIGGER EVENT occurs on the selected transition of the signal applied to the external trigger input. This signal is not one of the signals being displayed.

4) *Word Recognizer (WR).* When the WR is selected as the source of the TRIGGER EVENT, the WR unit generates a TRIGGER EVENT pulse when the logic levels present at the 16-channel inputs match a specific 16-bit word. The operator can select any 16-bit word using the WR channel switches on the 7D01 front panel.

B.7 Examining and Interpreting the Display

The logic analyzer has no time scale for measuring time intervals like that of an oscilloscope. Time is measured in units of one SAMPLE INTERVAL and is referenced to the TRIGGER EVENT. The examples in Figures B-13–B-15 show how this is done for the 7D01 4-channel display; the same idea may be extended to the 8- and 16-channel displays.

In Figure B-13, the post-trigger mode is used. The intensified dots on the left indicate when the TRIGGER EVENT occurred. The other set of dots is called the CURSOR and can be positioned anywhere along the waveforms using the CURSOR controls on the 7D01 front panel. The position of the CURSOR relative to the TRIGGER EVENT is displayed on the upper right-hand portion of the CRT screen. Here it is given as TRIG +45, which means that the CURSOR is 45 SAMPLE

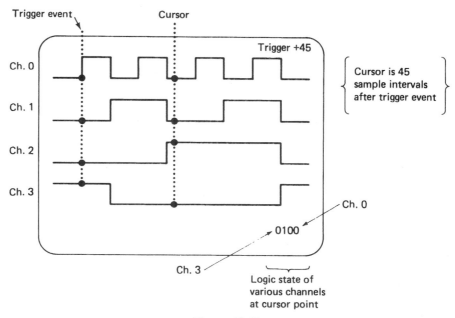

Figure B-13

INTERVALS after the TRIGGER EVENT. The data levels that are present on the various channel waveforms at the CURSOR point are displayed on the bottom of the CRT screen, with Channel 0 being the rightmost bit. Here it is given as 0100, which can be verified by looking at the waveform levels at the CURSOR position.

Figure B-14 illustrates the pre-trigger mode. Here the CURSOR is at -30 SAMPLE INTERVALS before the TRIGGER. The data levels at the CURSOR point are given as 0101.

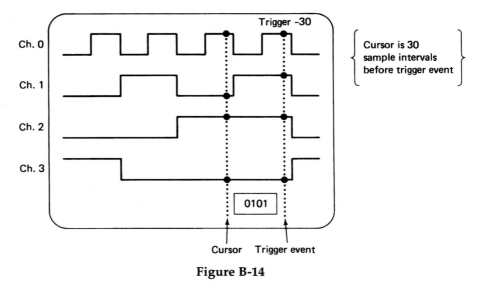

Figure B-14

Figure B-15 shows the CURSOR positioned right at the TRIGGER point, indicated by TRIG +0. The data levels at this point are 0111.

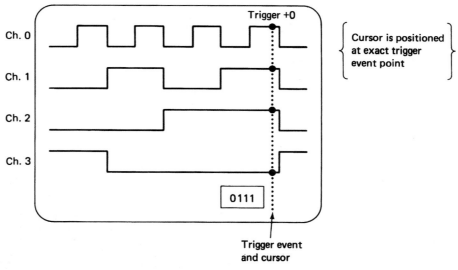

Figure B-15

EXAMPLE:

The waveforms in Figure B-15 were obtained using a SAMPLE INTERVAL of 50 nanoseconds. What is the time duration between the CURSOR and the TRIGGER EVENT?

SOLUTION:

The cursor is 30 SAMPLE INTERVALS before the TRIGGER or 30 × 50 n sec = 1500 n sec.

PART 2—USING THE STATE TABLE MODE

In Part 1, you saw how the 7D01 logic analyzer was used to sample, store, and display the logic levels present on up to 16 different signals simultaneously. The mode of display used was the TIMING DIAGRAM mode. Although this mode is very useful in many applications, it is not suitable for handling the large amounts of data present in the microprocessor and memory systems.

In Part 2, we will describe the STATE TABLE mode of operation. In this mode, all of the data in the logic analyzer's memory is displayed on the CRT in *tabular* form. Recall that the logic analyzer memory consists of shift registers, one per channel. These registers store the logic levels that were present on the data lines at each SAMPLE CLOCK edge during the STORE cycle.

The STATE TABLE mode is just another way the logic analyzer can display its memory data. The STORE cycle and TRIGGER operation are exactly the same as described in Part 1. Once the STORE cycle ends and the DISPLAY cycle begins, the logic analyzer will display the data in a table instead of as timing diagrams.

B.8 State Table Format

Figure B-16 shows a typical display in the TIMING DIAGRAM mode for four channels. The intensified dots on the left end of each waveform indicate the TRIGGER POINT. These dots also represent the CURSOR position, because the CURSOR is positioned at TRIG +0 as indicated.

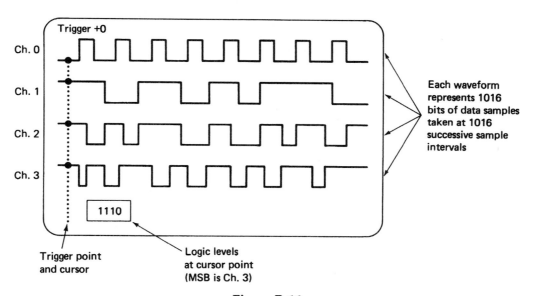

Figure B-16

You may recall that each channel waveform represents 1016 bits of data. These data correspond to samples that were taken at 1016 successive SAMPLE INTERVALS during the STORE cycle. The binary word shown at the lower part of the display tells us what the channel logic levels are at the CURSOR POINT, starting with channel 3 as the MSB. Since the CURSOR has been positioned at the TRIGGER POINT, this binary word also indicates the channel logic levels at the TRIGGER POINT.

Of course, the operator can move the CURSOR along the waveforms in steps of one SAMPLE INTERVAL. As this is done, the binary word will change to indicate the change in channel logic levels. If you were to record the binary words each time you moved the CURSOR one step, you would get a table of 4-bit words corresponding to the channel logic levels at the various sample intervals after the TRIGGER POINT. This is precisely what the logic analyzer does if you use it in the STATE TABLE mode.

B.8.A Binary Table

Figure B-17 shows what the display will look like when the operator selects the BINARY STATE TABLE display instead of the TIMING DIAGRAM display. The display is a table of *eighteen* 4-bit words. The top word in the table is *always* the CURSOR WORD. That is, it represents the logic levels present on the waveforms at the CURSOR POINT. The position of the CURSOR relative to the TRIGGER POINT is given as TRIG + 0 in this example.

The next 16 entries in the table show the logic levels present for the next 16 SAMPLE INTERVALS past the CURSOR POINT. Thus, the second table entry would be the data at TRIG + 1, the third entry would be at TRIG + 2, and so on, until the 17th entry, which is at TRIG + 16.

The 18th word (at the bottom of the display) is the TRIGGER WORD representing the logic levels that are present at the TRIGGER POINT. This TRIGGER WORD is *not* part of the data table; it is simply there as a reminder for the operator.

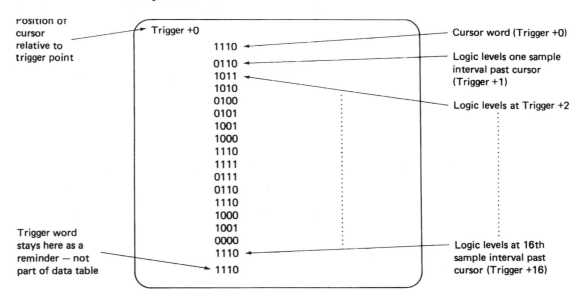

Figure B-17

B.8.B Blinking Trigger Word

Whenever the TRIGGER WORD appears as one of the 17 entries in the displayed data table, it will be blinking. For the example in Figure B-17, the TRIGGER WORD is the top entry in the table, since the CURSOR POINT is TRIG + 0. Thus, this 4-bit word will be blinking on the display

B.8.C 8- or 16-Channel Operation

The same binary table format can be used for 8- or 16-channel operation. The only difference is in the number of bits per word. We are using the 4-channel case here simply for convenience.

B.8.D Examining the Rest of the Data

The display contains only 17 data words, corresponding to the CURSOR WORD and the 16 following SAMPLE INTERVALS. The logic analyzer memory, however, holds a total of 1016 data words (508 for 8-channel operation, 254 for 16-channel operation). The operator can change the displayed data table by using the CURSOR position control. This is illustrated in the two tables of Figure B-18.

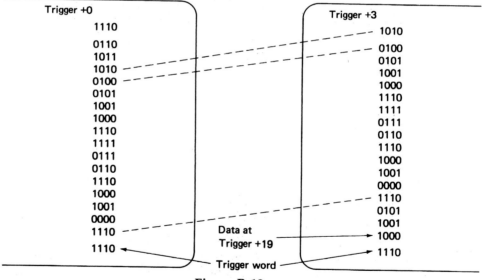

Figure B-18

The table on the left is the same as that in Figure B-17, where the CURSOR has been set at TRIG +0. The table on the right corresponds to a CURSOR position of TRIG +3. This means that the top word in this table is at TRIG +19. Thus, this new table contains three new entries at the bottom which were not contained in the original table. Of course, the new table has lost three of the entries from the top of the original table.

The operator can move the CURSOR to other positions relative to the TRIGGER POINT by using the logic analyzer CURSOR controls. In this manner, the operator can examine all of the data in the logic analyzer memory.

Note that the TRIG WORD at the bottom of both table displays is the same. This will not change with the CURSOR position because it is not part of the data tables. It is there to remind the operator what the TRIG WORD is.

B.8.E   Octal and Hex Tables

In many applications, it is more convenient to have the data tables displayed in octal or hexadecimal rather than in binary. The operator can select either octal or hex tables, and the logic analyzer will convert the binary data to the selected format.

PART 3—USING THE REFERENCE TABLE

The REF TABLE is used whenever the operator wishes to save the complete data table taken during a STORE operation so that it can be used as a reference to which subsequent new data can be compared. The following steps will illustrate the basic use of the REF TABLE.

B.8.F   Transferring 7D01 Data to the REF TABLE

After the logic analyzer has executed a STORE cycle, it will automatically display the data table in the manner described earlier. This data table will be referred to as the 7D01 data table to distinguish it from the REF TABLE. The 7D01 data table can be transferred to the REF TABLE memory by actuating the 7D01 REF control on the front panel. When this is done, there will be *two* tables displayed on the CRT, as shown in Figure B-19.

The 7D01 data table is on the left, and the REF TABLE is on the right. The two tables are identical because the 7D01 data table was just transferred to the REF TABLE memory.

7D01	Trigger +0	Ref	Trigger +0
Cursor word	1110		1110	Cursor word
	0110		0110
	1011		1011
	1010		1010
	0100		0100
	0101		0101
	1001		1001
	1000		1000
	1110		1110
	1111		1111
	0111		0111
	0110		0110
	1110		1110
	1000		1000
	1001		1001
	0000		0000
Trigger word	1110		1110	Trigger word
	1110		1110

Figure B-19

B.8.G Executing a New STORE Cycle

Once the data has been transferred to the REF TABLE, the operator can have the logic analyzer execute a STORE cycle to obtain a new set of data *without* affecting the REF TABLE. In other words, the REF TABLE will retain its current data while the logic analyzer fills the 7D01 data memory with new data. When the STORE cycle is completed, the logic analyzer will again display both tables. The 7D01 table will have the new set of data while the REF TABLE will have the old set of data.

B.8.H Comparing the 7D01 Data Table and the REF TABLE

The operator can now compare the new data table with the REF TABLE to see if and where any differences occur. This is extremely valuable in testing and troubleshooting situations where data from a known good circuit can be placed in the REF TABLE. The 7D01 helps the operator to see any differences in the two tables by intensifying any part of the 7D01 data table that is different from the REF TABLE. This is illustrated in Figure B-20.

Note that two bits in the 7D01 data table are intensified because they are different from the corresponding bits in the REF TABLE. The operator can use this information to help troubleshoot the circuit from which the new data was taken.

7D01	Trigger +0	Ref	Trigger +0
	1110		1110
	0110		0110
	1011		1011
	1010		1010
	0101		0100
	1001		1001
	1000		1000
	1110		1110
	0111		1111
	0111		0111
	0110		0110
	1110		1110
	1000		1000
	1001		1001
	0000		0000
	1110		1110
	1110		1110

Figure B-20

Appendix C

MANUFACTURERS' DATA SHEETS

LINEAR
INTEGRATED
CIRCUITS

TYPES LM124, LM224, LM324
QUADRUPLE OPERATIONAL AMPLIFIERS
BULLETIN NO. DL-S 12248, SEPTEMBER 1975 — REVISED OCTOBER 1979

- **Wide Range of Supply Voltages Single Supply . . . 3 V to 30 V or Dual Supplies**

- **Low Supply Current Drain Independent of Supply Voltage . . . 0.8 mA Typ**

- **Common-Mode Input Voltage Range Includes Ground Allowing Direct Sensing near Ground**

- **Low Input Bias and Offset Parameters Input Offset Voltage . . . 2 mV Typ Input Offset Current . . . 3 nA Typ (LM124) Input Bias Current . . . 45 nA Typ**

- **Differential Input Voltage Range Equal to Maximum-Rated Supply Voltage . . . ±32 V**

- **Open-Loop Differential Voltage Amplification . . . 100 V/mV Typ**

- **Internal Frequency Compensation**

schematic (each amplifier)

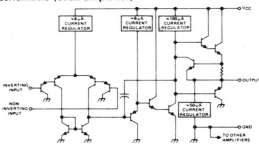

J OR N DUAL-IN-LINE OR W FLAT PACKAGE (TOP VIEW)

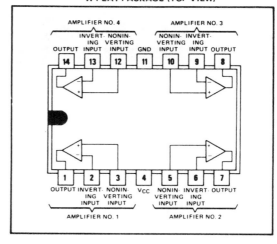

description

These devices consist of four independent, high-gain, frequency-compensated operational amplifiers that were designed specifically to operate from a single supply over a wide range of voltages. Operation from split supplies is also possible so long as the difference between the two supplies is 3 volts to 30 volts and Pin 4 is at least 1.5 volts more positive than the input common-mode voltage. The low supply current drain is independent of the magnitude of the supply voltage.

Applications include transducer amplifiers, d-c amplification blocks, and all the conventional operational amplifier circuits that now can be more easily implemented in single-supply-voltage systems. For example, the LM124 can be operated directly off of the standard five-volt supply that is used in digital systems and will easily provide the required interface electronics without requiring additional ± 15-volt supplies.

absolute maximum ratings over operating free-air temperature range (unless otherwise noted)

Supply voltage, V_{CC} (see Note 1) . . . . 32 V
Differential input voltage (see Note 2) . . . . ±32 V
Input voltage range (either input) . . . . −0.3 V to 32 V
Duration of output short-circuit (one amplifier) to ground at (or below) 25°C
  free-air temperature ($V_{CC} \leqslant 15$ V) (see Note 3) . . . . unlimited
Continuous total dissipation at (or below) 25°C free-air temperature (see Note 4) . . . . 900 mW
Operating free-air temperature range: LM124 . . . . −55°C to 125°C
  LM224 . . . . −25°C to 85°C
  LM324 . . . . 0°C to 70°C
Storage temperature range . . . . −65°C to 150°C
Lead temperature 1/16 inch (1,6 mm) from case for 60 seconds: J or W package . . . . 300°C
Lead temperature 1/16 inch (1,6 mm) from case for 10 seconds: N package . . . . 260°C

NOTES: 1. All voltage values, except differential voltages, are with respect to the network ground terminal.
   2. Differential voltages are at the noninverting input terminal with respect to the inverting input terminal.
   3. Short circuits from outputs to V_{CC} can cause excessive heating and eventual destruction.
   4. For operation above 25°C free-air temperature, refer to Dissipation Derating Table. In the J package, LM124 chips are alloy-mounted; LM224 and LM324 chips are glass-mounted.

TEXAS INSTRUMENTS
INCORPORATED
POST OFFICE BOX 225012 ● DALLAS, TEXAS 75265

 **MOTOROLA**

Specifications and Applications Information

MC1408
MC1508

EIGHT-BIT MULTIPLYING DIGITAL-TO-ANALOG CONVERTER

SILICON MONOLITHIC INTEGRATED CIRCUIT

EIGHT-BIT MULTIPLYING DIGITAL-TO-ANALOG CONVERTER

. . . designed for use where the output current is a linear product of an eight-bit digital word and an analog input voltage.

- Eight-Bit Accuracy Available in Both Temperature Ranges
  Relative Accuracy: ±0.19% Error maximum
  (MC1408L8, MC1408P8, MC1508L8)
- Seven and Six-Bit Accuracy Available with MC1408 Designated by 7 or 6 Suffix after Package Suffix
- Fast Settling Time — 300 ns typical
- Noninverting Digital Inputs are MTTL and CMOS Compatible
- Output Voltage Swing — +0.4 V to -5.0 V
- High-Speed Multiplying Input
  Slew Rate 4.0 mA/μs
- Standard Supply Voltages: +5.0 V and -5.0 V to -15 V

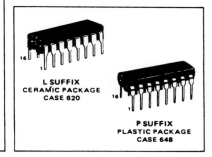

L SUFFIX
CERAMIC PACKAGE
CASE 620

P SUFFIX
PLASTIC PACKAGE
CASE 648

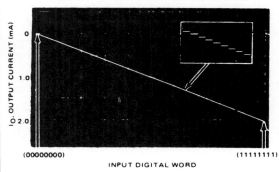

FIGURE 1 — D-to-A TRANSFER CHARACTERISTICS

I_O, OUTPUT CURRENT (mA)

INPUT DIGITAL WORD

(00000000)   (11111111)

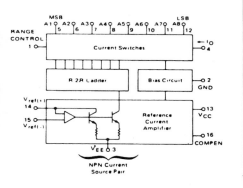

FIGURE 2 — BLOCK DIAGRAM

TYPICAL APPLICATIONS

- Tracking A-to-D Converters
- Successive Approximation A-to-D Converters
- 2 1/2 Digit Panel Meters and DVM's
- Waveform Synthesis
- Sample and Hold
- Peak Detector
- Programmable Gain and Attenuation
- CRT Character Generation
- Audio Digitizing and Decoding
- Programmable Power Supplies
- Analog-Digital Multiplication
- Digital-Digital Multiplication
- Analog-Digital Division
- Digital Addition and Subtraction
- Speech Compression and Expansion
- Stepping Motor Drive

MAXIMUM RATINGS (T_A = +25°C unless otherwise noted.)

Rating	Symbol	Value	Unit
Power Supply Voltage	V_{CC}	+5.5	Vdc
	V_{EE}	-16.5	
Digital Input Voltage	V_5 thru V_{12}	0 to +5.5	Vdc
Applied Output Voltage	V_O	+0.5, -5.2	Vdc
Reference Current	I_{14}	5.0	mA
Reference Amplifier Inputs	V_{14}, V_{15}	V_{CC}, V_{EE}	Vdc
Operating Temperature Range MC1508 MC1408 Series	T_A	 -55 to +125 0 to +75	°C
Storage Temperature Range	T_{stg}	-65 to +150	°C

ELECTRICAL CHARACTERISTICS (V_{CC} = +5.0 Vdc, V_{EE} = -15 Vdc, $\frac{V_{ref}}{R14}$ = 2.0 mA, MC1508L8: T_A = -55°C to +125°C. MC1408L Series: T_A = 0 to +75°C unless otherwise noted. All digital inputs at high logic level.)

Characteristic	Figure	Symbol	Min	Typ	Max	Unit
Relative Accuracy (Error relative to full scale I_O) MC1508L8, MC1408L8, MC1408P8 MC1408P7, MC1408L7, See Note 1 MC1408P6, MC1408L6, See Note 1	4	E_r	 – – –	 – – –	 ±0.19 ±0.39 ±0.78	%
Settling Time to within ±1/2 LSB (includes t_{PLH})(T_A=+25°C)See Note 2	5	t_S	–	300	–	ns
Propagation Delay Time T_A = +25°C	5	t_{PLH}, t_{PHL}	–	30	100	ns
Output Full Scale Current Drift		TCI_O	–	-20	–	PPM/°C
Digital Input Logic Levels (MSB) High Level, Logic "1" Low Level, Logic "0"	3	 V_{IH} V_{IL}	 2.0 –	 – –	 – 0.8	Vdc
Digital Input Current (MSB) High Level, V_{IH} = 5.0 V Low Level, V_{IL} = 0.8 V	3	 I_{IH} I_{IL}	 – –	 0 -0.4	 0.04 -0.8	mA
Reference Input Bias Current (Pin 15)	3	I_{15}	–	-1.0	-5.0	μA
Output Current Range V_{EE} = -5.0 V V_{EE} = -15 V, T_A = 25°C	3	I_{OR}	 0 0	 2.0 2.0	 2.1 4.2	mA
Output Current V_{ref} = 2.000 V, R14 = 1000 Ω	3	I_O	1.9	1.99	2.1	mA
Output Current (All bits low)	3	$I_{O(min)}$	–	0	4.0	μA
Output Voltage Compliance ($E_r \leq 0.19$% at T_A = +25°C) Pin 1 grounded Pin 1 open, V_{EE} below -10 V	3	V_O	 – –	 – –	 -0.55, +0.4 -5.0, +0.4	Vdc
Reference Current Slew Rate	6	$SR I_{ref}$	–	4.0		mA/μs
Output Current Power Supply Sensitivity		PSRR(-)	–	0.5	2.7	μA/V
Power Supply Current (All bits low)	3	I_{CC} I_{EE}	– –	+13.5 -7.5	+22 -13	mA
Power Supply Voltage Range (T_A = +25°C)	3	V_{CCR} V_{EER}	+4.5 -4.5	+5.0 -15	+5.5 -16.5	Vdc
Power Dissipation All bits low V_{EE} = -5.0 Vdc V_{EE} = -15 Vdc All bits high V_{EE} = -5.0 Vdc V_{EE} = -15 Vdc	3	P_D		 105 190 90 160	 170 305 – –	mW

Note 1. All current switches are tested to guarantee at least 50% of rated output current.
Note 2. All bits switched.

2114
1024 X 4 BIT STATIC RAM

	2114-2	2114-3	2114	2114L3	2114L
Max. Access Time (ns)	200	300	450	300	450
Max. Power Dissipation (mw)	710mw	710mw	710mw	370mw	370mw

- High Density 18 Pin Package
- Identical Cycle and Access Times
- Single +5V Supply
- No Clock or Timing Strobe Required
- Completely Static Memory

- Directly TTL Compatible: All Inputs and Outputs
- Common Data Input and Output Using Three-State Outputs
- Pin-Out Compatible with 3605 and 3625 Bipolar PROMs

The Intel® 2114 is a 4096-bit static Random Access Memory organized as 1024 words by 4-bits using N-channel Silicon-Gate MOS technology. It uses fully DC stable (static) circuitry throughout — in both the array and the decoding — and therefore requires no clocks or refreshing to operate. Data access is particularly simple since address setup times are not required. The data is read out nondestructively and has the same polarity as the input data. Common input/output pins are provided.

The 2114 is designed for memory applications where high performance, low cost, large bit storage, and simple interfacing are important design objectives. The 2114 is placed in an 18-pin package for the highest possible density.

It is directly TTL compatible in all respects: inputs, outputs, and a single +5V supply. A separate Chip Select ($\overline{CS}$) lead allows easy selection of an individual package when outputs are or-tied.

The 2114 is fabricated with Intel's N-channel Silicon-Gate technology — a technology providing excellent protection against contamination permitting the use of low cost plastic packaging.

PIN CONFIGURATION   **LOGIC SYMBOL**   **BLOCK DIAGRAM**

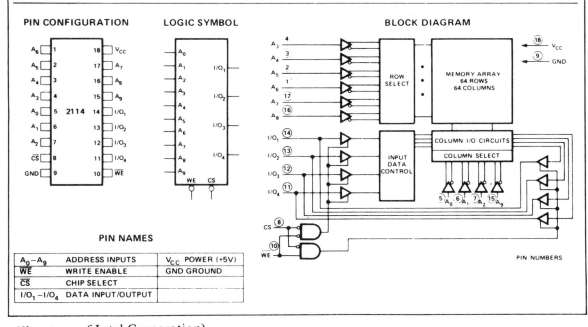

PIN NAMES

A_0–A_9	ADDRESS INPUTS	V_{CC} POWER (+5V)
$\overline{WE}$	WRITE ENABLE	GND GROUND
$\overline{CS}$	CHIP SELECT	
I/O_1–I/O_4	DATA INPUT/OUTPUT	

(Courtesy of Intel Corporation)

2114 FAMILY

A.C. CHARACTERISTICS $T_A = 0°C$ to $70°C$, $V_{CC} = 5V \pm 5\%$, unless otherwise noted.

READ CYCLE [1]

SYMBOL	PARAMETER	2114-2 Min.	2114-2 Max.	2114-3, 2114L3 Min.	2114-3, 2114L3 Max.	2114, 2114L Min.	2114, 2114L Max.	UNIT
t_{RC}	Read Cycle Time	200		300		450		ns
t_A	Access Time		200		300		450	ns
t_{CO}	Chip Selection to Output Valid		70		100		100	ns
t_{CX}	Chip Selection to Output Active	0		0		0		ns
t_{OTD}	Output 3-state from Deselection	0	40	0	80	0	100	ns
t_{OHA}	Output Hold from Address Change	10		10		10		ns

WRITE CYCLE [2]

SYMBOL	PARAMETER	2114-2 Min.	2114-2 Max.	2114-3, 2114L3 Min.	2114-3, 2114L3 Max.	2114, 2114L Min.	2114, 2114L Max.	UNIT
t_{WC}	Write Cycle Time	200		300		450		ns
t_W	Write Time	100		150		200		ns
t_{WR}	Write Release Time	20		0		0		ns
t_{OTW}	Output 3-state from Write	0	40	0	80	0	100	ns
t_{DW}	Data to Write Time Overlap	100		150		200		ns
t_{DH}	Data Hold From Write Time	0		0		0		ns

NOTES 1. A Read occurs during the overlap of a low $\overline{CS}$ and a high $\overline{WE}$.
2. A Write occurs during the overlap of a low $\overline{CS}$ and a low $\overline{WE}$.

A.C. CONDITIONS OF TEST

Input Pulse Levels . . . . 0.8 Volt to 2.4 Volt
Input Rise and Fall Times . . . . 10 nsec
Input and Output Timing Levels . . . . 1.5 Volts
Output Load . . . . 1 TTL Gate and $C_L = 50$ pF

National Semiconductor

CD4016BM/CD4016BC Quad Bilateral Switch

General Description

The CD4016BM/CD4016BC is a quad bilateral switch intended for the transmission or multiplexing of analog or digital signals. It is pin-for-pin compatible with CD4066BM/CD4066BC.

Features

- Wide supply voltage range   3V to 15V
- Wide range of digital and analog switching   ±7.5 V_{PEAK}
- "ON" resistance for 15V operation   400Ω (typ.)
- Matched "ON" resistance over 15V
  signal input $\Delta R_{ON} = 10\Omega$ (typ.)
- High degree of linearity   0.4% distortion (typ.)
  @ f_{IS} = 1 kHz, V_{IS} = 5 V_{p-p},
  $V_{DD} - V_{SS}$ = 10V, R_L = 10 kΩ
- Extremely low "OFF" switch leakage   0.1 nA (typ.)
  @ $V_{DD} - V_{SS}$ = 10V
  T_A = 25°C

- Extremely high control input impedance $10^{12}\Omega$ (typ.)
- Low crosstalk between switches   −50 dB (typ.)
  @ f_{IS} = 0.9 MHz, R_L = 1 kΩ
- Frequency response, switch "ON"   40 MHz (typ.)

Applications

- Analog signal switching/multiplexing
  - Signal gating
  - Squelch control
  - Chopper
  - Modulator/Demodulator
  - Commutating switch
- Digital signal switching/multiplexing
- CMOS logic implementation
- Analog-to-digital/digital-to-analog conversion
- Digital control of frequency, impedance, phase, and analog-signal gain

Schematic and Connection Diagrams

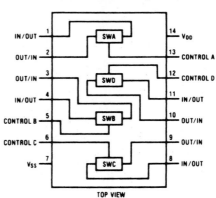

Dual-In-Line Package

Pin			Pin
IN/OUT	1	14	V_{DD}
OUT/IN	2	13	CONTROL A
OUT/IN	3	12	CONTROL D
IN/OUT	4	11	IN/OUT
CONTROL B	5	10	OUT/IN
CONTROL C	6	9	OUT/IN
V_{SS}	7	8	IN/OUT

TOP VIEW

TL/F/5661–1

Order Number CD4016BMJ or CD4016BCJ
NS Package J14A

Order Number CD4016BMN or CD4016BCN
NS Package N14A

AC Electrical Characteristics
$T_A = 25°C$, $C_L = 50\,pF$, $R_L = 200\,K$, $t_r = t_f = 20\,ns$, unless otherwise specified.

Symbol	Parameter	Conditions	Min	Typ	Max	Units
Clocked Operation						
t_{PHL}, t_{PLH}	Propagation Delay Time	$V_{DD} = 5V$		230	350	ns
		$V_{DD} = 10V$		80	160	ns
		$V_{DD} = 15V$		60	120	ns
t_{THL}, t_{TLH}	Transition Time	$V_{DD} = 5V$		100	200	ns
		$V_{DD} = 10V$		50	100	ns
		$V_{DD} = 15V$		40	80	ns
t_{WL}, t_{WM}	Minimum Clock Pulse-Width	$V_{DD} = 5V$		160	250	ns
		$V_{DD} = 10V$		60	110	ns
		$V_{DD} = 15V$		50	85	ns
t_{rCL}, t_{fCL}	Clock Rise and Fall Time	$V_{DD} = 5V$			15	μS
		$V_{DD} = 10V$			15	μS
		$V_{DD} = 15V$			15	μS
t_{SU}	Minimum Data Set-Up Time	$V_{DD} = 5V$		50	100	ns
		$V_{DD} = 10V$		20	40	ns
		$V_{DD} = 15V$		15	30	ns
f_{CL}	Maximum Clock Frequency	$V_{DD} = 5V$	2	3.5		MHz
		$V_{DD} = 10V$	4.5	8		MHz
		$V_{DD} = 15V$	6	11		MHz
C_{IN}	Input Capacitance	Clock Input		7.5	10	pF
		Other Inputs		5	7.5	pF
Reset Operation						
$t_{PHL(R)}$	Propagation Delay Time	$V_{DD} = 5V$		200	400	ns
		$V_{DD} = 10V$		100	200	ns
		$V_{DD} = 15V$		80	160	ns
$t_{WH(R)}$	Minimum Reset Pulse Width	$V_{DD} = 5V$		135	250	ns
		$V_{DD} = 10V$		40	80	ns
		$V_{DD} = 15V$		30	60	ns

Absolute Maximum Ratings
(Notes 1 and 2)

V_{DD} Supply Voltage	−0.5V to +18V
V_{IN} Input Voltage	−0.5V to V_{DD} + 0.5V
T_S Storage Temperature Range	−65°C to +150°C
P_D Package Dissipation	500 mW
Lead Temperature (Soldering, 10 seconds)	260°C

Recommended Operating Conditions (Note 2)

V_{DD} Supply Voltage	3V to 15V
V_{IN} Input Voltage	0V to V_{DD}
T_A Operating Temperature Range	
CD4016BM	−55°C to +125°C
CD4016BC	−40°C to +85°C

DC Electrical Characteristics CD4016BM (Note 2)

Symbol	Parameter	Conditions	−55°C Min	−55°C Max	25°C Min	25°C Typ	25°C Max	125°C Min	125°C Max	Units
I_{DD}	Quiescent Device Current	$V_{DD}=5V$, $V_{IN}=V_{DD}$ or V_{SS}		0.25		0.01	0.25		7.5	μA
		$V_{DD}=10V$, $V_{IN}=V_{DD}$ or V_{SS}		0.5		0.01	0.5		15	μA
		$V_{DD}=15V$, $V_{IN}=V_{DD}$ or V_{SS}		1.0		0.01	1.0		30	μA
Signal Inputs and Outputs										
R_{ON}	"ON" Resistance	$R_L = 10\,k\Omega$ to $\frac{V_{DD}-V_{SS}}{2}$ $V_C = V_{DD}$, $V_{IS} = V_{SS}$ or V_{DD}								
		$V_{DD}=10V$		600		250	660		960	Ω
		$V_{DD}=15V$		360		200	400		600	Ω
		$R_L = 10\,k\Omega$ to $\frac{V_{DD}-V_{SS}}{2}$ $V_C = V_{DD}$								
		$V_{DD}=10V$, $V_{IS}=4.75$ to $5.25V$		1870		850	2000		2600	Ω
		$V_{DD}=15V$, $V_{IS}=7.25$ to $7.75V$		775		400	850		1230	Ω
ΔR_{ON}	Δ"ON" Resistance Between any 2 of 4 Switches (In Same Package)	$R_L = 10\,k\Omega$ to $\frac{V_{DD}-V_{SS}}{2}$ $V_C = V_{DD}$, $V_{IS} = V_{SS}$ to V_{DD}								
		$V_{DD}=10V$				15				Ω
		$V_{DD}=15V$				10				Ω
I_{IS}	Input or Output Leakage Switch "OFF"	$V_C = 0$, $V_{DD}=15V$ $V_{IS}=15V$ and $0V$, $V_{OS}=0V$ and $15V$		±50		±0.1	±50		±500	nA
Control Inputs										
V_{ILC}	Low Level Input Voltage	$V_{IS}=V_{SS}$ and V_{DD} $V_{OS}=V_{DD}$ and V_{SS} $I_{IS}=\pm10\,\mu A$								
		$V_{DD}=5V$		0.9			0.7		0.5	V
		$V_{DD}=10V$		0.9			0.7		0.5	V
		$V_{DD}=15V$		0.9			0.7		0.5	V
V_{IHC}	High Level Input Voltage	$V_{DD}=5V$	3.5		3.5			3.5		V
		$V_{DD}=10V$ (see Note 6 and	7.0		7.0			7.0		V
		$V_{DD}=15V$ Figure 8)	11.0		11.0			11.0		V
I_{IN}	Input Current	$V_{DD}-V_{SS}=15V$ $V_{DD}\geq V_{IS}\geq V_{SS}$ $V_{DD}\geq V_C\geq V_{SS}$		±0.1		$\pm10^{-5}$	±0.1		±1.0	μA

DC Electrical Characteristics CD4016BC (Note 2) (Continued)

Symbol	Parameter	Conditions	−40°C Min	−40°C Max	25°C Min	25°C Typ	25°C Max	85°C Min	85°C Max	Units
I_{DD}	Quiescent Device Current	$V_{DD} = 5V$, $V_{IN} = V_{DD}$ or V_{SS}		1.0		0.01	1.0		7.5	μA
		$V_{DD} = 10V$, $V_{IN} = V_{DD}$ or V_{SS}		2.0		0.01	2.0		15	μA
		$V_{DD} = 15V$, $V_{IN} = V_{DD}$ or V_{SS}		4.0		0.01	4.0		'30	μA

Signal Inputs and Outputs

Symbol	Parameter	Conditions	−40°C Min	−40°C Max	25°C Min	25°C Typ	25°C Max	85°C Min	85°C Max	Units
R_{ON}	"ON" Resistance	$R_L = 10\,k\Omega$ to $\frac{V_{DD} - V_{SS}}{2}$ $V_C = V_{DD}$, $V_{IS} = V_{SS}$ or V_{DD}								
		$V_{DD} = 10V$		610		275	660		840	Ω
		$V_{DD} = 15V$		370		200	400		520	Ω
		$R_L = 10\,k\Omega$ to $\frac{V_{DD} - V_{SS}}{2}$ $V_C = V_{DD}$								
		$V_{DD} = 10V$, $V_{IS} = 4.75$ to $5.25V$		1900		850	2000		2380	Ω
		$V_{DD} = 15V$, $V_{IS} = 7.25$ to $7.75V$		790		400	850		1080	Ω
ΔR_{ON}	Δ"ON" Resistance Between any 2 of 4 Switches (In Same Package)	$R_L = 10\,k\Omega$ to $\frac{V_{DD} - V_{SS}}{2}$ $V_C = V_{DD}$, $V_{IS} = V_{SS}$ to V_{DD}								
		$V_{DD} = 10V$				15				Ω
		$V_{DD} = 15V$				10				Ω
I_{IS}	Input or Output Leakage Switch "OFF"	$V_C = 0$, $V_{DD} = 15V$ $V_{IS} = 0V$ or $15V$, $V_{OS} = 15V$ or $0V$		±50		±0.1	±50		±200	nA

Control Inputs

Symbol	Parameter	Conditions	−40°C Min	−40°C Max	25°C Min	25°C Typ	25°C Max	85°C Min	85°C Max	Units
V_{ILC}	Low Level Input Voltage	$V_{IS} = V_{SS}$ and V_{DD} $V_{OS} = V_{DD}$ and V_{SS} $I_{IS} = \pm 10\ \mu A$								
		$V_{DD} = 5V$		0.9			0.7		0.4	V
		$V_{DD} = 10V$		0.9			0.7		0.4	V
		$V_{DD} = 15V$		0.9			0.7		0.4	V
V_{IHC}	High Level Input Voltage	$V_{DD} = 5V$	3.5		3.5			3.5		V
		$V_{DD} = 10V$ (see Note 6 and	7.0		7.0			7.0		V
		$V_{DD} = 15V$ Figure 8)	11.0		11.0			11.0		V
I_{IN}	Input Current	$V_{CC} - V_{SS} = 15V$ $V_{DD} \geq V_{IS} \geq V_{SS}$ $V_{DD} \geq V_C \geq V_{SS}$		±0.3		±10⁻⁵	±0.3		±1.0	μA

AC Electrical Characteristics $T_A = 25°C$, $t_r = t_f = 20$ ns and $V_{SS} = 0V$ unless otherwise specified

Symbol	Parameter	Conditions	Min	Typ	Max	Units
t_{PHL}, t_{PLH}	Propagation Delay Time Signal Input to Signal Output	$V_C = V_{DD}$, $C_L = 50$ pF, (Figure 1) $R_L = 200k$				
		$V_{DD} = 5V$		58	100	ns
		$V_{DD} = 10V$		27	50	ns
		$V_{DD} = 15V$		20	40	ns
t_{PZH}, t_{PZL}	Propagation Delay Time Control Input to Signal Output High Impedance to Logical Level	$R_L = 1.0\ k\Omega$, $C_L = 50$ pF, (Figures 2 and 3)				
		$V_{DD} = 5V$		20	50	ns
		$V_{DD} = 10V$		18	40	ns
		$V_{DD} = 15V$		17	35	ns
t_{PHZ}, t_{PLZ}	Propagation Delay Time Control Input to Signal Output Logical Level to High Impedance	$R_L = 1.0\ k\Omega$, $C_L = 50$ pF, (Figures 2 and 3)				
		$V_{DD} = 5V$		15	40	ns
		$V_{DD} = 10V$		11	25	ns
		$V_{DD} = 15V$		10	22	ns
	Sine Wave Distortion	$V_C = V_{DD} = 5V$, $V_{SS} = -5$ $R_L = 10\ k\Omega$, $V_{IS} = 5\ V_{P-P}$, $f = 1$ kHz, (Figure 4)		0.4		%

AC Electrical Characteristics (Continued)

$T_A = 25°C$, $t_r = t_f = 20$ ns and $V_{SS} = 0V$ unless otherwise specified

Symbol	Parameter	Conditions	Min	Typ	Max	Units
	Frequency Response — Switch "ON" (Frequency at −3 dB)	$V_C = V_{DD} = 5V$, $V_{SS} = -5V$, $R_L = 1$ kΩ, $V_{IS} = 5$ V_{P-P}, 20 $\log_{10} V_{OS}/V_{OS}$ (1 kHz) −dB, (*Figure 4*)		40		MHz
	Feedthrough — Switch "OFF" (Frequency at −50 dB)	$V_{DD} = 5V$, $V_C = V_{SS} = -5V$, $R_L = 1$ kΩ, $V_{IS} = 5$ V_{P-P}, 20 $\log_{10} (V_{OS}/V_{IS}) = -50$ dB, (*Figure 4*)		1.25		MHz
	Crosstalk Between Any Two Switches (Frequency at −50 dB)	$V_{DD} = V_{C(A)} = 5V$; $V_{SS} = V_{C(B)} = -5V$, $R_L = 1$ kΩ $V_{IS(A)} = 5$ V_{P-P}, 20 $\log_{10} (V_{OS(B)}/V_{OS(A)}) = -50$ dB, (*Figure 5*)		0.9		MHz
	Crosstalk; Control Input to Signal Output	$V_{DD} = 10V$, $R_L = 10$ kΩ $R_{IN} = 1$ kΩ, $V_{CC} = 10V$ Square Wave, $C_L = 50$ pF (*Figure 6*)		150		mV$_{P-P}$
	Maximum Control Input	$R_L = 1$ kΩ, $C_L = 50$ pF, (*Figure 7*) $V_{OS(f)} = \frac{1}{2} V_{OS}$(1 kHz)				
		$V_{DD} = 5V$		6.5		MHz
		$V_{DD} = 10V$		8.0		MHz
		$V_{DD} = 15V$		9.0		MHz
C_{IS}	Signal Input Capacitance			4		pF
C_{OS}	Signal Output Capacitance	$V_{DD} = 10V$		4		pF
C_{IOS}	Feedthrough Capacitance	$V_C = 0V$		0.2		pF
C_{IN}	Control Input Capacitance			5	7.5	pF

Note 1: "Absolute Maximum Ratings" are those values beyond which the safety of the device cannot be guaranteed. They are not meant to imply that the devices should be operated at these limits. The tables of "Recommended Operating Conditions" and "Electrical Characteristics" provide conditions for actual device operation.

Note 2: $V_{SS} = 0V$ unless otherwise specified.

Note 3: These devices should not be connected to circuits with the power "ON".

Note 4: In all cases, there is approximately 5 pF of probe and jig capacitance on the output; however, this capacitance is included in C_L wherever it is specified.

Note 5: V_{IS} is the voltage at the in/out pin and V_{OS} is the voltage at the out/in pin. V_C is the voltage at the control input.

Note 6: If the switch input is held at V_{DD}, V_{IHC} is the control input level that will cause the switch output to meet the standard "B" series V_{OH} and I_{OH} output levels. If the analog switch input is connected to V_{SS}, V_{IHC} is the control input level — which allows the switch to sink standard "B" series $|I_{OH}|$, high level current, and still maintain a $V_{OL} \leq$ "B" series. These currents are shown in *Figure 8*.

AC Test Circuits and Switching Time Waveforms

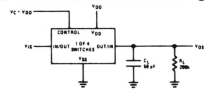 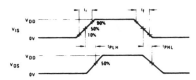

Figure 1. t_{PLH}, t_{PLH} Propagation Delay Time Signal Input to Signal Output

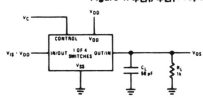 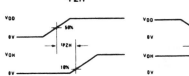 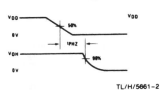

TL/H/5661–2

FIGURE 2. t_{PZH}, t_{PHZ} Propagation Delay Time Control to Signal Output

- **Package Options Include Plastic "Small Outline" Packages, Ceramic Chip Carriers and Flat Packages, and Plastic and Ceramic DIPs**

- **Dependable Texas Instruments Quality and Reliability**

description

These devices contain four independent 2-input-NAND gates.

The SN5400, SN54LS00, and SN54S00 are characterized for operation over the full military temperature range of −55°C to 125°C. The SN7400, SN74LS00, and SN74S00 are characterized for operation from 0°C to 70°C.

FUNCTION TABLE (each gate)

INPUTS		OUTPUT
A	B	Y
H	H	L
L	X	H
X	L	H

logic symbol†

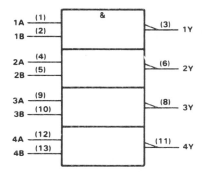

†This symbol is in accordance with ANSI/IEEE Std. 91-1984 and IEC Publication 617-12.
Pin numbers shown are for D, J, and N packages.

**SN5400 . . . J PACKAGE
SN54LS00, SN54S00 . . . J OR W PACKAGE
SN7400 . . . N PACKAGE
SN74LS00, SN74S00 . . . D OR N PACKAGE
(TOP VIEW)**

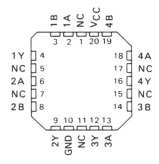

**SN5400 . . . W PACKAGE
(TOP VIEW)**

**SN54LS00, SN54S00 . . . FK PACKAGE
(TOP VIEW)**

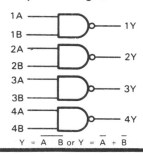

NC - No internal connection

logic diagram (positive logic)

$$Y = \overline{A \cdot B} \text{ or } Y = \overline{A} + \overline{B}$$

TEXAS
INSTRUMENTS
POST OFFICE BOX 655012 • DALLAS, TEXAS 75265

2-3

2

TTL Devices

SN5400, SN54LS00, SN54S00,
SN7400, SN74LS00, SN74S00
QUADRUPLE 2-INPUT POSITIVE-NAND GATES

schematics (each gate)

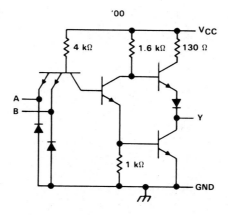

'00

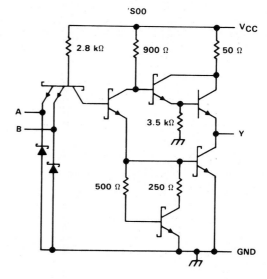

'LS00

'S00

Resistor values shown are nominal.

absolute maximum ratings over operating free-air temperature range (unless otherwise noted)

Supply voltage, V_CC (see Note 1) . . . . 7 V
Input voltage: '00, 'S00 . . . . 5.5 V
'LS00 . . . . 7 V
Operating free-air temperature range: SN54' . . . . −55°C to 125°C
SN74' . . . . 0°C to 70°C
Storage temperature range . . . . −65°C to 150°C

NOTE 1: Voltage values are with respect to network ground terminal.

2-4

TEXAS INSTRUMENTS
POST OFFICE BOX 655012 • DALLAS, TEXAS 75265

recommended operating conditions

		SN5400 MIN	NOM	MAX	SN7400 MIN	NOM	MAX	UNIT
V_{CC}	Supply voltage	4.5	5	5.5	4.75	5	5.25	V
V_{IH}	High-level input voltage	2			2			V
V_{IL}	Low-level input voltage			0.8			0.8	V
I_{OH}	High-level output current			−0.4			−0.4	mA
I_{OL}	Low-level output current			16			16	mA
T_A	Operating free-air temperature	−55		125	0		70	°C

electrical characteristics over recommended operating free-air temperature range (unless otherwise noted)

PARAMETER	TEST CONDITIONS †	SN5400 MIN	TYP‡	MAX	SN7400 MIN	TYP‡	MAX	UNIT
V_{IK}	V_{CC} = MIN, I_I = −12 mA			−1.5			−1.5	V
V_{OH}	V_{CC} = MIN, V_{IL} = 0.8 V, I_{OH} = −0.4 mA	2.4	3.4		2.4	3.4		V
V_{OL}	V_{CC} = MIN, V_{IH} = 2 V, I_{OL} = 16 mA		0.2	0.4		0.2	0.4	V
I_I	V_{CC} = MAX, V_I = 5.5 V			1			1	mA
I_{IH}	V_{CC} = MAX, V_I = 2.4 V			40			40	µA
I_{IL}	V_{CC} = MAX, V_I = 0.4 V			−1.6			−1.6	mA
I_{OS}§	V_{CC} = MAX	−20		−55	−18		−55	mA
I_{CCH}	V_{CC} = MAX, V_I = 0 V		4	8		4	8	mA
I_{CCL}	V_{CC} = MAX, V_I = 4.5 V		12	22		12	22	mA

† For conditions shown as MIN or MAX, use the appropriate value specified under recommended operating conditions.
‡ All typical values are at V_{CC} = 5 V, T_A = 25°C.
§ Not more than one output should be shorted at a time.

switching characteristics, V_{CC} = 5 V, T_A = 25°C (see note 2)

PARAMETER	FROM (INPUT)	TO (OUTPUT)	TEST CONDITIONS	MIN	TYP	MAX	UNIT
t_{PLH}	A or B	Y	R_L = 400 Ω, C_L = 15 pF		11	22	ns
t_{PHL}	A or B	Y	R_L = 400 Ω, C_L = 15 pF		7	15	ns

NOTE 2: Load circuits and voltage waveforms are shown in Section 1.

2

TTL Devices

Texas
INSTRUMENTS
POST OFFICE BOX 655012 • DALLAS, TEXAS 75265

recommended operating conditions

		SN54LS00			SN74LS00			UNIT
		MIN	NOM	MAX	MIN	NOM	MAX	
V_{CC}	Supply voltage	4.5	5	5.5	4.75	5	5.25	V
V_{IH}	High-level input voltage	2			2			V
V_{IL}	Low-level input voltage			0.7			0.8	V
I_{OH}	High-level output current			− 0.4			− 0.4	mA
I_{OL}	Low-level output current			4			8	mA
T_A	Operating free-air temperature	− 55		125	0		70	°C

electrical characteristics over recommended operating free-air temperature range (unless otherwise noted)

PARAMETER	TEST CONDITIONS †			SN54LS00			SN74LS00			UNIT
				MIN	TYP‡	MAX	MIN	TYP‡	MAX	
V_{IK}	V_{CC} = MIN,	I_I = − 18 mA				− 1.5			− 1.5	V
V_{OH}	V_{CC} = MIN,	V_{IL} = MAX,	I_{OH} = − 0.4 mA	2.5	3.4		2.7	3.4		V
V_{OL}	V_{CC} = MIN,	V_{IH} = 2 V,	I_{OL} = 4 mA		0.25	0.4		0.25	0.4	V
	V_{CC} = MIN,	V_{IH} = 2 V,	I_{OL} = 8 mA					0.35	0.5	
I_I	V_{CC} = MAX,	V_I = 7 V				0.1			0.1	mA
I_{IH}	V_{CC} = MAX,	V_I = 2.7 V				20			20	µA
I_{IL}	V_{CC} = MAX,	V_I = 0.4 V				− 0.4			− 0.4	mA
I_{OS} §	V_{CC} = MAX			− 20		− 100	− 20		− 100	mA
I_{CCH}	V_{CC} = MAX,	V_I = 0 V			0.8	1.6		0.8	1.6	mA
I_{CCL}	V_{CC} = MAX,	V_I = 4.5 V			2.4	4.4		2.4	4.4	mA

† For conditions shown as MIN or MAX, use the appropriate value specified under recommended operating conditions.
‡ All typical values are at V_{CC} = 5 V, T_A = 25°C.
§ Not more than one output should be shorted at a time, and the duration of the short-circuit should not exceed one second.

switching characteristics, V_{CC} = 5 V, T_A = 25°C (see note 2)

PARAMETER	FROM (INPUT)	TO (OUTPUT)	TEST CONDITIONS		MIN	TYP	MAX	UNIT
t_{PLH}	A or B	Y	R_L = 2 kΩ,	C_L = 15 pF		9	15	ns
t_{PHL}						10	15	ns

NOTE 2: Load circuits and voltage waveforms are shown in Section 1.

TEXAS INSTRUMENTS
POST OFFICE BOX 655012 • DALLAS, TEXAS 75265

2

TTL Devices

SN54HC00, SN74HC00
QUADRUPLE 2-INPUT POSITIVE-NAND GATES

D2684, DECEMBER 1982—REVISED MARCH 1984

- **Package Options Include Plastic "Small Outline" Packages, Ceramic Chip Carriers, and Standard Plastic and Ceramic 300-mil DIPs**

- **Dependable Texas Instruments Quality and Reliability**

description

These devices contain four independent 2-input NAND gates. They perform the Boolean functions $Y = \overline{A \cdot B}$ or $Y = \overline{A} + \overline{B}$ in positive logic.

The SN54HC00 is characterized for operation over the full military temperature range of $-55\,°C$ to $125\,°C$. The SN74HC00 is characterized for operation from $-40\,°C$ to $85\,°C$.

FUNCTION TABLE (each gate)

INPUTS		OUTPUT
A	**B**	**Y**
H	H	L
L	X	H
X	L	H

logic symbol[†]

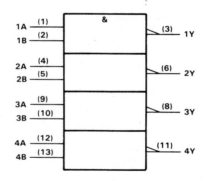

[†] This symbol is in accordance with ANSI/IEEE Std 91-1984 and IEC Publication 617-12.
Pin numbers shown are for D, J, or N packages.

SN54HC00 . . . J PACKAGE
SN74HC00 . . . D OR N PACKAGE
(TOP VIEW)

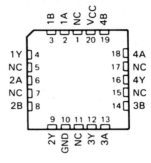

SN54HC00 . . . FK PACKAGE
(TOP VIEW)

NC – No internal connection

logic diagram (each gate)

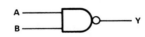

HCMOS Devices

2

TEXAS INSTRUMENTS
POST OFFICE BOX 655012 • DALLAS, TEXAS 75265

SN54HC00, SN74HC00
QUADRUPLE 2-INPUT POSITIVE-NAND GATES

absolute maximum ratings over operating free-air temperature range†

Supply voltage, V_{CC} .... −0.5 V to 7 V
Input clamp current, I_{IK} (V_I < 0 or V_I > V_{CC}) .... ±20 mA
Output clamp current, I_{OK} (V_O < 0 or V_O > V_{CC}) .... ±20 mA
Continuous output current, I_O (V_O = 0 to V_{CC}) .... ±25 mA
Continuous current through V_{CC} or GND pins .... ±50 mA
Lead temperature 1,6 mm (1/16 in) from case for 60 s: FK or J package .... 300°C
Lead temperature 1,6 mm (1/16 in) from case for 10 s: D or N package .... 260°C
Storage temperature range .... −65°C to 150°C

† Stresses beyond those listed under ''absolute maximum ratings'' may cause permanent damage to the device. These are stress ratings only, and functional operation of the device at these or any other conditions beyond those indicated under ''recommended operating conditions'' is not implied. Exposure to absolute-maximum-rated conditions for extended periods may affect device reliability.

recommended operating conditions

		SN54HC00 MIN	NOM	MAX	SN74HC00 MIN	NOM	MAX	UNIT
V_{CC} Supply voltage		2	5	6	2	5	6	V
V_{IH} High-level input voltage	V_{CC} = 2 V	1.5			1.5			V
	V_{CC} = 4.5 V	3.15			3.15			
	V_{CC} = 6 V	4.2			4.2			
V_{IL} Low-level input voltage	V_{CC} = 2 V	0		0.3	0		0.3	V
	V_{CC} = 4.5 V	0		0.9	0		0.9	
	V_{CC} = 6 V	0		1.2	0		1.2	
V_I Input voltage		0		V_{CC}	0		V_{CC}	V
V_O Output voltage		0		V_{CC}	0		V_{CC}	V
t_t Input transition (rise and fall) times	V_{CC} = 2 V	0		1000	0		1000	ns
	V_{CC} = 4.5 V	0		500	0		500	
	V_{CC} = 6 V	0		400	0		400	
T_A Operating free-air temperature		−55		125	−40		85	°C

electrical characteristics over recommended operating free-air temperature range (unless otherwise noted)

PARAMETER	TEST CONDITIONS	V_{CC}	T_A = 25°C MIN	TYP	MAX	SN54HC00 MIN	MAX	SN74HC00 MIN	MAX	UNIT
V_{OH}	V_I = V_{IH} or V_{IL}, I_{OH} = −20 µA	2 V	1.9	1.998		1.9		1.9		V
		4.5 V	4.4	4.499		4.4		4.4		
		6 V	5.9	5.999		5.9		5.9		
	V_I = V_{IH} or V_{IL}, I_{OH} = −4 mA	4.5 V	3.98	4.30		3.7		3.84		
	V_I = V_{IH} or V_{IL}, I_{OH} = −5.2 mA	6 V	5.48	5.80		5.2		5.34		
V_{OL}	V_I = V_{IH} or V_{IL}, I_{OL} = 20 µA	2 V		0.002	0.1		0.1		0.1	V
		4.5 V		0.001	0.1		0.1		0.1	
		6 V		0.001	0.1		0.1		0.1	
	V_I = V_{IH} or V_{IL}, I_{OL} = 4 mA	4.5 V		0.17	0.26		0.4		0.33	
	V_I = V_{IH} or V_{IL}, I_{OL} = 5.2 mA	6 V		0.15	0.26		0.4		0.33	
I_I	V_I = V_{CC} or 0	6 V		±0.1	±100		±1000		±1000	nA
I_{CC}	V_I = V_{CC} or 0, I_O = 0	6 V			2		40		20	µA
C_i		2 to 6 V		3	10		10		10	pF

TEXAS
INSTRUMENTS
POST OFFICE BOX 655012 • DALLAS, TEXAS 75265

2

HCMOS Devices

switching characteristics over recommended operating free-air temperature range (unless otherwise noted), C$_L$ = 50 pF (see Note 1)

PARAMETER	FROM (INPUT)	TO (OUTPUT)	V$_{CC}$	T$_A$ = 25°C			SN54HC00		SN74HC00		UNIT
				MIN	TYP	MAX	MIN	MAX	MIN	MAX	
t$_{pd}$	A or B	Y	2 V		45	90		135		115	ns
			4.5 V		9	18		27		23	
			6 V		8	15		23		20	
t$_t$		Y	2 V		38	75		110		95	ns
			4.5 V		8	15		22		19	
			6 V		6	13		19		16	

C$_{pd}$	Power dissipation capacitance per gate	No load, T$_A$ = 25°C	20 pF typ

NOTE 1: Load circuit and voltage waveforms are shown in Section 1.

HCMOS Devices

2

- Package Options Include Plastic "Small Outline" Packages, Ceramic Chip Carriers and Flat Packages, and Plastic and Ceramic DIPs

- Dependable Texas Instruments Quality and Reliability

description

These devices contain four independent 2-input-NOR gates.

The SN5402, SN54LS02, and SN54S02 are characterized for operation over the full military temperature range of −55°C to 125°C. The SN7402, SN74LS02, and SN74S02 are characterized for operation from 0°C to 70°C.

FUNCTION TABLE (each gate)

INPUTS		OUTPUT
A	B	Y
H	X	L
X	H	L
L	L	H

logic symbol†

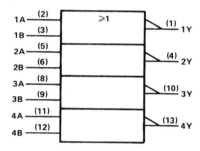

1A (2)
1B (3) ≥1 (1) 1Y

2A (5) (4) 2Y
2B (6)

3A (8) (10) 3Y
3B (9)

4A (11) (13) 4Y
4B (12)

†This symbol is in accordance with ANSI/IEEE Std. 91-1984 and IEC Publication 617-12.
Pin numbers shown are for D, J, and N packages.

logic diagram (positive logic)

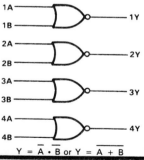

1A
1B ─── 1Y

2A
2B ─── 2Y

3A
3B ─── 3Y

4A
4B ─── 4Y

$$Y = \overline{A} \cdot \overline{B} \text{ or } Y = \overline{A + B}$$

SN5402 . . . J PACKAGE
SN54LS02, SN54S02 . . . J OR W PACKAGE
SN7402 . . . N PACKAGE
SN74LS02, SN74S02 . . . D OR N PACKAGE
(TOP VIEW)

```
1Y  [1   U  14]  VCC
1A  [2      13]  4Y
1B  [3      12]  4B
2Y  [4      11]  4A
2A  [5      10]  3Y
2B  [6       9]  3B
GND [7       8]  3A
```

SN5402 . . . W PACKAGE
(TOP VIEW)

```
1A  [1   U  14]  4Y
1B  [2      13]  4B
1Y  [3      12]  4A
VCC [4      11]  GND
2Y  [5      10]  3B
2A  [6       9]  3A
2B  [7       8]  3Y
```

SN54LS02, SN54S02 . . . FK PACKAGE
(TOP VIEW)

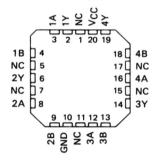

```
           1A 1Y NC VCC 4Y
            3  2  1 20 19
1B  [4              18]  4B
NC  [5              17]  NC
2Y  [6              16]  4A
NC  [7              15]  NC
2A  [8              14]  3Y
            9 10 11 12 13
           2B GND NC 3A 3B
```

NC - No internal connection

2

TTL Devices

TEXAS
INSTRUMENTS
POST OFFICE BOX 655012 • DALLAS, TEXAS 75265

SN5402, SN54LS02, SN54S02,
SN7402, SN74LS02, SN74S02
QUADRUPLE 2-INPUT POSITIVE-NOR GATES

schematics (each gate)

'02

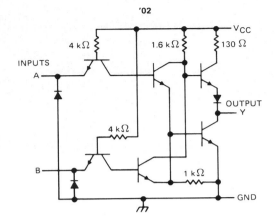

'LS02

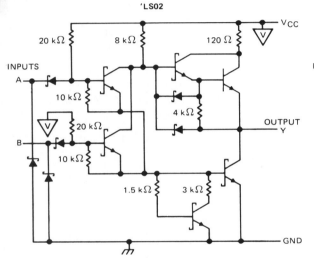

'S02

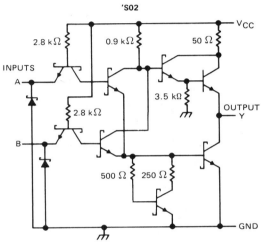

Resistor values shown are nominal.

absolute maximum ratings over operating free-air temperature range (unless otherwise noted)

Supply voltage, V_{CC} (see Note 1) .... 7 V
Input voltage: '02, 'S02 .... 5.5 V
          'LS02 .... 7 V
Off-state output voltage .... 7 V
Operating free-air temperature range: SN54' .... −55°C to 125°C
                  SN74' .... 0°C to 70°C
Storage temperature range .... −65°C to 150°C

NOTE 1. Voltage values are with respect to network ground terminal.

TEXAS
INSTRUMENTS

POST OFFICE BOX 655012 • DALLAS, TEXAS 75265

recommended operating conditions

		SN54LS02			SN74LS02			UNIT
		MIN	NOM	MAX	MIN	NOM	MAX	
V_{CC}	Supply voltage	4.5	5	5.5	4.75	5	5.25	V
V_{IH}	High-level input voltage	2			2			V
V_{IL}	Low-level input voltage			0.7			0.8	V
I_{OH}	High-level output current			− 0.4			− 0.4	mA
I_{OL}	Low-level output current			4			8	mA
T_A	Operating free-air temperature	− 55		125	0		70	°C

electrical characteristics over recommended operating free-air temperature range (unless otherwise noted)

PARAMETER	TEST CONDITIONS †		SN54LS02			SN74LS02			UNIT
			MIN	TYP‡	MAX	MIN	TYP‡	MAX	
V_{IK}	V_{CC} = MIN,	I_I = − 18 mA			− 1.5			− 1.5	V
V_{OH}	V_{CC} = MIN,	V_{IL} = MAX, I_{OH} = − 0.4 mA	2.5	3.4		2.7	3.4		V
V_{OL}	V_{CC} = MIN,	V_{IH} = 2 V, I_{OL} = 4 mA		0.25	0.4		0.25	0.4	V
	V_{CC} = MIN,	V_{IH} = 2 V, I_{OL} = 8 mA					0.35	0.5	
I_I	V_{CC} = MAX,	V_I = 7 V			0.1			0.1	mA
I_{IH}	V_{CC} = MAX,	V_I = 2.7 V			20			20	μA
I_{IL}	V_{CC} = MAX,	V_I = 0.4 V			− 0.4			− 0.4	mA
I_{OS} §	V_{CC} = MAX		− 20		− 100	− 20		− 100	mA
I_{CCH}	V_{CC} = MAX,	V_I = 0 V		1.6	3.2		1.6	3.2	mA
I_{CCL}	V_{CC} = MAX,	See Note 2		2.8	5.4		2.8	5.4	mA

† For conditions shown as MIN or MAX, use the appropriate value specified under recommended operating conditions.
‡ All typical values are at V_{CC} = 5 V, T_A = 25°C.
§ Not more than one output should be shorted at a time, and the duration of the short-circuit should not exceed one second.
NOTE 2: One input at 4.5 V, all others at GND.

switching characteristics, V_{CC} = 5 V, T_A = 25°C (see note 3)

PARAMETER	FROM (INPUT)	TO (OUTPUT)	TEST CONDITIONS		MIN	TYP	MAX	UNIT
t_{PLH}	A or B	Y	R_L = 2 kΩ,	C_L = 15 pF		10	15	ns
t_{PHL}						10	15	ns

NOTE 3: Load circuits and voltage waveforms are shown in Section 1.

Texas
INSTRUMENTS
POST OFFICE BOX 655012 • DALLAS, TEXAS 75265

- **Package Options Include Plastic "Small Outline" Packages, Ceramic Chip Carriers and Flat Packages, and Plastic and Ceramic DIPs**

- **Dependable Texas Instruments Quality and Reliability**

description

These devices contain six independent inverters.

The SN5404, SN54LS04, and SN54S04 are characterized for operation over the full military temperature range of −55°C to 125°C. The SN7404, SN74LS04, and SN74S04 are characterized for operation from 0°C to 70°C.

FUNCTION TABLE (each inverter)

INPUTS A	OUTPUT Y
H	L
L	H

logic symbol†

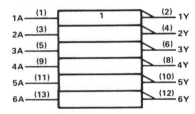

1A	(1)	1	(2)	1Y
2A	(3)		(4)	2Y
3A	(5)		(6)	3Y
4A	(9)		(8)	4Y
5A	(11)		(10)	5Y
6A	(13)		(12)	6Y

†This symbol is in accordance with ANSI/IEEE Std. 91-1984 and IEC Publication 617-12.
Pin numbers shown are for D, J, and N packages.

logic diagram (positive logic)

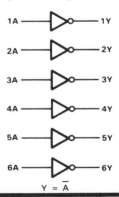

1A	1Y
2A	2Y
3A	3Y
4A	4Y
5A	5Y
6A	6Y

$$Y = \overline{A}$$

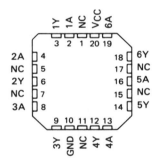

SN5404 . . . J PACKAGE
SN54LS04, SN54S04 . . . J OR W PACKAGE
SN7404 . . . N PACKAGE
SN74LS04, SN74S04 . . . D OR N PACKAGE
(TOP VIEW)

1A	1	14	V_CC
1Y	2	13	6A
2A	3	12	6Y
2Y	4	11	5A
3A	5	10	5Y
3Y	6	9	4A
GND	7	8	4Y

SN5404 . . . W PACKAGE
(TOP VIEW)

1A	1	14	1Y
2Y	2	13	6A
2A	3	12	6Y
V_CC	4	11	GND
3A	5	10	5Y
3Y	6	9	5A
4A	7	8	4Y

SN54LS04, SN54S04 . . . FK PACKAGE
(TOP VIEW)

2A	4	18	6Y
NC	5	17	NC
2Y	6	16	5A
NC	7	15	NC
3A	8	14	5Y

Top: 1Y 1A NC V_CC 6A (3 2 1 20 19)
Bottom: 3Y GND NC 4Y 4A (9 10 11 12 13)

NC - No internal connection

2

TTL Devices

TEXAS
INSTRUMENTS

POST OFFICE BOX 655012 • DALLAS, TEXAS 75265

schematics (each gate)

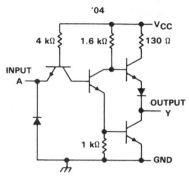

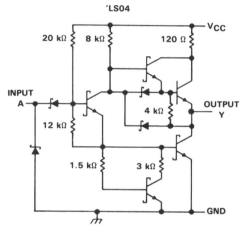

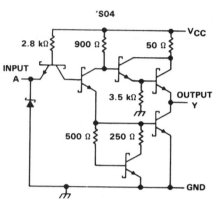

Resistor values shown are nominal.

absolute maximum ratings over operating free-air temperature range (unless otherwise noted)

Supply voltage, V_{CC} (see Note 1) . . . . 7 V
Input voltage: '04, 'S04 . . . . 5.5 V
           'LS04 . . . . 7 V
Operating free-air temperature range: SN54' . . . . −55°C to 125°C
                            SN74' . . . . 0°C to 70°C
Storage temperature range . . . . −65°C to 150°C

NOTE 1: Voltage values are with respect to network ground terminal.

TEXAS
INSTRUMENTS
POST OFFICE BOX 655012 • DALLAS, TEXAS 75265

2

TTL Devices

recommended operating conditions

		SN54LS04			SN74LS04			UNIT
		MIN	NOM	MAX	MIN	NOM	MAX	
V_{CC}	Supply voltage	4.5	5	5.5	4.75	5	5.25	V
V_{IH}	High-level input voltage	2			2			V
V_{IL}	Low-level input voltage			0.7			0.8	V
I_{OH}	High-level output current			−0.4			−0.4	mA
I_{OL}	Low-level output current			4			8	mA
T_A	Operating free-air temperature	−55		125	0		70	°C

electrical characteristics over recommended operating free-air temperature range (unless otherwise noted)

PARAMETER	TEST CONDITIONS †		SN54LS04			SN74LS04			UNIT
			MIN	TYP ‡	MAX	MIN	TYP ‡	MAX	
V_{IK}	V_{CC} = MIN,	I_I = −18 mA			−1.5			−1.5	V
V_{OH}	V_{CC} = MIN, V_{IL} = MAX,	I_{OH} = −0.4 mA	2.5	3.4		2.7	3.4		V
V_{OL}	V_{CC} = MIN, V_{IH} = 2 V,	I_{OL} = 4 mA		0.25	0.4			0.4	V
	V_{CC} = MIN, V_{IH} = 2 V,	I_{OL} = 8 mA					0.25	0.5	
I_I	V_{CC} = MAX,	V_I = 7 V			0.1			0.1	mA
I_{IH}	V_{CC} = MAX,	V_I = 2.7 V			20			20	μA
I_{IL}	V_{CC} = MAX,	V_I = 0.4 V			−0.4			−0.4	mA
I_{OS} §	V_{CC} = MAX		−20		−100	−20		−100	mA
I_{CCH}	V_{CC} = MAX,	V_I = 0 V		1.2	2.4		1.2	2.4	mA
I_{CCL}	V_{CC} = MAX,	V_I = 4.5 V		3.6	6.6		3.6	6.6	mA

† For conditions shown as MIN or MAX, use the appropriate value specified under recommended operating conditions.
‡ All typical values are at V_{CC} = 5 V, T_A = 25°C.
§ Not more than one output should be shorted at a time, and the duration of the short-circuit should not exceed one second.

switching characteristics, V_{CC} = 5 V, T_A = 25°C (see note 2)

PARAMETER	FROM (INPUT)	TO (OUTPUT)	TEST CONDITIONS		MIN	TYP	MAX	UNIT
t_{PLH}	A	Y	R_L = 2 kΩ,	C_L = 15 pF		9	15	ns
t_{PHL}						10	15	ns

NOTE 2: Load circuits and voltage waveforms are shown in Section 1.

TEXAS
INSTRUMENTS
POST OFFICE BOX 655012 • DALLAS, TEXAS 75265

2

TTL Devices

- **Package Options Include Both Plastic and Ceramic Chip Carriers in Addition to Plastic and Ceramic DIPs**

- **Dependable Texas Instruments Quality and Reliability**

description

These devices contain six independent inverters. The open-collector outputs require pull-up resistors to perform correctly. They may be connected to other open-collector outputs to implement active-low wired-OR or active-high wired-AND functions. Open collector devices are often used to generate high V_{OH} levels.

The SN5405, SN54H05, SN54LS05 and SN54S05 are characterized for operation over the full military temperature range of $-55\,°C$ to $125\,°C$. The SN7405, SN74H05, SN74LS05 and SN74S05 are characterized for operation from $0\,°C$ to $70\,°C$.

FUNCTION TABLE (each inverter)

INPUT	OUTPUT
A	Y
H	L
L	H

logic diagram (each inverter)

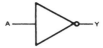

A ───▷○─── Y

positive logic

$$Y = \overline{A}$$

SN5405, SN54H05 . . . J PACKAGE
SN54LS05, SN54S05 . . . J OR W PACKAGE
SN7405, SN74H05 . . . J OR N PACKAGE
SN74LS05, SN74S05 . . . D, J OR N PACKAGE
(TOP VIEW)

```
       ┌───U───┐
1A  □1      14□ VCC
1Y  □2      13□ 6A
2A  □3      12□ 6Y
2Y  □4      11□ 5A
3A  □5      10□ 5Y
3Y  □6       9□ 4A
GND □7       8□ 4Y
       └───────┘
```

SN5405, SN54H05 . . . W PACKAGE
(TOP VIEW)

```
       ┌───U───┐
1A  □1      14□ 1Y
2Y  □2      13□ 6A
2A  □3      12□ 6Y
VCC □4      11□ GND
3A  □5      10□ 5Y
3Y  □6       9□ 5A
4A  □7       8□ 4Y
       └───────┘
```

SN54LS05, SN54S05 . . . FK PACKAGE
SN74LS05, SN74S05 . . . FN PACKAGE
(TOP VIEW)

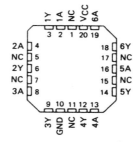

NC - No internal connection

3

TTL DEVICES

TEXAS INSTRUMENTS
POST OFFICE BOX 225012 ● DALLAS, TEXAS 75265

recommended operating conditions

		SN5405			SN7405			UNIT
		MIN	NOM	MAX	MIN	NOM	MAX	
V_{CC}	Supply voltage	4.5	5	5.5	4.75	5	5.25	V
V_{IH}	High-level input voltage	2			2			V
V_{IL}	Low-level input voltage			0.8			0.8	V
V_{OH}	High-level output voltage			5.5			5.5	V
I_{OL}	Low-level output current			16			16	mA
T_A	Operating free-air temperature	−55		125	0		70	°C

electrical characteristics over recommended operating free-air temperature range (unless otherwise noted)

PARAMETER	TEST CONDITIONS†		MIN	TYP‡	MAX	UNIT
V_{IK}	$V_{CC} = $ MIN,	$I_I = -12$ mA			−1.5	V
I_{OH}	$V_{CC} = $ MIN, $V_{IL} = 0.8$ V,	$V_{OH} = 5.5$ V			0.25	mA
V_{OL}	$V_{CC} = $ MIN, $V_{IH} = 2$ V,	$I_{OL} = 16$ mA		0.2	0.4	V
I_I	$V_{CC} = $ MAX,	$V_I = 5.5$ V			1	mA
I_{IH}	$V_{CC} = $ MAX,	$V_I = 2.4$ V			40	µA
I_{IL}	$V_{CC} = $ MAX,	$V_I = 0.4$ V			−1.6	mA
I_{CCH}	$V_{CC} = $ MAX,	$V_I = 0$ V		6	12	mA
I_{CCL}	$V_{CC} = $ MAX,	$V_I = 4.5$ V		18	33	mA

† For conditions shown as MIN or MAX, use the appropriate value specified under recommended operating conditions.
‡ All typical values are at $V_{CC} = 5$ V, $T_A = 25$°C.

switching characteristics, $V_{CC} = 5$ V, $T_A = 25$°C (see note 2)

PARAMETER	FROM (INPUT)	TO (OUTPUT)	TEST CONDITIONS		MIN	TYP	MAX	UNIT
t_{PLH}	A	Y	$R_L = 4$ kΩ,	$C_L = 15$ pF		40	55	ns
t_{PHL}			$R_L = 400$ Ω,	$C_L = 15$ pF		8	15	ns

NOTE 2: See General Information Section for load circuits and voltage waveforms.

TEXAS
INSTRUMENTS
POST OFFICE BOX 225012 • DALLAS, TEXAS 75265

TTL DEVICES

3

TYPES SN54H05, SN74H05
HEX INVERTERS WITH OPEN-COLLECTOR OUTPUTS

recommended operating conditions

		SN54H05 MIN	SN54H05 NOM	SN54H05 MAX	SN74H05 MIN	SN74H05 NOM	SN74H05 MAX	UNIT
V_{CC}	Supply voltage	4.5	5	5.5	4.75	5	5.25	V
V_{IH}	High-level input voltage	2			2			V
V_{IL}	Low-level input voltage			0.8			0.8	V
V_{OH}	High-level output voltage			5.5			5.5	V
I_{OL}	Low-level output current			20			20	mA
T_A	Operating free-air temperature	−55		125	0		70	°C

electrical characteristics over recommended operating free-air temperature range (unless otherwise noted)

PARAMETER	TEST CONDITIONS†		MIN	TYP‡	MAX	UNIT
V_{IK}	V_{CC} = MIN,	I_I = −8 mA			−1.5	V
I_{OH}	V_{CC} = MIN, V_{IL} = 0.8 V,	V_{OH} = 5.5 V			0.25	mA
V_{OL}	V_{CC} = MIN, V_{IH} = 2 V,	I_{OL} = 20 mA		0.2	0.4	V
I_I	V_{CC} = MAX,	V_I = 5.5 V			1	mA
I_{IH}	V_{CC} = MAX,	V_I = 2.4 V			50	µA
I_{IL}	V_{CC} = MAX,	V_I = 0.4 V			−2	mA
I_{CCH}	V_{CC} = MAX,	V_I = 0 V		16	26	mA
I_{CCL}	V_{CC} = MAX,	V_I = 4.5 V		40	58	mA

† For conditions shown as MIN or MAX, use the appropriate value specified under recommended operating conditions.
‡ All typical values are at V_{CC} = 5 V, T_A = 25°C.

switching characteristics, V_{CC} = 5 V, T_A = 25°C (see note 2)

PARAMETER	FROM (INPUT)	TO (OUTPUT)	TEST CONDITIONS		MIN	TYP	MAX	UNIT
t_{PLH}	A	Y	R_L = 280 Ω,	C_L = 25 pF		10	15	ns
t_{PHL}						7.5	12	ns

NOTE 2: See General Information Section for load circuits and voltage waveforms.

TEXAS
INSTRUMENTS
POST OFFICE BOX 225012 • DALLAS, TEXAS 75265

SN5410, SN54LS10, SN54S10, SN7410, SN74LS10, SN74S10
TRIPLE 3-INPUT POSITIVE-NAND GATES

DECEMBER 1983–REVISED MARCH 1988

- **Package Options Include Plastic ''Small Outline'' Packages, Ceramic Chip Carriers and Flat Packages, and Plastic and Ceramic DIPs**

- **Dependable Texas Instruments Quality and Reliability**

description

These devices contain three independent 3-input NAND gates.

The SN5410, SN54LS10, and SN54S10 are characterized for operation over the full military temperature range of −55°C to 125°C. The SN7410, SN74LS10, and SN74S10 are characterized for operation from 0°C to 70°C.

FUNCTION TABLE (each gate)

INPUTS			OUTPUT
A	B	C	Y
H	H	H	L
L	X	X	H
X	L	X	H
X	X	L	H

logic symbol†

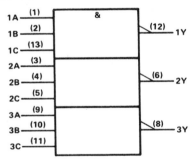

†This symbol is in accordance with ANSI/IEEE Std. 91-1984 and IEC Publication 617-12.
Pin numbers shown are for D, J, and N packages.

positive logic

$$Y = \overline{A \cdot B \cdot C} \text{ or } Y = \overline{A} + \overline{B} + \overline{C}$$

SN5410 . . . J PACKAGE
SN54LS10, SN54S10 . . . J OR W PACKAGE
SN7410 . . . N PACKAGE
SN74LS10, SN74S10 . . . D OR N PACKAGE
(TOP VIEW)

```
       ┌───┬─∪─┬───┐
1A  [ 1        14 ]  VCC
1B  [ 2        13 ]  1C
2A  [ 3        12 ]  1Y
2B  [ 4        11 ]  3C
2C  [ 5        10 ]  3B
2Y  [ 6         9 ]  3A
GND [ 7         8 ]  3Y
       └───────────┘
```

SN5410 . . . W PACKAGE
(TOP VIEW)

```
       ┌───┬─∪─┬───┐
1A  [ 1        14 ]  1C
1B  [ 2        13 ]  3Y
1Y  [ 3        12 ]  3C
VCC [ 4        11 ]  GND
2Y  [ 5        10 ]  3B
2A  [ 6         9 ]  3A
2B  [ 7         8 ]  2C
       └───────────┘
```

SN54LS10, SN54S10 . . . FK PACKAGE
(TOP VIEW)

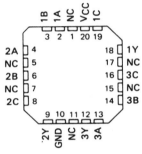

NC - No internal connection

logic diagram (positive logic)

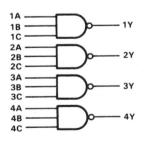

TEXAS
INSTRUMENTS

POST OFFICE BOX 655012 • DALLAS, TEXAS 75265

2

TTL Devices

2-53

54/7411
54H/74H11
54S/74S11
54LS/74LS11

TRIPLE 3-INPUT AND GATE

CONNECTION DIAGRAMS
PINOUT A

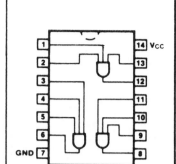

PINOUT B

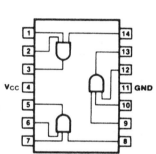

ORDERING CODE: See Section 9

PKGS	PIN OUT	COMMERCIAL GRADE Vcc = +5.0 V ±5%, TA = 0°C to +70°C	MILITARY GRADE Vcc = +5.0 V ±10%, TA = -55°C to +125°C	PKG TYPE
Plastic DIP (P)	A	7411PC, 74H11PC 74S11PC, 74LS11PC		9A
Ceramic DIP (D)	A	7411DC, 74H11DC 74S11DC, 74LS11DC	5411DM, 54H11DM 54S11DM, 54LS11DM	6A
Flatpak (F)	A	74S11FC, 74LS11FC	54S11FM, 54LS11FM	3I
	B	7411FC, 74H11FC	5411FM, 54H11FM	

INPUT LOADING/FAN-OUT: See Section 3 for U.L definitions

PINS	54/74 (U.L.) HIGH/LOW	54/74H (U.L.) HIGH/LOW	54/74S (U.L.) HIGH/LOW	54/74LS (U.L.) HIGH/LOW
Inputs	1.0/1.0	1.25/1.25	1.25/1.25	0.5/0.25
Outputs	20/10	12.5/12.5	25/12.5	10/5.0 (2.5)

DC AND AC CHARACTERISTICS: See Section 3*

SYMBOL	PARAMETER	54/74 Min	54/74 Max	54/74H Min	54/74H Max	54/74S Min	54/74S Max	54/74LS Min	54/74LS Max	UNITS	CONDITIONS	
ICCH	Power Supply		15		30		24		3.6	mA	VIN = Open	Vcc = Max
ICCL	Current		24		48		42		6.6		VIN = Gnd	
tPLH	Propagation Delay		27		12	2.5	7.0		13	ns	Figs. 3-1, 3-5	
tPHL			19		12	2.5	7.5		11			

*DC limits apply over operating temperature range; AC limits apply at TA = +25°C and Vcc = +5.0 V.

54/7413
54LS/74LS13
DUAL 4-INPUT SCHMITT TRIGGER

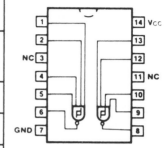

ORDERING CODE: See Section 9

PKGS	PIN OUT	COMMERCIAL GRADE V_{CC} = +5.0 V ±5%, T_A = 0°C to +70°C	MILITARY GRADE V_{CC} = +5.0 V ±10%, T_A = -55°C to +125°C	PKG TYPE
Plastic DIP (P)	A	7413PC, 74LS13PC		9A
Ceramic DIP (D)	A	7413DC, 74LS13DC	5413DM, 54LS13DM	6A
Flatpak (F)	A	7413FC, 74LS13FC	5413FM, 54LS13FM	3I

INPUT LOADING/FAN-OUT: See Section 3 for U.L. definitions

PINS	54/74 (U.L.) HIGH/LOW	54/74LS (U.L.) HIGH/LOW
Inputs	1.0/1.0	0.5/0.25
Outputs	20/10	10/5.0 (2.5)

DC AND AC CHARACTERISTICS: See Section 3*

SYMBOL	PARAMETER	54/74 Min	54/74 Max	54/74LS Min	54/74LS Max	UNITS	CONDITIONS	
V_{T+}	Positive-going Threshold Voltage	1.5	2.0	1.5	2.0	V	V_{CC} = +5.0 V	
V_{T-}	Negative-going Threshold Voltage	0.6	1.1	0.6	1.1	V	V_{CC} = +5.0 V	
$V_{T+} - V_{T-}$	Hysteresis Voltage	0.4		0.4		V	V_{CC} = +5.0 V	
I_{T+}	Input Current at Positive-going Threshold	-0.65**		-0.14**		mA	V_{CC} = +5.0 V, V_{IN} = V_{T+}	
I_{T-}	Input Current at Negative-going Threshold	-0.85**		-0.18**		mA	V_{CC} = +5.0 V, V_{IN} = V_{T-}	
I_{OS}	Output Short Circuit Current	-18	-55	-20	-100	mA	V_{CC} = Max	
I_{CCH}	Power Supply Current		23		6.0	mA	V_{IN} = Gnd	V_{CC} = Max
I_{CCL}			32		7.0		V_{IN} = Open	
t_{PLH}	Propagation Delay		27		22	ns	Fig. 3-1, 3-15	
t_{PHL}			22		27			

*DC limits apply over operating temperature range, AC limits apply at T_A = +25°C and V_{CC} = +5.0 V. **Typical Value

SN5414, SN54LS14, SN7414, SN74LS14
HEX SCHMITT-TRIGGER INVERTERS

DECEMBER 1983—REVISED MARCH 1988

- **Operation from Very Slow Edges**
- **Improved Line-Receiving Characteristics**
- **High Noise Immunity**

description

Each circuit functions as an inverter, but because of the Schmitt action, it has different input threshold levels for positive (V_{T+}) and for negative going (V_{T-}) signals.

These circuits are temperature-compensated and can be triggered from the slowest of input ramps and still give clean, jitter-free output signals.

The SN5414 and SN54LS14 are characterized for operation over the full military temperature range of –55°C to 125°C. The SN7414 and the SN74LS14 are characterized for operation from 0°C to 70°C.

logic symbol†

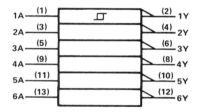

† This symbol is in accordance with ANSI/IEEE Std 91-1984 and IEC Publication 617-12.
Pin numbers shown are for D, J, N, and W packages.

logic diagram (positive logic)

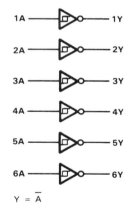

$$Y = \overline{A}$$

SN5414, SN54LS14 . . . J OR W PACKAGE
SN7414 . . . N PACKAGE
SN74LS14 . . . D OR N PACKAGE
(TOP VIEW)

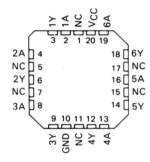

SN54LS14 . . . FK PACKAGE
(TOP VIEW)

NC—No internal connection

2

TTL Devices

TEXAS INSTRUMENTS
POST OFFICE BOX 655012 • DALLAS, TEXAS 75265

SN5414, SN54LS14, SN7414, SN74LS14
HEX SCHMITT-TRIGGER INVERTERS

schematics

'14

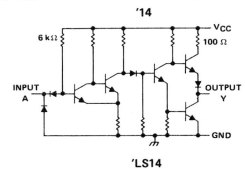

'LS14

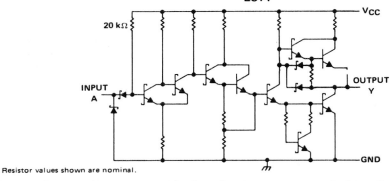

Resistor values shown are nominal.

absolute maximum ratings over operating free-air temperature range (unless otherwise noted)

Supply voltage, V_{CC} (see Note 1) . . . . 7 V
Input voltage: '14 . . . . 5.5 V
              'LS14 . . . . 7 V
Operating free-air temperature: SN54' . . . . − 55°C to 125°C
                              SN74' . . . . 0°C to 70°C
Storage temperature range . . . . − 65°C to 150°C

NOTE 1: Voltage values are with respect to network ground terminal.

TEXAS INSTRUMENTS
POST OFFICE BOX 655012 • DALLAS, TEXAS 75265

2

TTL Devices

recommended operating conditions

		SN54LS14			SN74LS14			UNIT
		MIN	NOM	MAX	MIN	NOM	MAX	
V_{CC}	Supply voltage	4.5	5	5.5	4.75	5	5.25	V
I_{OH}	High-level output current			− 0.4			− 0.4	mA
I_{OL}	Low-level output current			4			8	mA
T_A	Operating free-air temperature	− 55		125	0		70	°C

electrical characteristics over recommended operating free-air temperature range (unless otherwise noted)

PARAMETER	TEST CONDITIONS†			SN54LS14			SN74LS14			UNIT
				MIN	TYP‡	MAX	MIN	TYP‡	MAX	
V_{T+}	$V_{CC} = 5$ V			1.4	1.6	1.9	1.4	1.6	1.9	V
V_{T-}	$V_{CC} = 5$ V			0.5	0.8	1	0.5	0.8	1	V
Hysteresis $(V_{T+} - V_{T-})$	$V_{CC} = 5$ V			0.4	0.8		0.4	0.8		V
V_{IK}	$V_{CC} = $ MIN,	$I_I = - 18$ mA				− 1.5			− 1.5	V
V_{OH}	$V_{CC} = $ MIN,	$V_I = 0.5$ V,	$I_{OH} = - 0.4$ mA	2.5	3.4		2.7	3.4		V
V_{OL}	$V_{CC} = $ MIN,	$V_I = 1.9$ V	$I_{OL} = 4$ mA		0.25	0.4		0.25	0.4	V
			$I_{OL} = 8$ mA					0.35	0.5	
I_{T+}	$V_{CC} = 5$ V,	$V_I = V_{T+}$			− 0.14			− 0.14		mA
I_{T-}	$V_{CC} = 5$ V,	$V_I = V_{T-}$			− 0.18			− 0.18		mA
I_I	$V_{CC} = $ MAX,	$V_I = 7$ V				0.1			0.1	mA
I_{IH}	$V_{CC} = $ MAX,	$V_{IH} = 2.7$ V				20			20	µA
I_{IL}	$V_{CC} = $ MAX,	$V_{IL} = 0.4$ V				− 0.4			− 0.4	mA
I_{OS}§	$V_{CC} = $ MAX			− 20		− 100	− 20		− 100	mA
I_{CCH}	$V_{CC} = $ MAX				8.6	16		8.6	16	mA
I_{CCL}	$V_{CC} = $ MAX				12	21		12	21	mA

† For conditions shown as MIN or MAX, use the appropriate value specified under recommended operating conditions.
‡ All typical values are at $V_{CC} = 5$ V, $T_A = 25$°C.
§ Not more than one output should be shorted at a time, and duration of the short-circuit should not exceed one second.

switching characteristics, $V_{CC} = 5$ V, $T_A = 25$°C

PARAMETER	FROM (INPUT)	TO (OUTPUT)	TEST CONDITIONS		MIN	TYP	MAX	UNIT
t_{PLH}	A	Y	$R_L = 2$ kΩ,	$C_L = 15$ pF		15	22	ns
t_{PHL}						15	22	ns

TEXAS
INSTRUMENTS
POST OFFICE BOX 655012 • DALLAS, TEXAS 75265

2

TTL Devices

TYPICAL CHARACTERISTICS OF 'LS14 CIRCUITS

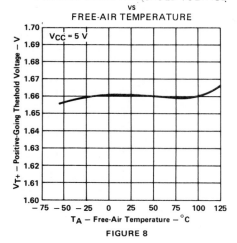

POSITIVE-GOING THRESHOLD VOLTAGE
vs
FREE-AIR TEMPERATURE

FIGURE 8

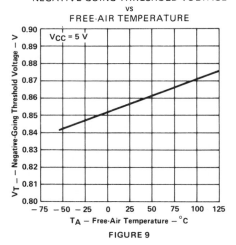

NEGATIVE-GOING THRESHOLD VOLTAGE
vs
FREE-AIR TEMPERATURE

FIGURE 9

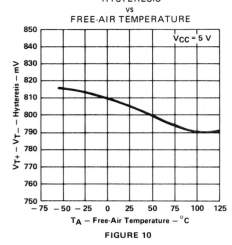

HYSTERESIS
vs
FREE-AIR TEMPERATURE

FIGURE 10

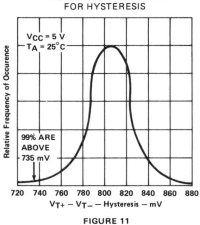

DISTRIBUTION OF UNITS
FOR HYSTERESIS

FIGURE 11

Data for temperatures below 0°C and above 70°C and supply voltages below 4.75 V and above 5.25 V are applicable for SN54LS14 only.

TEXAS
INSTRUMENTS
POST OFFICE BOX 655012 • DALLAS, TEXAS 75265

2

TTL Devices

SN54LS14, SN74LS14
HEX SCHMITT-TRIGGER INVERTERS

TYPICAL CHARACTERISTICS OF 'LS14 CIRCUITS

THRESHOLD VOLTAGES AND HYSTERESIS
vs
SUPPLY VOLTAGE

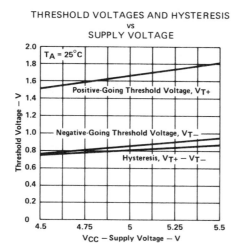

FIGURE 12

OUTPUT VOLTAGE
vs
INPUT VOLTAGE

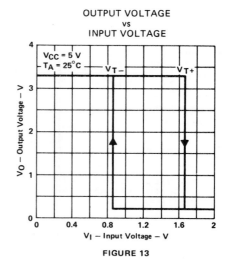

FIGURE 13

Data for temperatures below 0°C and above 70°C and supply voltages below 4.75 V and above 5.25 V are applicable for SN54LS14 only.

2

TTL Devices

2-84

TEXAS
INSTRUMENTS

POST OFFICE BOX 655012 • DALLAS, TEXAS 75265

TYPICAL APPLICATION DATA

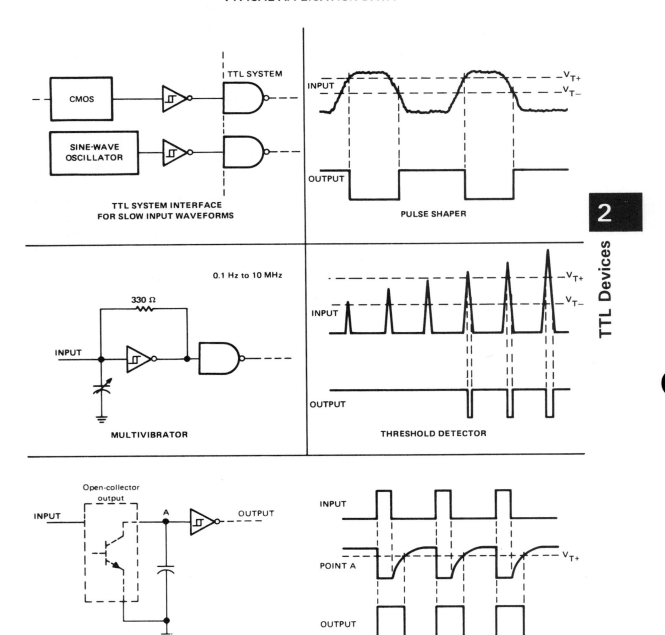

TTL SYSTEM INTERFACE
FOR SLOW INPUT WAVEFORMS

PULSE SHAPER

0.1 Hz to 10 MHz

MULTIVIBRATOR

THRESHOLD DETECTOR

PULSE STRETCHER

TEXAS
INSTRUMENTS
POST OFFICE BOX 655012 • DALLAS, TEXAS 75265

2-85

2

TTL Devices

SN5427, SN54LS27, SN7427, SN74LS27
TRIPLE 3-INPUT POSITIVE-NOR GATES

DECEMBER 1983- REVISED MARCH 1988

- Package Options Include Plastic "Small Outline" Packages, Ceramic Chip Carriers and Flat Packages, and Plastic and Ceramic DIPs

- Dependable Texas Instruments Quality and Reliability

description

These devices contain three independent 3-input NOR gates.

The SN5427 and SN54LS27 are characterized for operation over the full military temperature range of −55°C to 125°C. The SN7427 and SN74LS27 are characterized for operation from 0°C to 70°C.

FUNCTION TABLE (each gate)

INPUTS			OUTPUT
A	B	C	Y
H	X	X	L
X	H	X	L
X	X	H	L
L	L	L	H

logic symbol†

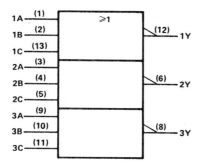

1A (1)
1B (2)
1C (13)
≥1
(12) 1Y
2A (3)
2B (4)
2C (5)
(6) 2Y
3A (9)
3B (10)
3C (11)
(8) 3Y

† This symbol is in accordance with ANSI/IEEE Std 91-1984 and IEC Publication 617-12.
Pin numbers shown are for D, J, N, and W packages.

SN5427, SN54LS27 . . . J OR W PACKAGE
SN7427 . . . N PACKAGE
SN74LS27 . . . D OR N PACKAGE
(TOP VIEW)

1A	1	14	V_{CC}
1B	2	13	1C
2A	3	12	1Y
2B	4	11	3C
2C	5	10	3B
2Y	6	9	3A
GND	7	8	3Y

SN54LS27 . . . FK PACKAGE
(TOP VIEW)

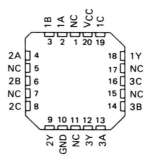

NC - No internal connection

logic diagram

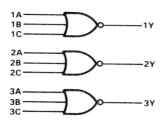

1A
1B — 1Y
1C

2A
2B — 2Y
2C

3A
3B — 3Y
3C

positive logic

$$Y = \overline{A + B + C} \text{ or } Y = \overline{A} \cdot \overline{B} \cdot \overline{C}$$

2

TTL Devices

TEXAS INSTRUMENTS
POST OFFICE BOX 225012 ● DALLAS, TEXAS 75265

- Package Options Include Plastic "Small Outline" Packages, Ceramic Chip Carriers and Flat Packages, and Plastic and Ceramic DIPs

- Dependable Texas Instruments Quality and Reliability

description

These devices contain four independent 2-input OR gates.

The SN5432, SN54LS32 and SN54S32 are characterized for operation over the full military range of −55°C to 125°C. The SN7432, SN74LS32 and SN74S32 are characterized for operation from 0°C to 70°C.

FUNCTION TABLE (each gate)

INPUTS		OUTPUT
A	B	Y
H	X	H
X	H	H
L	L	L

logic symbol†

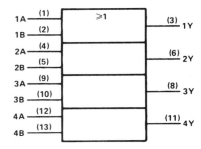

1A (1)
1B (2)
    ≥1
(3) 1Y

2A (4)
2B (5)
(6) 2Y

3A (9)
3B (10)
(8) 3Y

4A (12)
4B (13)
(11) 4Y

† This symbol is in accordance with ANSI IEEE Std 91 1984 and IEC Publication 617 12.
Pin numbers shown are for D, J, N, or W packages.

SN5432, SN54LS32, SN54S32 . . . J OR W PACKAGE
SN7432 . . . N PACKAGE
SN74LS32, SN74S32 . . . D OR N PACKAGE
(TOP VIEW)

```
        ___
1A  [ 1   14 ]  VCC
1B  [ 2   13 ]  4B
1Y  [ 3   12 ]  4A
2A  [ 4   11 ]  4Y
2B  [ 5   10 ]  3B
2Y  [ 6    9 ]  3A
GND [ 7    8 ]  3Y
```

SN54LS32, SN54S32 . . . FK PACKAGE
(TOP VIEW)

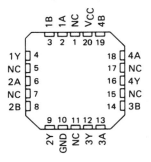

```
           1B  1A  NC VCC 4B
            3   2   1  20  19
1Y  [ 4              18 ]  4A
NC  [ 5              17 ]  NC
2A  [ 6              16 ]  4Y
NC  [ 7              15 ]  NC
2B  [ 8              14 ]  3B
            9  10  11  12  13
           2Y  GND NC  3Y  3A
```

NC - No internal connection

logic diagram

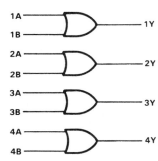

1A
1B
    1Y

2A
2B
    2Y

3A
3B
    3Y

4A
4B
    4Y

positive logic

$Y = A + B$ or $Y = \overline{\overline{A} \cdot \overline{B}}$

TEXAS INSTRUMENTS
POST OFFICE BOX 655012 • DALLAS, TEXAS 75265

2 TTL Devices

54/7442A • 54LS/74LS42
54/7443A • 54/7444A
1-of-10 DECODER

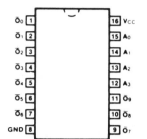

DESCRIPTION - The '42, '43 and '44 are multipurpose decoders. For any valid input combination, one and only one output is LOW. For all invalid input combinations all outputs are HIGH. The '42 accepts four BCD inputs and provides ten mutually exclusive outputs; the '43 accepts four lines of EXCESS-3 encoded data and provides ten mutually exclusive outputs; the '44 accepts four lines of EXCESS-3 Gray encoded data and provides ten mutually exclusive totem pole outputs.

- **MULTIFUNCTION CAPABILITY**
- **MUTUALLY EXCLUSIVE OUTPUTS**
- **DEMULTIPLEXING CAPABILITY**
- **FULLY TTL AND CMOS COMPATIBLE**

ORDERING CODE: See Section 9

PKGS	PIN OUT	COMMERCIAL GRADE V_{CC} = +5.0 V ±5%, T_A = 0° C to +70° C	MILITARY GRADE V_{CC} = +5.0 V ±10%, T_A = -55° C to +125° C	PKG TYPE
Plastic DIP (P)	A	7442APC, 74LS42PC 7443APC, 7444APC		9B
Ceramic DIP (D)	A	7442ADC, 74LS42DC 7443ADC, 7444ADC	5442ADM, 54LS42DM 5443ADM, 5444ADM	6B
Flatpak (F)	A	7442AFC, 74LS42FC 7443AFC, 7444AFC	5442AFM, 54LS42FM 5443AFM, 5444AFM	4L

LOGIC SYMBOL

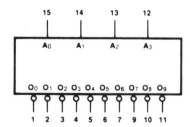

V_{CC} = Pin 16
GND = Pin 8

42 • 43 • 44

INPUT LOADING/FAN-OUT: See Section 3 for U.L. definitions

PIN NAMES	DESCRIPTION	54/74 (U.L.) HIGH/LOW	54/74LS (U.L.) HIGH/LOW
$A_0 - A_3$	BCD Inputs ('42)	1.0/1.0	0.5/0.25
$A_0 - A_3$	EXCESS-3 Inputs ('43)	1.0/1.0	
$A_0 - A_3$	EXCESS-3 GRAY Inputs ('44)	1.0/1.0	
$\overline{O}_0 - \overline{O}_0$	Decimal Outputs (Active LOW)	20/10	10/5.0 (2.5)

FUNCTIONAL DESCRIPTION — Logically, the '42, '43 and '44 differ only in their input codes. The '42 accepts the standard 8421 BCD code. The '43 accepts the EXCESS-3 decimal code while the '44 accepts the EXCESS-3 Gray code. For any input combination within the assigned ten states, only one output is LOW, as shown in the Truth Table. For all invalid input combinations, all ten outputs are HIGH.

The '42 can be used as a conventional 1-of-8 decoder by treating the most significant input A_3 as an active LOW Enable. Similarly, it can be used as an 8-output demultiplexer by using A_3 as the data input.

TRUTH TABLE

'42A • 'LS42 BCD INPUT				'43A EXCESS-3 INPUT				'44A EXCESS-3 GRAY INPUT				ALL TYPES DECIMAL OUTPUT									
A_3	A_2	A_1	A_0	A_3	A_2	A_1	A_0	A_3	A_2	A_1	A_0	$\overline{O}_0$	$\overline{O}_1$	$\overline{O}_2$	$\overline{O}_3$	$\overline{O}_4$	$\overline{O}_5$	$\overline{O}_6$	$\overline{O}_7$	$\overline{O}_8$	$\overline{O}_9$
L	L	L	L	L	L	H	H	L	L	H	L	L	H	H	H	H	H	H	H	H	H
L	L	L	H	L	H	L	L	L	H	H	L	H	L	H	H	H	H	H	H	H	H
L	L	H	L	L	H	L	H	L	H	H	H	H	H	L	H	H	H	H	H	H	H
L	L	H	H	L	H	H	L	L	H	L	H	H	H	H	L	H	H	H	H	H	H
L	H	L	L	L	H	H	H	L	H	L	L	H	H	H	H	L	H	H	H	H	H
L	H	L	H	H	L	L	L	H	H	L	L	H	H	H	H	H	L	H	H	H	H
L	H	H	L	H	L	L	H	H	H	L	H	H	H	H	H	H	H	L	H	H	H
L	H	H	H	H	L	H	L	H	H	H	H	H	H	H	H	H	H	H	L	H	H
H	L	L	L	H	L	H	H	H	H	H	L	H	H	H	H	H	H	H	L	H
H	L	L	H	H	H	L	L	H	L	H	L	H	H	H	H	H	H	H	H	H	L
H	L	H	L	H	H	L	H	H	L	H	H	H	H	H	H	H	H	H	H	H	H
H	L	H	H	H	H	H	L	H	L	L	H	H	H	H	H	H	H	H	H	H	H
H	H	L	L	H	H	H	H	H	L	L	L	H	H	H	H	H	H	H	H	H	H
H	H	L	H	L	L	L	L	L	L	L	L	H	H	H	H	H	H	H	H	H	H
H	H	H	L	L	L	L	H	L	L	L	H	H	H	H	H	H	H	H	H	H	H
H	H	H	H	L	L	H	L	L	L	H	H	H	H	H	H	H	H	H	H	H	H

H = HIGH Voltage Level
L = LOW Voltage Level

(Courtesy Of Fairchild — A Schlumberger Company)

'46A, '47A, 'LS47 feature	'48, 'LS48 feature	'LS49 feature
• **Open-Collector Outputs Drive Indicators Directly** • **Lamp-Test Provision** • **Leading/Trailing Zero Suppression**	• **Internal Pull-Ups Eliminate Need for External Resistors** • **Lamp-Test Provision** • **Leading/Trailing Zero Suppression**	• **Open-Collector Outputs** • **Blanking Input**

SN5446A, SN5447A, SN54LS47, SN5448,
SN54LS48 . . . J PACKAGE
SN7446A, SN7447A,
SN7448 . . . N PACKAGE
SN74LS47, SN74LS48 . . . D OR N PACKAGE
(TOP VIEW)

SN54LS47, SN54LS48 . . . FK PACKAGE
(TOP VIEW)

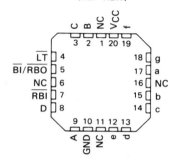

SN54LS49 . . . J OR W PACKAGE
SN74LS49 . . . D OR N PACKAGE
(TOP VIEW)

SN54LS49 . . . FK PACKAGE
(TOP VIEW)

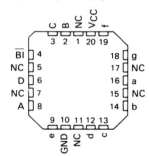

NC – No internal connection

2

TTL Devices

TEXAS
INSTRUMENTS
POST OFFICE BOX 655012 • DALLAS, TEXAS 75265

● All Circuit Types Feature Lamp Intensity Modulation Capability

TYPE	DRIVER OUTPUTS				TYPICAL POWER DISSIPATION	PACKAGES
	ACTIVE LEVEL	OUTPUT CONFIGURATION	SINK CURRENT	MAX VOLTAGE		
SN5446A	low	open-collector	40 mA	30 V	320 mW	J, W
SN5447A	low	open-collector	40 mA	15 V	320 mW	J, W
SN5448	high	2-kΩ pull-up	6.4 mA	5.5 V	265 mW	J, W
SN54LS47	low	open-collector	12 mA	15 V	35 mW	J, W
SN54LS48	high	2-kΩ pull-up	2 mA	5.5 V	125 mW	J, W
SN54LS49	high	open-collector	4 mA	5.5 V	40 mW	J, W
SN7446A	low	open-collector	40 mA	30 V	320 mW	J, N
SN7447A	low	open-collector	40 mA	15 V	320 mW	J, N
SN7448	high	2-kΩ pull-up	6.4 mA	5.5 V	265 mW	J, N
SN74LS47	low	open-collector	24 mA	15 V	35 mW	J, N
SN74LS48	high	2-kΩ pull-up	6 mA	5.5 V	125 mW	J, N
SN74LS49	high	open-collector	8 mA	5.5 V	40 mW	J, N

2

TTL Devices

logic symbols†

'46A, '47A, 'LS47

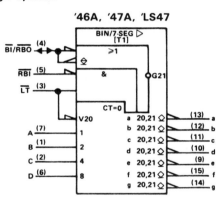

'48, 'LS48

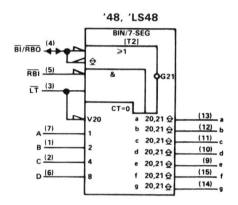

'LS49

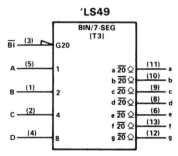

† These symbols are in accordance with ANSI/IEEE Std 91-1984 and IEC Publication 617-12.
Pin numbers shown are for D, J, N, and W packages.

TEXAS
INSTRUMENTS
POST OFFICE BOX 655012 • DALLAS, TEXAS 75265

logic diagrams (positive logic)

'46A, '47A, 'LS47

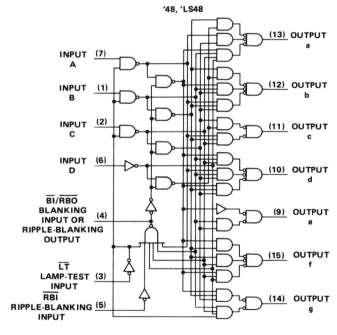

'48, 'LS48

Pin numbers shown are for D, J, N, and W packages.

2

TTL Devices

2-179

SN54LS49, SN74LS49
BCD-TO-SEVEN-SEGMENT DECODERS/DRIVERS

logic diagrams (continued)

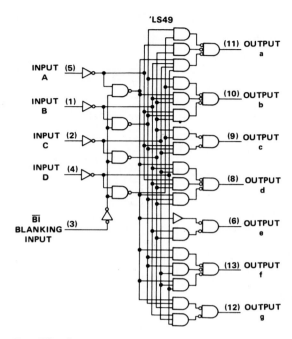

Pin numbers shown are for D, J, N, and W packages.

TEXAS
INSTRUMENTS
POST OFFICE BOX 655012 • DALLAS, TEXAS 75265

54/7474
54H/74H74
54S/74S74
54LS/74LS74

DUAL D-TYPE POSITIVE EDGE-TRIGGERED FLIP-FLOP

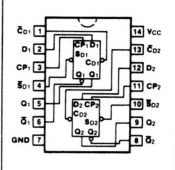

DESCRIPTION — The '74 devices are dual D-type flip-flops with Direct Clear and Set inputs and complementary (Q, $\bar{Q}$) outputs. Information at the input is transferred to the outputs on the positive edge of the clock pulse. Clock triggering occurs at a voltage level of the clock pulse and is not directly related to the transition time of the positive going pulse. After the Clock Pulse input threshold voltage has been passed, the Data input is locked out and information present will not be transferred to the outputs until the next rising edge of the Clock Pulse input.

PINOUT B

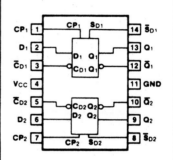

TRUTH TABLE
(Each Half)

INPUT	OUTPUTS	
@ t_n	@ t_{n+1}	
D	Q	$\bar{Q}$
L	L	H
H	H	L

Asynchronous Inputs:
LOW input to $\bar{S}_D$ sets Q to HIGH level
LOW input to $\bar{C}_D$ sets Q to LOW level
Clear and Set are independent of clock
Simultaneous LOW on $\bar{C}_D$ and $\bar{S}_D$ makes both Q and $\bar{Q}$ HIGH

H = HIGH Voltage Level
L = LOW Voltage Level
t_n = Bit time before clock pulse.
t_{n+1} = Bit time after clock pulse.

LOGIC SYMBOL

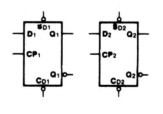

V_{CC} = Pin 14 (4)
GND = Pin 7 (11)

ORDERING CODE: See Section 9

PKGS	PIN OUT	COMMERCIAL GRADE V_{CC} = +5.0 V ±5%, T_A = 0°C to +70°C	MILITARY GRADE V_{CC} = +5.0 V ±10%, T_A = -55°C to +125°C	PKG TYPE
Plastic DIP (P)	A	7474PC, 74H74PC 74S74PC, 74LS74PC		9A
Ceramic DIP (D)	A	7474DC, 74H74DC 74S74DC, 74LS74DC	5474DM, 54H74DM 54S74DM, 54LS74DM	6A
Flatpak (F)	A	74S74FC, 74LS74FC	54S74FM, 54LS74FM	3I
	B	7474FC, 74H74FC	5474FM, 54H74FM	

INPUT LOADING/FAN-OUT: See Section 3 for U.L. definitions

PIN NAMES	DESCRIPTION	54/74 (U.L.) HIGH/LOW	54/74H (U.L.) HIGH/LOW	54/74S (U.L.) HIGH/LOW	54/74LS (U.L.) HIGH/LOW
D_1, D_2	Data Inputs	1.0/1.0	1.25/1.25	1.25/1.25	0.5/0.25
CP_1, CP_2	Clock Pulse Inputs (Active Rising Edge)	2.0/2.0	2.5/2.5	2.5/2.5	1.0/0.5
$\bar{C}_{D1}$, $\bar{C}_{D2}$	Direct Clear Inputs (Active LOW)	3.0/2.0	3.75/2.5	3.75/3.75	1.5/0.75
$\bar{S}_{D1}$, $\bar{S}_{D2}$	Direct Set Inputs (Active LOW)	2.0/1.0	2.5/1.25	2.5/2.5	1.0/0.5
Q_1, $\bar{Q}_1$, Q_2, $\bar{Q}_2$	Outputs	20/10	12.5/12.5	25/12.5	10/5.0 (2.5)

LOGIC DIAGRAM (one half shown)

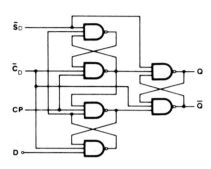

DC CHARACTERISTICS OVER OPERATING TEMPERATURE RANGE (unless otherwise specified)

SYMBOL	PARAMETER		54/74 Min	54/74 Max	54/74H Min	54/74H Max	54/74S Min	54/74S Max	54/74LS Min	54/74LS Max	UNITS	CONDITIONS
I_{CC}	Power Supply Current	XM		30		42		50		8.0	mA	V_{CC} = Max, V_{CP} = 0 V
		XC		30		50		50		8.0		

AC CHARACTERISTICS: V_{CC} = +5.0 V, T_A = +25° C (See Section 3 for waveforms and load configurations)

SYMBOL	PARAMETER	54/74 C_L = 15 pF R_L = 400 Ω Min	54/74 Max	54/74H C_L = 25 pF R_L = 280 Ω Min	54/74H Max	54/74S C_L = 15 pF R_L = 280 Ω Min	54/74S Max	54/74LS C_L = 15 pF Min	54/74LS Max	UNITS	CONDITIONS
f_{max}	Maximum Clock Frequency	15		35		75		30		MHz	Figs. 3-1, 3-8
t_{PLH} t_{PHL}	Propagation Delay CP_n to Q_n or $\bar{Q}_n$		25 40		15 20		9.0 11		25 35	ns	Figs. 3-1, 3-8
t_{PLH} t_{PHL}	Propagation Delay $\bar{C}_{Dn}$ or $\bar{S}_{Dn}$ to Q_n or $\bar{Q}_n$		25 40		20 30		6.0 13.5		15 35	ns	$V_{CP} \geq$ 2.0 V Figs. 3-1, 3-10
t_{PLH} t_{PHL}	Propagation Delay $\bar{C}_{Dn}$ or $\bar{S}_{Dn}$ to Q_n or $\bar{Q}_n$		25 40		20 30		6.0 8.0		15 24	ns	$V_{CP} \leq$ 0.8 V Figs. 3-1, 3-10

(Courtesy of Fairchild — A Schlumberger Company)

AC OPERATING REQUIREMENTS: $V_{CC} = +5.0$ V, $T_A = +25°$C

SYMBOL	PARAMETER	54/74		54/74H		54/74S		54/74LS		UNITS	CONDITIONS
		Min	Max	Min	Max	Min	Max	Min	Max		
t_s (H)	Setup Time HIGH D_n to CP_n	20		10		3.0		10		ns	Fig. 3-6
t_h (H)	Hold Time HIGH D_n to CP_n	5.0		0		0		5.0		ns	
t_s (L)	Setup Time LOW D_n to CP_n	20		15		3.0		20		ns	Fig. 3-6
t_h (L)	Hold Time LOW D_n to CP_n	5.0		0		0		5.0		ns	
t_w (H) t_w (L)	CP_n Pulse Width	30 37		15 13.5		6.0 7.3		18 15.5		ns	Fig. 3-8
t_w (L)	$\overline{C}_{Dn}$ or $\overline{S}_{Dn}$ Pulse Width LOW	30		25		7.0		15		ns	Fig. 3-10

FUNCTION TABLE
(each latch)

INPUTS		OUTPUTS	
D	C	Q	$\overline{Q}$
L	H	L	H
H	H	H	L
X	L	Q_0	$\overline{Q_0}$

H = high level, L = low level, X = irrelevant

Q_0 = the level of Q before the high-to-low transition of G

description

These latches are ideally suited for use as temporary storage for binary information between processing units and input/output or indicator units. Information present at a data (D) input is transferred to the Q output when the enable (C) is high and the Q output will follow the data input as long as the enable remains high. When the enable goes low, the information (that was present at the data input at the time the transition occurred) is retained at the Q output until the enable is permitted to go high.

The '75 and 'LS75 feature complementary Q and $\overline{Q}$ outputs from a 4-bit latch, and are available in various 16-pin packages. For higher component density applications, the '77 and 'LS77 4-bit latches are available in 14-pin flat packages.

These circuits are completely compatible with all popular TTL families. All inputs are diode-clamped to minimize transmission-line effects and simplify system design. Series 54 and 54LS devices are characterized for operation over the full military temperature range of −55°C to 125°C; Series 74, and 74LS devices are characterized for operation from 0°C to 70°C.

SN5475, SN54LS75 . . . J OR W PACKAGE
SN7475 . . . N PACKAGE
SN74LS75 . . . D OR N PACKAGE
(TOP VIEW)

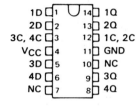

SN5477, SN54LS77 . . . W PACKAGE
(TOP VIEW)

NC - No internal connection

logic symbols†

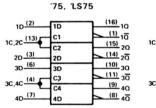

†These symbols are in accordance with ANSI/IEEE Std 91-1984 and IEC Publication 617-12.

absolute maximum ratings over operating free-air temperature range (unless otherwise noted)

Supply voltage, V_{CC} (See Note 1)	7 V
Input voltage: '75, '77	5.5 V
'LS75, 'LS77	7 V
Interemitter voltage (see Note 2)	5.5 V
Operating free-air temperature range: SN54'	−55°C to 125°C
SN74'	0°C to 70°C
Storage temperature range	−65°C to 150°C

NOTES: 1. Voltage values are with respect to network ground terminal.

    2. This is the voltage between two emitters of a multiple-emitter input transistor and is not applicable to the 'LS75 and 'LS77.

TEXAS
INSTRUMENTS

POST OFFICE BOX 655012 • DALLAS, TEXAS 75265

2

TTL Devices

CONNECTION DIAGRAM
PINOUT A

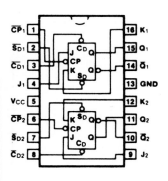

54/7476
54H/74H76
54LS/74LS76

DUAL JK FLIP-FLOP
(With Separate Sets, Clears and Clocks)

DESCRIPTION — The '76 and 'H76 are dual JK master/slave flip-flops with separate Direct Set, Direct Clear and Clock Pulse inputs for each flip-flop. Inputs to the master section are controlled by the clock pulse. The clock pulse also regulates the state of the coupling transistors which connect the master and slave sections. The sequence of operation is as follows: 1) isolate slave from master; 2) enter information from J and K inputs to master; 3) disable J and K inputs; 4) transfer information from master to slave.

TRUTH TABLE

INPUTS		OUTPUT
@ t_n		@ t_{n+1}
J	K'	Q
L	L	Q_n
L	H	L
H	L	H
H	H	$\bar{Q}_n$

H = HIGH Voltage Level
L = LOW Voltage Level
t_n = Bit time before clock pulse.
t_{n+1} = Bit time after clock pulse.

CLOCK WAVEFORM

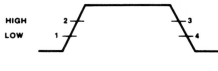

Asynchronous Inputs:
  LOW input to $\bar{S}_D$ sets Q to HIGH level
  LOW input to $\bar{C}_D$ sets Q to LOW level
  Clear and Set are independent of clock
  Simultaneous LOW on $\bar{C}_D$ and $\bar{S}_D$
  makes both Q and $\bar{Q}$ HIGH

The 'LS76 is a dual JK, negative edge-triggered flip-flop also offering individual Direct Set, Direct Clear and Clock Pulse inputs. When the Clock Pulse input is HIGH, the JK inputs are enabled and data is accepted. This data will be transferred to the outputs according to the Truth Table on the HIGH-to-LOW clock transitions.

ORDERING CODE: See Section 9

PKGS	PIN OUT	COMMERCIAL GRADE Vcc = +5.0 V ±5%, T_A = 0°C to +70°C	MILITARY GRADE Vcc = +5.0 V ±10%, T_A = -55°C to +125°C	PKG TYPE
Plastic DIP (P)	A	7476PC, 74H76PC 74LS76PC		9B
Ceramic DIP (D)	A	7476DC, 74H76DC 74LS76DC	5476DM, 54H76DM 54LS76DM	6B
Flatpak (F)	A	7476FC, 74H76FC 74LS76FC	5476FM, 54H76FM 54LS76FM	4L

LOGIC SYMBOL

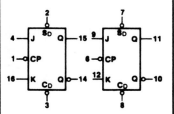

Vcc = Pin 5
GND = Pin 13

(Courtesy of Fairchild — A Schlumberger Company)

INPUT LOADING/FAN-OUT: See Section 3 for U.L. definitions

PIN NAMES	DESCRIPTION	54/74 (U.L.) HIGH/LOW	54/74H (U.L.) HIGH/LOW	54/74LS (U.L.) HIGH/LOW
J_1, J_2, K_1, K_2	Data Inputs	1.0/1.0	1.25/1.25	0.5/0.25
$\overline{CP}_1, \overline{CP}_2$	Clock Pulse Inputs (Active Falling Edge)	2.0/2.0	2.5/2.5	2.0/0.5
$\overline{C}_{D1}, \overline{C}_{D2}$	Direct Clear Inputs (Active LOW)	2.0/2.0	2.5/2.5	1.5/0.5
$\overline{S}_{D1}, \overline{S}_{D2}$	Direct Set Inputs (Active LOW)	2.0/2.0	2.5/2.5	1.5/0.5
$Q_1, \overline{Q}_1, Q_2, \overline{Q}_2$	Outputs	20/10	12.5/12.5	10/5.0 (2.5)

LOGIC DIAGRAMS (one half shown)
'76, 'H76

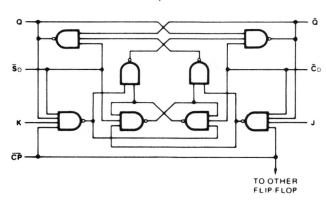

'LS76

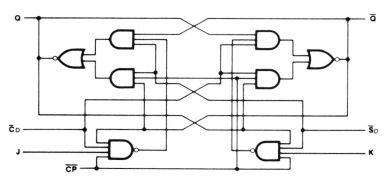

DC CHARACTERISTICS OVER OPERATING TEMPERATURE RANGE (unless otherwise specified)

SYMBOL	PARAMETER	54/74		54/74H		54/74LS		UNITS	CONDITIONS
		Min	Max	Min	Max	Min	Max		
I_{CC}	Power Supply Current		40		50		8.0	mA	V_{CC} = Max, V_{CP} = 0 V

AC CHARACTERISTICS: V_{CC} = +5.0 V, T_A = +25°C (See Section 3 for waveforms and load configurations)

SYMBOL	PARAMETER	54/74 C_L = 15 pF R_L = 400 Ω		54/74H C_L = 25 pF R_L = 280 Ω		54/74LS C_L = 15 pF		UNITS	CONDITIONS
		Min	Max	Min	Max	Min	Max		
f_{max}	Maximum Clock Frequency	15		25		30		MHz	Figs. 3-1, 3-9
t_{PLH} t_{PHL}	Propagation Delay $\overline{CP}_n$ to Q_n or $\overline{Q}_n$		25 40		21 27		20 30	ns	Figs. 3-1, 3-9
t_{PLH} t_{PHL}	Propagation Delay $\overline{C}_{Dn}$ or $\overline{S}_{Dn}$ to Q_n or $\overline{Q}_n$		25 40		13 24		20 30	ns	Figs. 3-1, 3-10

AC OPERATING REQUIREMENTS: V_{CC} = +5.0 V, T_A = +25°C

SYMBOL	PARAMETER	54/74		54/74H		54/74LS		UNITS	CONDITIONS
		Min	Max	Min	Max	Min	Max		
t_s (H)	Setup Time HIGH J_n or K_n to $\overline{CP}_n$	0		0		20		ns	
t_h (H)	Hold Time HIGH J_n or K_n to $\overline{CP}_n$	0		0		0		ns	Fig. 3-18 ('76, 'H76)
t_s (L)	Setup Time LOW J_n or K_n to $\overline{CP}_n$	0		0		20		ns	Fig. 3-7 ('LS76)
t_h (L)	Hold Time LOW J_n or K_n to $\overline{CP}_n$	0		0		0		ns	
t_w (H) t_w (L)	$\overline{CP}_n$ Pulse Width	20 47		12 28		20 13.5		ns	Fig. 3-9
t_w (L)	$\overline{C}_{Dn}$ or $\overline{S}_{Dn}$ Pulse Width LOW	25		16		25		ns	Fig. 3-10

(Courtesy of Fairchild — A Schlumberger Company)

SN5483A, SN54LS83A, SN7483A, SN74LS83A
4-BIT BINARY FULL ADDDERS WITH FAST CARRY

MARCH 1974 — REVISED MARCH 1988

- **Full-Carry Look-Ahead across the Four Bits**
- **Systems Achieve Partial Look-Ahead Performance with the Economy of Ripple Carry**
- **SN54283/SN74283 and SN54LS283/SN74LS283 Are Recommended For New Designs as They Feature Supply Voltage and Ground on Corner Pins to Simplify Board Layout**

TYPE	TYPICAL ADD TIMES		TYPICAL POWER DISSIPATION PER 4-BIT ADDER
	TWO 8-BIT WORDS	TWO 16-BIT WORDS	
'83A	23 ns	43 ns	310 mW
'LS83A	25 ns	45 ns	95 mW

description

These improved full adders perform the addition of two 4-bit binary numbers. The sum (Σ) outputs are provided for each bit and the resultant carry (C4) is obtained from the fourth bit. These adders feature full internal look ahead across all four bits generating the carry term in ten nanoseconds typically. This provides the system designer with partial look-ahead performance at the economy and reduced package count of a ripple-carry implementation.

The adder logic, including the carry, is implemented in its true form meaning that the end-around carry can be accomplished without the need for logic or level inversion.

Designed for medium-speed applications, the circuits utilize transistor-transistor logic that is compatible with most other TTL families and other saturated low-level logic families.

Series 54 and 54LS circuits are characterized for operation over the full military temperature range of $-55°C$ to $125°C$, and Series 74 and 74LS circuits are characterized for operation from $0°C$ to $70°C$.

logic symbol†

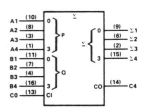

A1 (10), A2 (8), A3 (3), A4 (1), B1 (11), B2 (7), B3 (4), B4 (16), C0 (13) CI; outputs Σ (9) Σ1, (6) Σ2, (2) Σ3, (15) Σ4, CO (14) C4

†This symbol is in accordance with ANSI/IEEE Std 91-1984 and IEC Publication 617-12.
Pin numbers are for D, J, N, and W packages.

SN5483A, SN54LS83A . . . J OR W PACKAGE
SN7483A . . . N PACKAGE
SN74LS83A . . . D OR N PACKAGE
(TOP VIEW)

```
A4   [1   16] B4
Σ3   [2   15] Σ4
A3   [3   14] C4
B3   [4   13] C0
VCC  [5   12] GND
Σ2   [6   11] B1
B2   [7   10] A1
A2   [8    9] Σ1
```

SN54LS83A . . . FK PACKAGE
(TOP VIEW)

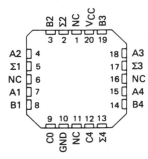

```
        B2 Σ2 NC VCC B3
         3  2  1  20 19
A2 [4            18] A3
Σ1 [5            17] Σ3
NC [6            16] NC
A1 [7            15] A4
B1 [8            14] B4
         9 10 11 12 13
        C0 GND NC C4 Σ4
```

NC - No internal connection

FUNCTION TABLE

INPUT				OUTPUT					
				WHEN C0 = L		WHEN C2 = L	WHEN C0 = H		WHEN C2 = H
A1	B1	A2	B2	Σ1	Σ2	C2	Σ1	Σ2	C2
A3	B3	A4	B4	Σ3	Σ4	C4	Σ3	Σ4	C4
L	L	L	L	L	L	L	H	L	L
H	L	L	L	H	L	L	L	H	L
L	H	L	L	H	L	L	L	H	L
H	H	L	L	L	H	L	H	H	L
L	L	H	L	L	H	L	H	H	L
H	L	H	L	H	H	L	L	L	H
L	H	H	L	H	H	L	L	L	H
H	H	H	L	L	L	H	H	L	H
L	L	L	H	L	H	L	H	H	L
H	L	L	H	H	H	L	L	L	H
L	H	L	H	H	H	L	L	L	H
H	H	L	H	L	L	H	H	L	H
L	L	H	H	L	L	H	H	L	H
H	L	H	H	H	L	H	L	H	H
L	H	H	H	H	L	H	L	H	H
H	H	H	H	L	H	H	H	H	H

H = high level, L = low level

NOTE: Input conditions at A1, B1, A2, B2, and C0 are used to determine outputs Σ1 and Σ2 and the value of the internal carry C2. The values at C2, A3, B3, A4, and B4 are then used to determine outputs Σ3, Σ4, and C4.

TTL Devices 2

TEXAS INSTRUMENTS
POST OFFICE BOX 655012 • DALLAS, TEXAS 75265

logic diagram (positive logic)

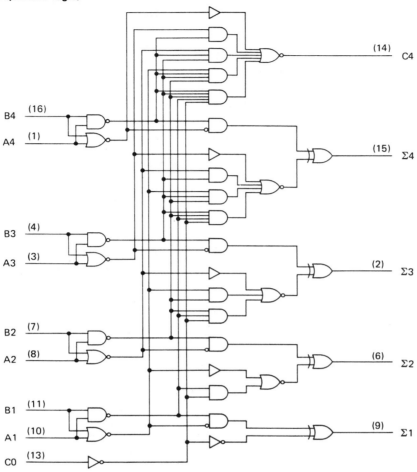

2

TTL Devices

Pin numbers shown are for D, J, N, and W packages.

absolute maximum ratings over operating free-air temperature range (unless otherwise noted)

Supply voltage, V_{CC} (see Note 1)	7 V
Input voltage: '83A	5.5 V
'LS83A	7 V
Interemitter voltage (see Note 2)	5.5 V
Operating free-air temperature range: SN5483A, SN54LS83A	−55°C to 125°C
SN7483A, SN74LS83A	0°C to 70°C
Storage temperature range	−65°C to 150°C

NOTES: 1. Voltage values, except interemitter voltage, are with respect to network ground terminal.
          2. This is the voltage between two emitters of a multiple-emitter transistor. This rating applies for the '83A only between the
               following pairs: A1 and B1, A2 and B2, A3 and B3, A4 and B4.

TEXAS INSTRUMENTS

POST OFFICE BOX 655012 • DALLAS. TEXAS 75265

TYPE	TYPICAL POWER DISSIPATION	TYPICAL DELAY (4-BIT WORDS)
'85	275 mW	23 ns
'LS85	52 mW	24 ns
'S85	365 mW	11 ns

description

These four-bit magnitude comparators perform comparison of straight binary and straight BCD (8-4-2-1) codes. Three fully decoded decisions about two 4-bit words (A, B) are made and are externally available at three outputs. These devices are fully expandable to any number of bits without external gates. Words of greater length may be compared by connecting comparators in cascade. The A > B, A < B, and A = B outputs of a stage handling less-significant bits are connected to the corresponding A > B, A < B, and A = B inputs of the next stage handling more-significant bits. The stage handling the least-significant bits must have a high-level voltage applied to the A = B input. The cascading paths of the '85, 'LS85, and 'S85 are implemented with only a two-gate-level delay to reduce overall comparison times for long words. An alternate method of cascading which further reduces the comparison time is shown in the typical application data.

SN5485, SN54LS85, SN54S85 . . . J OR W PACKAGE
SN7485 . . . N PACKAGE
SN74LS85, SN74S85 . . . D OR N PACKAGE
(TOP VIEW)

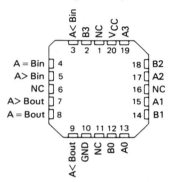

SN54LS85, SN54S85 . . . FK PACKAGE
(TOP VIEW)

NC - No internal connection

FUNCTION TABLE

COMPARING INPUTS				CASCADING INPUTS			OUTPUTS		
A3, B3	A2, B2	A1, B1	A0, B0	A > B	A < B	A = B	A > B	A < B	A = B
A3 > B3	X	X	X	X	X	X	H	L	L
A3 < B3	X	X	X	X	X	X	L	H	L
A3 = B3	A2 > B2	X	X	X	X	X	H	L	L
A3 = B3	A2 < B2	X	X	X	X	X	L	H	L
A3 = B2	A2 = B2	A1 > B1	X	X	X	X	H	L	L
A3 = B3	A2 = B2	A1 < B1	X	X	X	X	L	H	L
A2 = B3	A2 = B2	A1 = B1	A0 > B0	X	X	X	H	L	L
A3 = B3	A2 = B2	A1 = B1	A0 < B0	X	X	X	L	H	L
A3 = B3	A2 = B2	A1 = B1	A0 = B0	H	L	L	H	L	L
A3 = B3	A2 = B2	A1 = B1	A0 = B0	L	H	L	L	H	L
A3 = B3	A2 = B2	A1 = B1	A0 = B0	X	X	H	L	L	H
A3 = B3	A2 = B2	A1 = B1	A0 = B0	H	H	L	L	L	L
A3 = B3	A2 = B2	A1 = B1	A0 = B0	L	L	L	H	H	L

TEXAS INSTRUMENTS
POST OFFICE BOX 655012 • DALLAS, TEXAS 75265

2-263

2

TTL Devices

logic diagrams (positive logic)

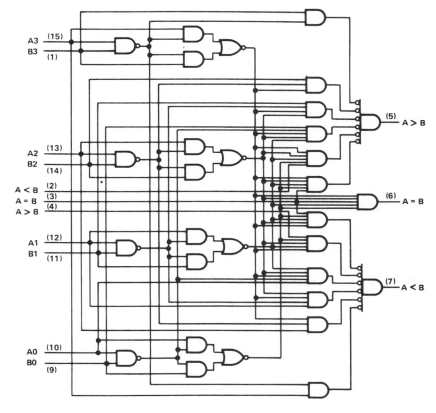

logic symbol†

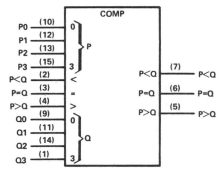

†This symbol is in accordancae with ANSI/IEEE Std 91-1984 and IEC Publication 617-12.
Pin numbers shown are for D, J, N, and W packages.

2-264

**TEXAS
INSTRUMENTS**
POST OFFICE BOX 655012 • DALLAS, TEXAS 75265

2

TTL Devices

TYPICAL APPLICATION DATA

COMPARISON OF TWO N-BIT WORDS

This application demonstrates how these magnitude comparators can be cascaded to compare longer words. The example illustrated shows the comparison of two 24-bit words; however, the design is expandable to n-bits. As an example, one comparator can be used with five of the 24-bit comparators illustrated to expand the word length to 120-bits. Typical comparison times for various word lengths using the '85, 'LS85, or 'S85 are:

WORD LENGTH	NUMBER OF PKGS	'85	'LS85	'S85
1-4 bits	1	23 ns	24 ns	11 ns
5-24 bits	2-6	46 ns	48 ns	22 ns
25-120 bits	8-31	69 ns	72 ns	33 ns

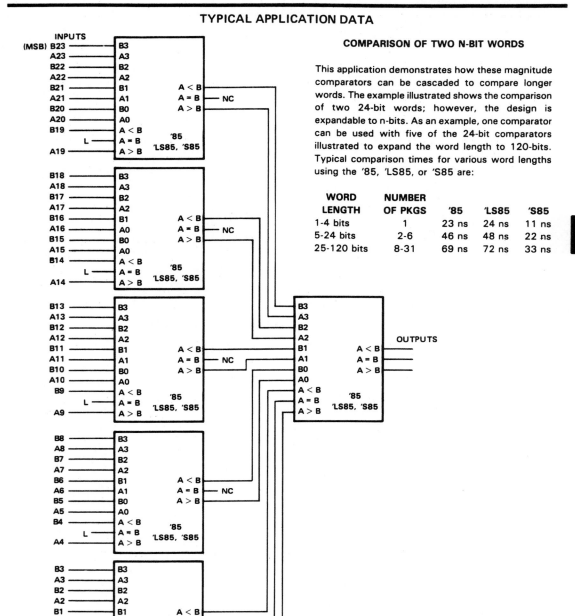

COMPARISON OF TWO 24-BIT WORDS

TTL Devices

2

TEXAS INSTRUMENTS
POST OFFICE BOX 655012 • DALLAS, TEXAS 75265

- Package Options Include Plastic "Small Outline" Packages, Ceramic Chip Carriers and Flat Packages, and Standard Plastic and Ceramic 300-mil DIPs

- Dependable Texas Instruments Quality and Reliability

TYPE	TYPICAL AVERAGE PROPAGATION DELAY TIME	TYPICAL TOTAL POWER DISSIPATION
'86	14 ns	150 mW
'LS86A	10 ns	30.5 mW
'S86	7 ns	250 mW

SN5486, SN54LS86A, SN54S86 . . . J OR W PACKAGE
SN7486 . . . N PACKAGE
SN74LS86A, SN74S86 . . . D OR N PACKAGE
(TOP VIEW)

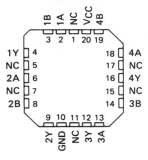

```
1A   [1      14] VCC
1B   [2      13] 4B
1Y   [3      12] 4A
2A   [4      11] 4Y
2B   [5      10] 3B
2Y   [6       9] 3A
GND  [7       8] 3Y
```

SN54LS86A, SN54S86 . . . FK PACKAGE
(TOP VIEW)

```
        1B 1A NC VCC 4B
         3  2  1 20 19
1Y [ 4                18 ] 4A
NC [ 5                17 ] NC
2A [ 6                16 ] 4Y
NC [ 7                15 ] NC
2B [ 8                14 ] 3B
         9 10 11 12 13
        2Y GND NC 3Y 3A
```

NC — No internal connection

description

These devices contain four independent 2-input Exclusive-OR gates. They perform the Boolean functions $Y = A \oplus B = \overline{A}B + A\overline{B}$ in positive logic.

A common application is as a true/complement element. If one of the inputs is low, the other input will be reproduced in true form at the output. If one of the inputs is high, the signal on the other input will be reproduced inverted at the output.

The SN5486, 54LS86A, and the SN54S86 are characterized for operation over the full military temperature range of −55°C to 125°C. The SN7486, SN74LS86A, and the SN74S86 are characterized for operation from 0°C to 70°C.

exclusive-OR logic

An exclusive-OR gate has many applications, some of which can be represented better by alternative logic symbols.

EXCLUSIVE-OR

These are five equivalent Exclusive-OR symbols valid for an '86 or 'LS86A gate in positive logic; negation may be shown at any two ports.

LOGIC IDENTITY ELEMENT	EVEN-PARITY	ODD-PARITY ELEMENT
The output is active (low) if all inputs stand at the same logic level (i.e., A = B).	The output is active (low) if an even number of inputs (i.e., 0 or 2) are active.	The output is active (high) if an odd number of inputs (i.e., only 1 of the 2) are active.

TEXAS INSTRUMENTS

POST OFFICE BOX 655012 • DALLAS, TEXAS 75265

TTL Devices

2

SN5486, SN54LS86A, SN54S86,
SN7486, SN74LS86A, SN74S86
QUADRUPLE 2-INPUT EXCLUSIVE-OR GATES

schematics of inputs and outputs

'86

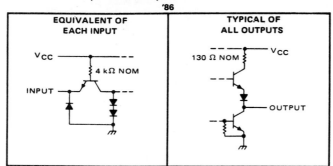

'LS86A

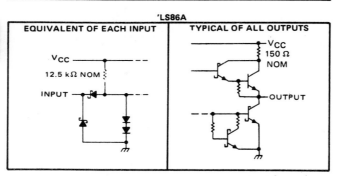

'S86

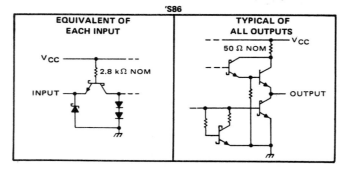

logic symbol†

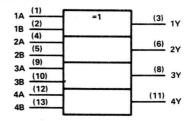

†This symbol is in accordance with
ANSI/IEEE Std. 91-1984 and IEC Publication 617-12.
Pin numbers shown are for D, J, N, and W packages.

FUNCTION TABLE

INPUTS		OUTPUT
A	**B**	**Y**
L	L	L
L	H	H
H	L	H
H	H	L

H = high level, L = low level

TEXAS
INSTRUMENTS
POST OFFICE BOX 655012 • DALLAS, TEXAS 75265

SN5490A, SN5492A, SN5493A, SN54LS90, SN54LS92, SN54LS93, SN7490A, SN7492A, SN7493A, SN74LS90, SN74LS92, SN74LS93
DECADE, DIVIDE-BY-TWELVE AND BINARY COUNTERS

MARCH 1974 — REVISED MARCH 1988

'90A, 'LS90 . . . Decade Counters

'92A, 'LS92 . . . Divide By-Twelve Counters

'93A, 'LS93 . . . 4-Bit Binary Counters

TYPES	TYPICAL POWER DISSIPATION
'90A	145 mW
'92A, '93A	130 mW
'LS90, 'LS92, 'LS93	45 mW

description

Each of these monolithic counters contains four master-slave flip-flops and additional gating to provide a divide-by-two counter and a three-stage binary counter for which the count cycle length is divide-by-five for the '90A and 'LS90, divide-by-six for the '92A and 'LS92, and the divide-by-eight for the '93A and 'LS93.

All of these counters have a gated zero reset and the '90A and 'LS90 also have gated set-to-nine inputs for use in BCD nine's complement applications.

To use their maximum count length (decade, divide-by-twelve, or four-bit binary) of these counters, the CKB input is connected to the Q_A output. The input count pulses are applied to CKA input and the outputs are as described in the appropriate function table. A symmetrical divide-by-ten count can be obtained from the '90A or 'LS90 counters by connecting the Q_D output to the CKA input and applying the input count to the CKB input which gives a divide-by-ten square wave at output Q_A.

SN5490A, SN54LS90 . . . J OR W PACKAGE
SN7490A . . . N PACKAGE
SN74LS90 . . . D OR N PACKAGE
(TOP VIEW)

```
        ___ ___
CKB  [1]  U  [14] CKA
R0(1)[2]     [13] NC
R0(2)[3]     [12] Q_A
 NC  [4]     [11] Q_D
V_CC [5]     [10] GND
R9(1)[6]     [9]  Q_B
R9(2)[7]     [8]  Q_C
```

SN5492A, SN54LS92 . . . J OR W PACKAGE
SN7492A . . . N PACKAGE
SN74LS92 . . . D OR N PACKAGE
(TOP VIEW)

```
        ___ ___
CKB  [1]  U  [14] CKA
 NC  [2]     [13] NC
 NC  [3]     [12] Q_A
 NC  [4]     [11] Q_B
V_CC [5]     [10] GND
R0(1)[6]     [9]  Q_C
R0(2)[7]     [8]  Q_D
```

SN5493A, SN54LS93 . . . J OR W PACKAGE
SN7493 . . . N PACKAGE
SN74LS93 . . . D OR N PACKAGE
(TOP VIEW)

```
        ___ ___
CKB  [1]  U  [14] CKA
R0(1)[2]     [13] NC
R0(2)[3]     [12] Q_A
 NC  [4]     [11] Q_D
V_CC [5]     [10] GND
 NC  [6]     [9]  Q_B
 NC  [7]     [8]  Q_C
```

NC — No internal connection

2 — TTL Devices

PRODUCTION DATA documents contain information current as of publication date. Products conform to specifications per the terms of Texas Instruments standard warranty. Production processing does not necessarily include testing of all parameters.

TEXAS
INSTRUMENTS

POST OFFICE BOX 655012 • DALLAS, TEXAS 75265

SN5490A, '92A, '93A, SN54LS90, 'LS92, 'LS93, SN7490A, '92A, '93A, SN74LS90, 'LS92, 'LS93
DECADE, DIVIDE-BY-TWELVE, AND BINARY COUNTERS

logic symbols†

'90

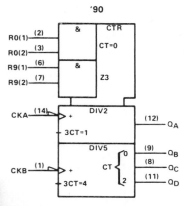

'92

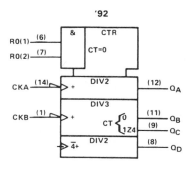

'93A, 'LS93

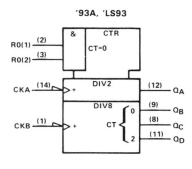

†These symbols are in accordance with ANSI/IEEE Std. 91-1984 and IEC Publication 617-12.

2

TTL Devices

TEXAS
INSTRUMENTS
POST OFFICE BOX 655012 • DALLAS, TEXAS 75265

'90A, 'LS90
BCD COUNT SEQUENCE
(See Note A)

COUNT	OUTPUT			
	Q_D	Q_C	Q_B	Q_A
0	L	L	L	L
1	L	L	L	H
2	L	L	H	L
3	L	L	H	H
4	L	H	L	L
5	L	H	L	H
6	L	H	H	L
7	L	H	H	H
8	H	L	L	L
9	H	L	L	H

'90A, 'LS90
BI-QUINARY (5-2)
(See Note B)

COUNT	OUTPUT			
	Q_A	Q_D	Q_C	Q_B
0	L	L	L	L
1	L	L	L	H
2	L	L	H	L
3	L	L	H	H
4	L	H	L	L
5	H	L	L	L
6	H	L	L	H
7	H	L	H	L
8	H	L	H	H
9	H	H	L	L

'92A, 'LS92
COUNT SEQUENCE
(See Note C)

COUNT	OUTPUT			
	Q_D	Q_C	Q_B	Q_A
0	L	L	L	L
1	L	L	L	H
2	L	L	H	L
3	L	L	H	H
4	L	H	L	L
5	L	H	L	H
6	H	L	L	L
7	H	L	L	H
8	H	L	H	L
9	H	L	H	H
10	H	H	L	L
11	H	H	L	H

'90A, 'LS90
RESET/COUNT FUNCTION TABLE

RESET INPUTS				OUTPUT			
$R_{0(1)}$	$R_{0(2)}$	$R_{9(1)}$	$R_{9(2)}$	Q_D	Q_C	Q_B	Q_A
H	H	L	X	L	L	L	L
H	H	X	L	L	L	L	L
X	X	H	H	H	L	L	H
X	L	X	L	COUNT			
L	X	L	X	COUNT			
L	X	X	L	COUNT			
X	L	L	X	COUNT			

'93A, 'LS93
COUNT SEQUENCE
(See Note C)

COUNT	OUTPUT			
	Q_D	Q_C	Q_B	Q_A
0	L	L	L	L
1	L	L	L	H
2	L	L	H	L
3	L	L	H	H
4	L	H	L	L
5	L	H	L	H
6	L	H	H	L
7	L	H	H	H
8	H	L	L	L
9	H	L	L	H
10	H	L	H	L
11	H	L	H	H
12	H	H	L	L
13	H	H	L	H
14	H	H	H	L
15	H	H	H	H

'92A, 'LS92, '93A, 'LS93
RESET/COUNT FUNCTION TABLE

RESET INPUTS		OUTPUT			
$R_{0(1)}$	$R_{0(2)}$	Q_D	Q_C	Q_B	Q_A
H	H	L	L	L	L
L	X	COUNT			
X	L	COUNT			

NOTES: A. Output Q_A is connected to input CKB for BCD count.
B. Output Q_D is connected to input CKA for bi-quinary count.
C. Output Q_A is connected to input CKB.
D. H = high level, L = low level, X = irrelevant

TTL Devices

2

SN5490A, '92A, '93A, SN54LS90, 'LS92, 'LS93, SN7490A, '92A, '93A, SN74LS90, 'LS92, 'LS93 DECADE, DIVIDE-BY-TWELVE, AND BINARY COUNTERS

logic diagrams (positive logic)

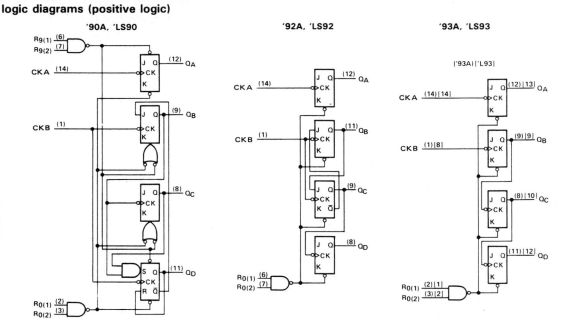

'90A, 'LS90   '92A, 'LS92   '93A, 'LS93

The J and K inputs shown without connection are for reference only and are functionally at a high level.
Pin numbers shown in ( ) are for the 'LS93 and '93A and pin numbers shown in [ ] are for the 54L93.

schematics of inputs and outputs

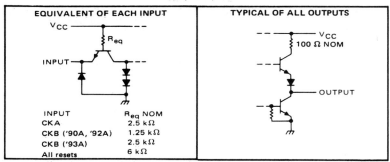

'90A, '92A, '93A

EQUIVALENT OF EACH INPUT	TYPICAL OF ALL OUTPUTS

INPUT	R_{eq} NOM
CKA	2.5 kΩ
CKB ('90A, '92A)	1.25 kΩ
CKB ('93A)	2.5 kΩ
All resets	6 kΩ

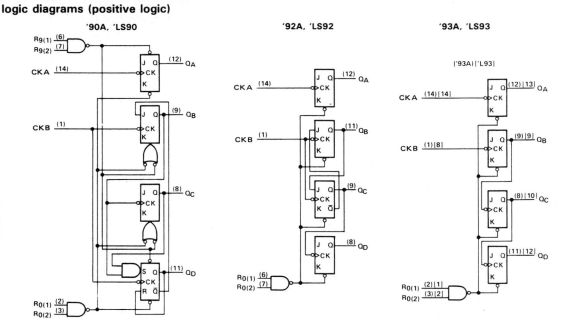

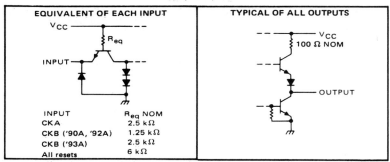

TEXAS INSTRUMENTS
POST OFFICE BOX 655012 • DALLAS, TEXAS 75265

- **Package Options Include Plastic and Ceramic DIPs**

- **Dependable Texas Instruments Quality and Reliability**

description

The SN54111 and SN74111 are d-c coupled, variable-skew, J-K flip-flops which utilize TTL circuitry to obtain 25-MHz performance typically. They are termed "variable-skew" because they allow the maximum clock skew in a system to be a direct function of the clock pulse width. The J and K inputs are enabled to accept data only during a short period (30 nanoseconds maximum hold time) starting with, and immediately following the rising edge of the clock pulse. After this, inputs may be changed while the clock is at the high level without affecting the state of the master. At the threshold level of the falling edge of the clock pulse, the data stored in the master will be transferred to the output. The effective allowable clock skew then is minimum propagation delay time minus hold time, plus clock pulse width. This means that the system designer can set the maximum allowable clock skew needed by varying the clock pulse width. Thus system design is made easier and the requirements for sophisticated clock distribution systems are minimized or, in some cases, entirely eliminated. These flip-flops have an additional feature-the synchronous input has reduced sensitivity to data change while the clock is high because the data need be present for only a short period of time and the system's susceptibility to noise is thereby effectively reduced.

The SN54111 is characterized for operation over the full military temperature range of −55°C to 125°C; the SN74111 is characterized for operation from 0°C to 70°C.

SN54111 . . . J OR W PACKAGE
SN74111 . . . J OR N PACKAGE
(TOP VIEW)

```
      1K    [ 1   U  16 ]  VCC
    1PRE    [ 2      15 ]  2K
    1CLR    [ 3      14 ]  2PRE
      1J    [ 4      13 ]  2CLR
    1CLK    [ 5      12 ]  2J
      1Q    [ 6      11 ]  2CLK
      1Q    [ 7      10 ]  2Q
     GND    [ 8       9 ]  2Q
```

logic symbol

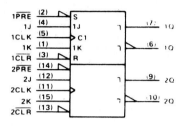

Pin numbers shown are for J and N packages

FUNCTION TABLE

INPUTS					OUTPUTS	
$\overline{PRE}$	$\overline{CLR}$	CLK	J	K	Q	$\overline{Q}$
L	H	X	X	X	H	L
H	L	X	X	X	L	H
L	L	X	X	X	H†	H†
H	H	⊓	L	L	Q_0	$\overline{Q}_0$
H	H	⊓	H	L	H	L
H	H	⊓	L	H	L	H
H	H	⊓	H	H	TOGGLE	

† This configuration is non-stable; that is, it will not persist when preset or clear return to their inactive (high) level.

POST OFFICE BOX 225012 • DALLAS, TEXAS 75265

TTL DEVICES

TYPES SN54111, SN74111
DUAL J-K MASTER-SLAVE
FLIP-FLOPS WITH DATA LOCKOUT

logic diagram

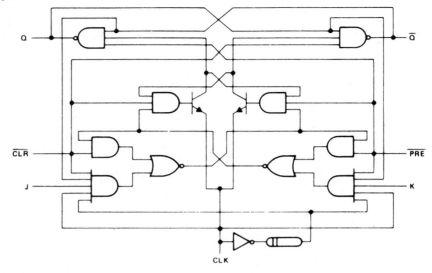

schematics of inputs and outputs

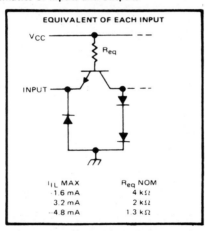

EQUIVALENT OF EACH INPUT

I_{IL} MAX	R_{eq} NOM
-1.6 mA	4 kΩ
-3.2 mA	2 kΩ
-4.8 mA	1.3 kΩ

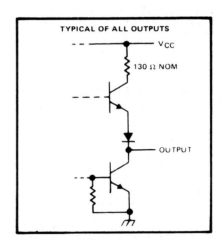

TYPICAL OF ALL OUTPUTS

130 Ω NOM

absolute maximum ratings over operating free-air temperature range (unless otherwise noted)

Supply voltage, V_{CC} (see Note 1)	7 V
Input voltage	5.5 V
Operating free-air temperature range: SN54'	55°C to 125°C
SN74'	0°C to 70°C
Storage temperature range	-65°C to 150°C

NOTE 1 Voltage values are with respect to network ground terminal

TEXAS INSTRUMENTS

POST OFFICE BOX 225012 • DALLAS TEXAS 75265

TTL DEVICES

recommended operating conditions

			SN54111			SN74111			UNIT
			MIN	NOM	MAX	MIN	NOM	MAX	
V_{CC}	Supply voltage		4.5	5	5.5	4.75	5	5.25	V
V_{IH}	High-level input voltage		2			2			V
V_{IL}	Low-level input voltage				0.8			0.8	V
I_{OH}	High-level output current				−0.8			−0.8	mA
I_{OL}	Low-level output current				16			16	mA
t_w	Pulse duration	CLK high or low	25			25			ns
		$\overline{PRE}$ or $\overline{CLR}$ low	25			25			
t_{su}	Input setup time before CLK ↑		0			0			ns
t_h	Input hold time data after CLK ↑		30			30			ns
T_A	Operating free-air temperature		−55		125	0		70	°C

electrical characteristics over recommended operating free-air temperature range (unless otherwise noted)

PARAMETER		TEST CONDITIONS †	SN54111			SN74111			UNIT
			MIN	TYP‡	MAX	MIN	TYP‡	MAX	
V_{IK}		V_{CC} = MIN, I_I = −12 mA			−1.5			−1.5	V
V_{OH}		V_{CC} = MIN, V_{IH} = 2 V, V_{IL} = 0.8 V, I_{OH} = −0.8 mA	2.4	3.4		2.4	3.4		V
V_{OL}		V_{CC} = MIN, V_{IH} = 2 V, V_{IL} = 0.8 V, I_{OL} = 16 mA		0.2	0.4		0.2	0.4	V
I_I		V_{CC} = MAX, V_I = 5.5 V			1			1	mA
I_{IH}	J or K	V_{CC} = MAX, V_I = 2.4 V			40			40	μA
	$\overline{CLR}$ or $\overline{PRE}$				80			80	
	CLK				120			120	
I_{IL}	J or K	V_{CC} = MAX, V_I = 0.4 V			−1.6			−1.6	mA
	$\overline{CLR}$★				−3.2			−3.2	
	$\overline{PRE}$★				−3.2			−3.2	
	CLK				−4.8			−4.8	
I_{OS}§		V_{CC} = MAX	−20		−57	−18		−57	mA
I_{CC}		V_{CC} = MAX, See Note 2		14	20.5		14	20.5	mA

† For conditions shown as MIN or MAX, use the appropriate value specified under recommended operating conditions.
‡ All typical values are at V_{CC} = 5 V, T_A = 25°C.
§ Not more than one output should be shorted at a time.
★ Clear is tested with preset high and preset is tested with clear high.
NOTE 2: With all outputs open, I_{CC} is measured with the Q and $\overline{Q}$ outputs high in turn. At the time of measurement, the clock input is at 4.5 V.

switching characteristics, V_{CC} = 5 V, T_A = 25°C (see note 3)

PARAMETER	FROM (INPUT)	TO (OUTPUT)	TEST CONDITIONS	MIN	TYP	MAX	UNIT
f_{max}				20	25		MHz
t_{PLH}	$\overline{PRE}$ or $\overline{CLR}$	Q or $\overline{Q}$	R_L = 400 Ω, C_L = 15 pF		12	18	ns
t_{PHL}					21	30	ns
t_{PLH}	CLK	Q or $\overline{Q}$			12	17	ns
t_{PHL}					20	30	ns

NOTE 3: See General Information Section for load circuits and voltage waveforms.

TTL DEVICES

TEXAS
INSTRUMENTS
POST OFFICE BOX 225012 • DALLAS, TEXAS 75265

TYPES SN54121, SN54L121, SN74121
MONOSTABLE MULTIVIBRATORS
WITH SCHMITT-TRIGGER INPUTS

REVISED MAY 1983

- **Programmable Output Pulse Width**
  With R_{int} . . . 35 ns Typ
  With R_{ext}/C_{ext} . . . 40 ns to 28 Seconds
- **Internal Compensation for Virtual Temperature Independence**
- **Jitter-Free Operation up to 90% Duty Cycle**
- **Inhibit Capability**

SN54121 . . . J OR W PACKAGE
SN54L121 . . . J PACKAGE
SN74121 . . . J OR N PACKAGE

(TOP VIEW)

```
         ___  ___
  Q̄  [ 1      14 ]  VCC
 NC  [ 2      13 ]  NC
 A1  [ 3      12 ]  NC
 A2  [ 4      11 ]  Rext/Cext
  B  [ 5      10 ]  Cext
  Q  [ 6       9 ]  Rint
GND  [ 7       8 ]  NC
```

NC - No internal connection.

FUNCTION TABLE

INPUTS			OUTPUTS	
A1	A2	B	Q	Q̄
L	X	H	L	H
X	L	H	L†	H†
X	X	L	L†	H†
H	H	X	L†	H†
H	↓	H	⊓	⊔
↓	H	H	⊓	⊔
↓	↓	H	⊓	⊔
L	X	↑	⊓	⊔
X	L	↑	⊓	⊔

For explanation of function table symbols, see page
† These lines of the function table assume that the indicated steady-state conditions at the A and B inputs have been setup long enough to complete any pulse started before the setup.

description

These multivibrators feature dual negative-transition-triggered inputs and a single positive-transition-triggered input which can be used as an inhibit input. Complementary output pulses are provided.

Pulse triggering occurs at a particular voltage level and is not directly related to the transition time of the input pulse. Schmitt-trigger input circuitry (TTL hysteresis) for the B input allows jitter-free triggering from inputs with transition rates as slow as 1 volt/second, providing the circuit with an excellent noise immunity of typically 1.2 volts. A high immunity to V_{CC} noise of typically 1.5 volts is also provided by internal latching circuitry.

Once fired, the outputs are independent of further transitions of the inputs and are a function only of the timing components. Input pulses may be of any duration relative to the output pulse. Output pulse length may be varied from 40 nanoseconds to 28 seconds by choosing appropriate timing components. With no external timing components (i.e., R_{int} connected to V_{CC}, C_{ext} and R_{ext}/C_{ext} open), an output pulse of typically 30 or 35 nanoseconds is achieved which may be used as a d-c triggered reset signal. Output rise and fall times are TTL compatible and independent of pulse length.

Pulse width stability is achieved through internal compensation and is virtually independent of V_{CC} and temperature. In most applications, pulse stability will only be limited by the accuracy of external timing components.

Jitter-free operation is maintained over the full temperature and V_{CC} ranges for more than six decades of timing capacitance (10 pF to 10 μF) and more than one decade of timing resistance (2 kΩ to 30 kΩ for the SN54121/SN54L121 and 2 kΩ to 40 kΩ for the SN74121). Throughout these ranges, pulse width is defined by the relationship $t_{W(out)} = C_{ext}R_T \ln 2 \approx 0.7\ C_{ext}R_T$. In circuits where pulse cutoff is not critical, timing capacitance up to 1000 μF and timing resistance as low as 1.4 kΩ may be used. Also, the range of jitter-free output pulse widths is extended if V_{CC} is held to 5 volts and free-air temperature is 25°C. Duty cycles as high as 90% are achieved when using maximum recommended R_T. Higher duty cycles are available if a certain amount of pulse-width jitter is allowed.

TEXAS INSTRUMENTS
POST OFFICE BOX 225012 • DALLAS, TEXAS 75265

3-471

TTL DEVICES

3

logic diagram (positive logic)

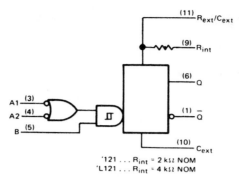

'121 . . . R_{int} = 2 kΩ NOM
'L121 . . . R_{int} = 4 kΩ NOM

Pin numbers shown on logic notation are for J or N packages.

NOTES: 1. An external capacitor may be connected between C_{ext} (positive) and R_{ext}/C_{ext}.
2. To use the internal timing resistor, connect R_{int} to V_{CC}. For improved pulse width accuracy and repeatability, connect an external resistor between R_{ext}/C_{ext} and V_{CC} with R_{int} open-circuited.

schematics of inputs and outputs

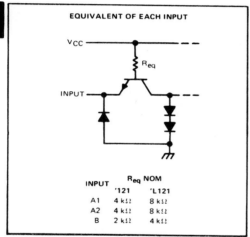

EQUIVALENT OF EACH INPUT

INPUT	R_{eq} NOM	
	'121	'L121
A1	4 kΩ	8 kΩ
A2	4 kΩ	8 kΩ
B	2 kΩ	4 kΩ

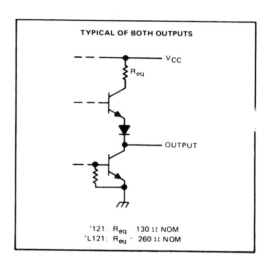

TYPICAL OF BOTH OUTPUTS

'121: R_{eq} 130 Ω NOM
'L121: R_{eq} 260 Ω NOM

3

TTL DEVICES

TEXAS INSTRUMENTS
POST OFFICE BOX 225012 ● DALLAS, TEXAS 75265

absolute maximum ratings over operating free-air temperature range (unless otherwise noted)

Supply voltage, V_{CC} (see Note 1) '121 . . . . 7 V

'L121 . . . . 8 V

Input voltage: . . . . 5.5 V

Operating free-air temperature range: SN54121, SN54L121 . . . . − 55°C to 125°C

SN74121 . . . . 0°C to 70°C

Storage temperature range . . . . − 65°C to 150°C

NOTE 1: Voltage values are with respect to network ground terminal.

recommended operating conditions

			SN54121 SN74121			SN54L121			UNIT
			MIN	NOM	MAX	MIN	NOM	MAX	
V_{CC}	Supply voltage	54 Family	4.5	5	5.5	4.5	5	5.5	V
		74 Family	4.75	5	5.25				
I_{OH}	High-level output current				− 0.4			− 0.2	mA
I_{OL}	Low-level output current				16			8	mA
dv/dt	Rate of rise or fall of input pulse	Schmitt input, B		1			1		V/s
		Logic inputs, A1, A2		1			1		V/µs
$t_{w(in)}$	Input pulse width		50			100			ns
R_{ext}	External timing capacitance	54 Family	1.4		30	1.4		30	kΩ
		74 Family	1.4		40				
C_{ext}	External timing capacitance		0		1000	0		1000	µF
	Duty cycle	$R_T = 2 kΩ$			67			67	%
		$R_T = MAX R_{ext}$			90			90	
T_A	Operating free-air termperature	54 Family	− 55		125	− 55		125	°C
		74 Family	0		70				

TEXAS
INSTRUMENTS
POST OFFICE BOX 225012 ● DALLAS, TEXAS 75265

electrical characteristics over recommended operating free-air temperature range (unless otherwise noted)

PARAMETER		TEST CONDITIONS†		SN54121 SN74121 MIN	TYP‡	MAX	SN54L121 MIN	TYP‡	MAX	UNIT
V_{T+}	Positive-going threshold voltage at A input	V_{CC} = MIN			1.4	2		1.4	2	V
V_{T-}	Negative-going threshold voltage at A input	V_{CC} = MIN		0.8	1.4		0.8	1.4		V
V_{T+}	Positive-going threshold voltage at B input	V_{CC} = MIN			1.55	2		1.55	2	V
V_{T-}	Negative-going threshold voltage at B input	V_{CC} = MIN		0.8	1.35		0.8	1.35		V
V_{IK}	Input clamp voltage	V_{CC} = MIN,	I_I = -12 mA			-1.5			-1.5	V
V_{OH}	High-level output voltage	V_{CC} = MIN,	I_{OH} = MAX	2.4	3.4		2.4	3.4		V
V_{OL}	Low-level output voltage	V_{CC} = MIN,	I_{OL} = MAX		0.2	0.4		0.2	0.4	V
I_I	Input current at maximum input voltage	V_{CC} = MAX,	V_I = 5.5 V			1			1	mA
I_{IH}	High-level input current	V_{CC} = MAX, V_I = 2.4 V	A1 or A2			40			20	μA
			B			80			40	
I_{IL}	Low-level input current	V_{CC} = MAX, V_I = 0.4 V	A1 or A2			-1.6			-0.8	mA
			B			-3.2			-1.6	
I_{OS}	Short-circuit output current♦	V_{CC} = MAX	54 Family	-20		-55	-10		-27	mA
			74 Family	-18		-55				
I_{CC}	Supply current	V_{CC} = MAX	Quiescent		13	25		7	12	mA
			Triggered		23	40		9	20	

† For conditions shown as MIN or MAX, use the appropriate value specified under recommended operating conditions.
‡ All typical values are at V_{CC} 5 V, T_A 25 C.
♦ Not more than one output should be shorted at a time.

3

TTL DEVICES

switching characteristics, V_{CC} = 5 V, T_A = 25°C

PARAMETER		TEST CONDITIONS		'121 MIN	TYP	MAX	'L121 MIN	TYP	MAX	UNIT
t_{PLH}	Propagation delay time, low-to-high-level Q output from either A input		C_{ext} 80 pF, R_{int} to V_{CC}		45	70			140	ns
t_{PLH}	Propagation delay time, low-to-high-level Q output from B input				35	55			110	ns
t_{PHL}	Propagation delay time, high-to-low-level Q output from either A input	C_L = 15 pF, R_L = 400 Ω for '121, R_L = 800 Ω for 'L121, See Note 2			50	80			160	ns
t_{PHL}	Propagation delay time, high-to-low-level Q output from B input				40	65			130	ns
$t_{w(out)}$	Pulse width obtained using internal timing resistor		C_{ext} 80 pF, R_{int} to V_{CC}	70	110	150	70	225	260	ns
$t_{w(out)}$	Pulse width obtained with zero timing capacitance		C_{ext} = 0, R_{int} to V_{CC}		30	50		35	70	ns
$t_{w(out)}$	Pulse width obtained using external timing resistor		C_{ext} = 100 pF, R_T = 10 kΩ	600	700	800	600	700	850	ns
			C_{ext} = 1 μF, R_T = 10 kΩ	6	7	8	6	7	8	ms

NOTE 2 See General Information Section for load circuits and voltage waveforms.

TEXAS
INSTRUMENTS
POST OFFICE BOX 225012 • DALLAS, TEXAS 75265

54/74125
54LS/74LS125A
QUAD BUS BUFFER GATE
(With 3-State Outputs)

CONNECTION DIAGRAM
PINOUT A

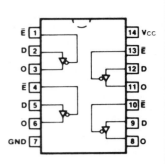

ORDERING CODE: See Section 9

PKGS	PIN OUT	COMMERCIAL GRADE $V_{CC} = +5.0$ V $\pm 5\%$, $T_A = 0°C$ to $+70°C$	MILITARY GRADE $V_{CC} = +5.0$ V $\pm 10\%$, $T_A = -55°C$ to $+125°C$	PKG TYPE
Plastic DIP (P)	A	74125PC, 74LS125APC		9A
Ceramic DIP (D)	A	74125DC, 74LS125ADC	54125DM, 54LS125ADM	6A
Flatpak (F)	A	74125FC, 74LS125AFC	54125FM, 54LS125AFM	3I

TRUTH TABLE

INPUTS		OUTPUT
Ē	D	
L	L	L
L	H	H
H	X	Z

H = HIGH Voltage Level
L = LOW Voltage Level
X = Immaterial
Z = High Impedance

INPUT LOADING/FAN-OUT: See Section 3 for U.L. definitions

PINS	54/74 (U.L.) HIGH/LOW	54/74LS (U.L.) HIGH/LOW
Inputs	1.0/1.0	0.5/0.25
Outputs	130/10	65/15
	(50)	(25)/(7.5)

DC AND AC CHARACTERISTICS: See Seciton 3*

SYMBOL	PARAMETER		54/74 Min	54/74 Max	54/74LS Min	54/74LS Max	UNITS	CONDITIONS
V_{OH}	Output HIGH Voltage	XM	2.4				V	$I_{OH} = -2.0$ mA
		XC	2.4					$I_{OH} = -5.2$ mA
		XM			2.4			$I_{OH} = -1.0$ mA
		XC			2.4			$I_{OH} = -2.6$ mA
I_{OS}	Output Short Circuit Current	XM	-30	-70	-30	-130	mA	$V_{CC} = $ Max
		XC	-28	-70	-30	-130		
I_{CC}	Power Supply Current			54		20	mA	Outputs OFF, $V_{IN} = $ Gnd $V_E = 4.5$ V, $V_{CC} = $ Max
t_{PLH}	Propagation Delay			13		15	ns	Figs. 3-3, 3-5
t_{PHL}	Data to Output			18		18		
t_{PZH}	Output Enable Time			17		16	ns	Figs. 3-3, 3-11, 3-12
t_{PZL}				25		25		
t_{PLZ}	Output Disable Time			8.0		25	ns	Figs. 3-3, 3-11, 3-12
t_{PHZ}				12		25		

The V_{OH} conditions note: $V_{CC} = $ Min, $V_{IN} = V_{IH}$ or V_{IL}

*DC limits apply over operating temperature range; AC limits apply at $T_A = +25°C$ and $V_{CC} = +5.0$ V.

SN54LS138, SN54S138, SN74LS138, SN74S138A
3-LINE TO 8-LINE DECODERS/DEMULTIPLEXERS

DECEMBER 1972–REVISED MARCH 1988

- **Designed Specifically for High-Speed:**
  Memory Decoders
  Data Transmission Systems
- **3 Enable Inputs to Simplify Cascading and/or Data Reception**
- **Schottky-Clamped for High Performance**

description

These Schottky-clamped TTL MSI circuits are designed to be used in high-performance memory decoding or data-routing applications requiring very short propagation delay times. In high-performance memory systems, these docoders can be used to minimize the effects of system decoding. When employed with high-speed memories utilizing a fast enable circuit, the delay times of these decoders and the enable time of the memory are usually less than the typical access time of the memory. This means that the effective system delay introduced by the Schottky-clamped system decoder is negligible.

The 'LS138, SN54S138, and SN74S138A decode one of eight lines dependent on the conditions at the three binary select inputs and the three enable inputs. Two active-low and one active-high enable inputs reduce the need for external gates or inverters when expanding. A 24-line decoder can be implemented without external inverters and a 32-line decoder requires only one inverter. An enable input can be used as a data input for demultiplexing applications.

All of these decoder/demultiplexers feature fully buffered inputs, each of which represents only one normalized load to its driving circuit. All inputs are clamped with high-performance Schottky diodes to suppress line-ringing and to simplify system design.

The SN54LS138 and SN54S138 are characterized for operation over the full military temperature range of −55°C to 125°C. The SN74LS138 and SN74S138A are characterized for operation from 0°C to 70°C.

SN54LS138, SN54S138 . . . J OR W PACKAGE
SN74LS138, SN74S138A . . . D OR N PACKAGE
(TOP VIEW)

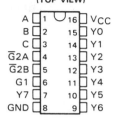

SN54LS138, SN54S138 . . . FK PACKAGE
(TOP VIEW)

NC—No internal connection

logic symbols†

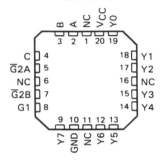

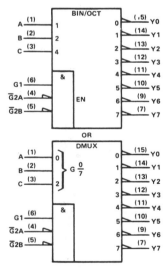

†These symbols are in accordance with ANSI/IEEE Std 91-1984 and IEC Publication 617-12.
Pin numbers shown are for D, J, N, and W packages.

Copyright © 1972, Texas Instruments Incorporated

TEXAS INSTRUMENTS
POST OFFICE BOX 655012 • DALLAS, TEXAS 75265

TTL Devices 2

SN54LS138, SN54S138, SN74LS138, SN74S138A
3-LINE-TO 8-LINE DECODERS/DEMULTIPLEXERS

logic diagram and function table

'LS138, SN54S138, SN74S138A

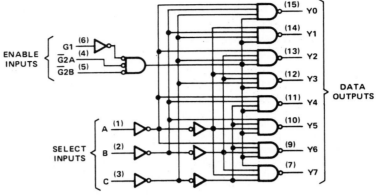

Pin numbers shown are for D, J, N, and W packages.

'LS138, SN54138, SN74S138A
FUNCTION TABLE

INPUTS					OUTPUTS							
ENABLE		SELECT										
G1	Ḡ2*	C	B	A	Y0	Y1	Y2	Y3	Y4	Y5	Y6	Y7
X	H	X	X	X	H	H	H	H	H	H	H	H
L	X	X	X	X	H	H	H	H	H	H	H	H
H	L	L	L	L	L	H	H	H	H	H	H	H
H	L	L	L	H	H	L	H	H	H	H	H	H
H	L	L	H	L	H	H	L	H	H	H	H	H
H	L	L	H	H	H	H	H	L	H	H	H	H
H	L	H	L	L	H	H	H	H	L	H	H	H
H	L	H	L	H	H	H	H	H	H	L	H	H
H	L	H	H	L	H	H	H	H	H	H	L	H
H	L	H	H	H	H	H	H	H	H	H	H	L

* $\overline{G2}$ = $\overline{G2A}$ + $\overline{G2B}$
H = high level, L = low level, X = irrelevant

2-426

TEXAS
INSTRUMENTS
POST OFFICE BOX 655012 • DALLAS TEXAS 75265

54S/74S139
54LS/74LS139
DUAL 1-OF-4 DECODER

CONNECTION DIAGRAM
PINOUT A

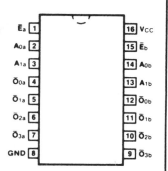

DESCRIPTION — The '139 is a high speed dual 1-of-4 decoder/demultiplexer. The device has two independent decoders, each accepting two inputs and providing four mutually exclusive active LOW outputs. Each decoder has an active LOW Enable input which can be used as a data input for a 4-output demultiplexer. Each half of the '139 can be used as a function generator providing all four minterms of two variables. The '139 is fabricated with the Schottky barrier diode process for high speed.

- **SCHOTTKY PROCESS FOR HIGH SPEED**
- **MULTIFUNCTION CAPABILITY**
- **TWO COMPLETELY INDEPENDENT 1-OF-4 DECODERS**
- **ACTIVE LOW MUTUALLY EXCLUSIVE OUTPUTS**

LOGIC SYMBOL

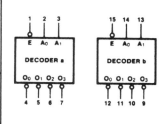

V_{CC} = Pin 16
GND = Pin 8

ORDERING CODE: See Section 9

PKGS	PIN OUT	COMMERCIAL GRADE V_{CC} = +5.0 V ±5%, T_A = 0°C to +70°C	MILITARY GRADE V_{CC} = +5.0 V ±10%, T_A = -55°C to +125°C	PKG TYPE
Plastic DIP (P)	A	74S139PC, 74LS139PC		9B
Ceramic DIP (D)	A	74S139DC, 74LS139DC	54S139DM, 54LS139DM	6B
Flatpak (F)	A	74S139FC, 74LS139FC	54S139FM, 54LS139FM	4L

INPUT LOADING/FAN-OUT: See Section 3 for U.L. definitions

PIN NAMES	DESCRIPTION	54/74S (U.L.) HIGH/LOW	54/74LS (U.L.) HIGH/LOW
A_0, A_1	Address Inputs	1.25/1.25	0.5/0.25
$\bar{E}$	Enable Input (Active LOW)	1.25/1.25	0.5/0.25
$\bar{O}_0 - \bar{O}_3$	Outputs (Active LOW)	25/12.5	10/5.0 (2.5)

FUNCTIONAL DESCRIPTION — The '139 is a high speed dual 1-of-4 decoder/demultiplexer fabricated with the Schottky barrier diode process. The device has two independent decoders, each of which accepts two binary weighted inputs (A_0, A_1) and provides four mutually exclusive active LOW outputs ($\overline{O}_0 - \overline{O}_3$). Each decoder has an active LOW enable ($\overline{E}$). When $\overline{E}$ is HIGH all outputs are forced HIGH. The enable can be used as the data input for a 4-output demultiplexer application. Each half of the '139 generates all four minterms of two variables. These four minterms are useful in some applications, replacing multiple gate functions as shown in *Figure a*, and thereby reducing the number of packages required in a logic network.

TRUTH TABLE

INPUTS			OUTPUTS			
$\overline{E}$	A_0	A_1	$\overline{O}_0$	$\overline{O}_1$	$\overline{O}_2$	$\overline{O}_3$
H	X	X	H	H	H	H
L	L	L	L	H	H	H
L	H	L	H	L	H	H
L	L	H	H	H	L	H
L	H	H	H	H	H	L

H = HIGH Voltage Level
L = LOW Voltage Level
X = Immaterial

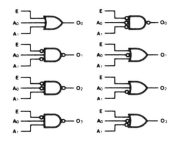

Fig. a

LOGIC DIAGRAM

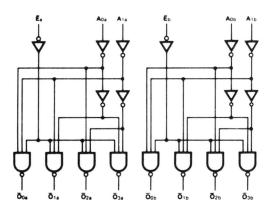

(Courtesy of Fairchild — A Schlumberger Company)

DC CHARACTERISTICS OVER OPERATING TEMPERATURE RANGE (unless otherwisespecified)

SYMBOL	PARAMETER	54/74LS		54/74S		UNITS	CONDITIONS
		Min	Max	Min	Max		
I_{CC}	Power Supply Current		11		90	mA	V_{CC} = Max

AC CHARACTERISTICS: V_{CC} = +5.0 V, T_A = +25°C (See Section 3 for waveforms and load configurations)

SYMBOL	PARAMETER	54/74LS C_L = 15 pF		54/74S C_L = 15 pF R_L = 280 Ω		UNITS	CONDITIONS
		Min	Max	Min	Max		
t_{PLH} t_{PHL}	Propagation Delay A_0 or A_1 to $\overline{O}_n$		18 27		12 12	ns	Figs. 3-1, 3-4, 3-5
t_{PLH} t_{PHL}	Propagation Delay $\overline{E}$ to $\overline{O}_n$		15 24		8.0 10	ns	Figs. 3-1, 3-5

'147, 'LS147

- Encodes 10-Line Decimal to 4-Line BCD

- Applications Include:

  Keyboard Encoding
  Range Selection: '148, 'LS148

- Encodes 8 Data Lines to 3-Line Binary (Octal)

- Applications Include:

  N-Bit Encoding
  Code Converters and Generators

TYPE	TYPICAL DATA DELAY	TYPICAL POWER DISSIPATION
'147	10 ns	225 mW
'148	10 ns	190 mW
'LS147	15 ns	60 mW
'LS148	15 ns	60 mW

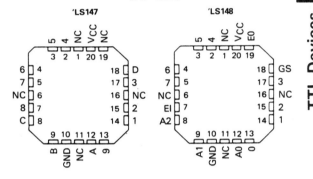

SN54147, SN54LS147,
SN54148, SN54LS148 . . . J OR W PACKAGE
SN74147, SN74148 . . . N PACKAGE
SN74LS147, SN74LS148 . . . D OR N PACKAGE
(TOP VIEW)

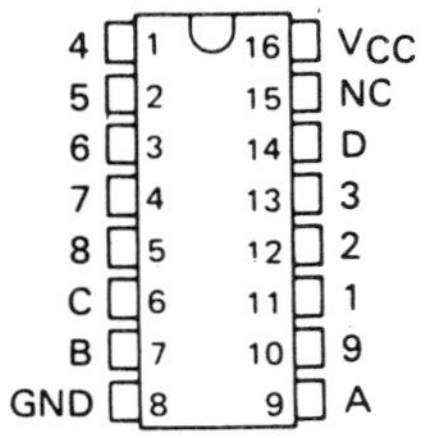

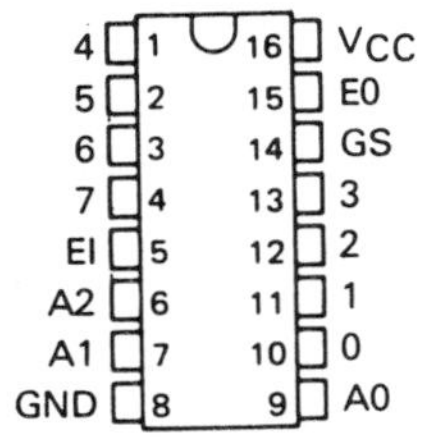

SN54LS147, SN54LS148 . . . FK PACKAGE
(TOP VIEW)

NC - No internal connection

description

These TTL encoders feature priority decoding of the inputs to ensure that only the highest-order data line is encoded. The '147 and 'LS147 encode nine data lines to four-line (8-4-2-1) BCD. The implied decimal zero condition requires no input condition as zero is encoded when all nine data lines are at a high logic level. The '148 and 'LS148 encode eight data lines to three-line (4-2-1) binary (octal). Cascading circuitry (enable input EI and enable output EO) has been provided to allow octal expansion without the need for external circuitry. For all types, data inputs and outputs are active at the low logic level. All inputs are buffered to represent one normalized Series 54/74 or 54LS/74LS load, respectively.

'147, 'LS147
FUNCTION TABLE

1	2	3	4	5	6	7	8	9	D	C	B	A
H	H	H	H	H	H	H	H	H	H	H	H	H
X	X	X	X	X	X	X	X	L	L	H	H	L
X	X	X	X	X	X	X	L	H	L	H	H	H
X	X	X	X	X	X	L	H	H	H	L	L	L
X	X	X	X	X	L	H	H	H	H	L	L	H
X	X	X	X	L	H	H	H	H	H	L	H	L
X	X	X	L	H	H	H	H	H	H	L	H	H
X	X	L	H	H	H	H	H	H	H	H	L	L
X	L	H	H	H	H	H	H	H	H	H	L	H
L	H	H	H	H	H	H	H	H	H	H	H	L

(Headers: INPUTS | OUTPUTS)

'148, 'LS148
FUNCTION TABLE

EI	0	1	2	3	4	5	6	7	A2	A1	A0	GS	EO
H	X	X	X	X	X	X	X	X	H	H	H	H	H
L	H	H	H	H	H	H	H	H	H	H	H	H	L
L	X	X	X	X	X	X	X	L	L	L	L	L	H
L	X	X	X	X	X	X	L	H	L	L	H	L	H
L	X	X	X	X	X	L	H	H	L	H	L	L	H
L	X	X	X	X	L	H	H	H	L	H	H	L	H
L	X	X	X	L	H	H	H	H	H	L	L	L	H
L	X	X	L	H	H	H	H	H	H	L	H	L	H
L	X	L	H	H	H	H	H	H	H	H	L	L	H
L	L	H	H	H	H	H	H	H	H	H	H	L	H

(Headers: INPUTS | OUTPUTS)

H = high logic level, L = low logic level, X = irrelevant

TEXAS
INSTRUMENTS

POST OFFICE BOX 655012 • DALLAS, TEXAS 75265

2

TTL Devices

SN54147, SN54148, SN54LS147, SN54LS148,
SN74147, SN74148 (TIM9907), SN74LS147, SN74LS148
10-LINE TO 4-LINE AND 8-LINE TO 3-LINE PRIORITY ENCODERS

logic symbols†

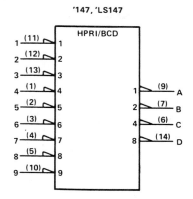

†These symbols are in accordance with ANSI/IEEE Std. 91-1984 and
IEC Publication 617-12.
Pin numbers shown are for D, J, N, and W packages.

logic diagrams

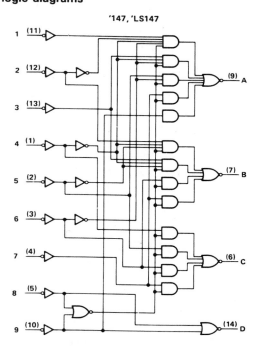

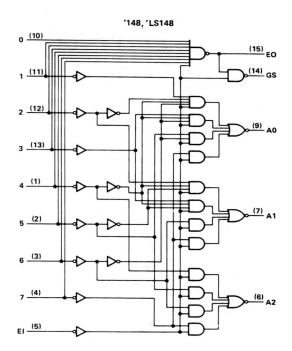

Pin numbers shown are for D, J, N, and W packages.

TEXAS
INSTRUMENTS
POST OFFICE BOX 655012 • DALLAS. TEXAS 75265

2

TTL Devices

TYPICAL APPLICATION DATA

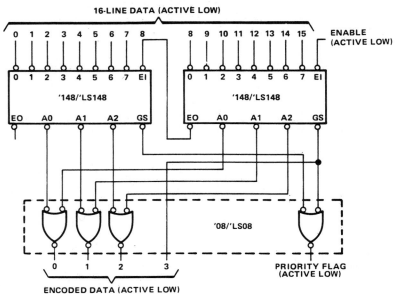

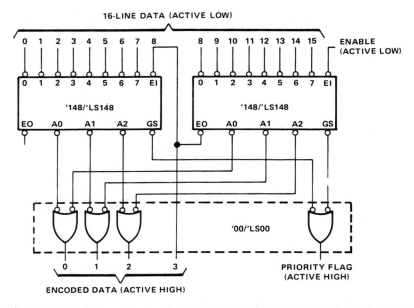

Since the '147/'LS147 and '148/'LS148 are combinational logic circuits, wrong addresses can appear during input transients. Moreover, for the '148/'LS148 a change from high to low at input EI can cause a transient low on the GS output when all inputs are high. This must be considered when strobing the outputs.

**TEXAS
INSTRUMENTS**

POST OFFICE BOX 655012 • DALLAS, TEXAS 75265

54/74151A
54S/74S151
54LS/74LS151

8-INPUT MULTIPLEXER

CONNECTION DIAGRAM
PINOUT A

I_3 [1]	[16] V_{CC}
I_2 [2]	[15] I_4
I_1 [3]	[14] I_5
I_0 [4]	[13] I_6
Z [5]	[12] I_7
$\bar{Z}$ [6]	[11] S_0
$\bar{E}$ [7]	[10] S_1
GND [8]	[9] S_2

DESCRIPTION — The '151 is a high speed 8-input digital multiplexer. It provides in one package, the ability to select one line of data from up to eight sources. The '151 can be used as a universal function generator to generate any logic function of four variables. Both assertion and negation outputs are provided.

LOGIC SYMBOL

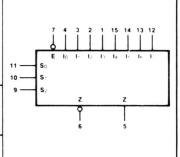

V_{CC} = Pin 16
GND = Pin 8

ORDERING CODE: See Section 9

PKGS	PIN OUT	COMMERCIAL GRADE V_{CC} = +5.0 V ±5%, T_A = 0°C to +70°C	MILITARY GRADE V_{CC} = +5.0 V ±10%, T_A = -55°C to +125°C	PKG TYPE
Plastic DIP (P)	A	74151APC, 74S151PC 74LS151PC		9B
Ceramic DIP (D)	A	74151ADC, 74S151DC 74LS151DC	54151ADM, 54S151DM 54LS151DM	6B
Flatpak (F)	A	74151AFC, 74S151FC 74LS151FC	54151AFM, 54S151FM 54LS151FM	4L

INPUT LOADING/FAN-OUT: See Section 3 for U.L. definitions

PIN NAMES	DESCRIPTION	54/74 (U.L.) HIGH/LOW	54/74S (U.L.) HIGH/LOW	54/74LS (U.L.) HIGH/LOW
$I_0 - I_7$	Data Inputs	1.0/1.0	1.25/1.25	0.5/0.25
$S_0 - S_2$	Select Inputs	1.0/1.0	1.25/1.25	0.5/0.25
$\bar{E}$	Enable Input (Active LOW)	1.0/1.0	1.25/1.25	0.5/0.25
Z	Data Output	20/10	25/12.5	10/5.0 (2.5)
$\bar{Z}$	Inverted Data Output	20/10	25/12.5	10/5.0 (2.5)

(Courtesy of Fairchild — A Schlumberger Company)

FUNCTIONAL DESCRIPTION — The '151 is a logical implementation of a single pole, 8-position switch with the switch position controlled by the state of three Select inputs, S_0, S_1, S_2. Both assertion and negation outputs are provided. The Enable input ($\overline{E}$) is active LOW. When it is not activated, the negation output is HIGH and the assertion output is LOW regardless of all other inputs. The logic function provided at the output is:

$$Z = \overline{E} \bullet (I_0 \bullet \overline{S}_0 \bullet \overline{S}_1 \bullet \overline{S}_2 + I_1 \bullet S_0 \bullet \overline{S}_1 \bullet \overline{S}_2 + I_2 \bullet \overline{S}_0 \bullet S_1 \bullet \overline{S}_2 + I_3 \bullet S_0 \bullet S_1 \bullet \overline{S}_2 +$$
$$I_4 \bullet \overline{S}_0 \bullet \overline{S}_1 \bullet S_2 + I_5 \bullet S_0 \bullet \overline{S}_1 \bullet S_2 + I_6 \bullet \overline{S}_0 \bullet S_1 \bullet S_2 + I_7 \bullet S_0 \bullet S_1 \bullet S_2).$$

The '151 provides the ability, in one package, to select from eight sources of data or control information. By proper manipulation of the inputs, the '151 can provide any logic function of four variables and its negation.

TRUTH TABLE

INPUTS				OUTPUTS	
$\overline{E}$	S_2	S_1	S_0	$\overline{Z}$	Z
H	X	X	X	H	L
L	L	L	L	$\overline{I_0}$	I_0
L	L	L	H	$\overline{I_1}$	I_1
L	L	H	L	$\overline{I_2}$	I_2
L	L	H	H	$\overline{I_3}$	I_3
L	H	L	L	$\overline{I_4}$	I_4
L	H	L	H	$\overline{I_5}$	I_5
L	H	H	L	$\overline{I_6}$	I_6
L	H	H	H	$\overline{I_7}$	I_7

H = HIGH Voltage Level
L = LOW Voltage Level

LOGIC DIAGRAM

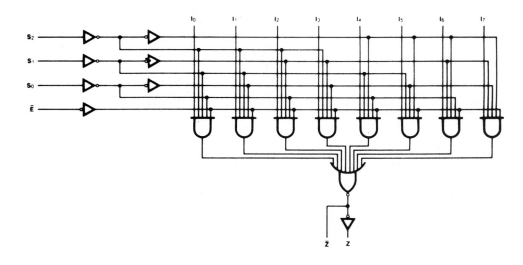

54/74173
54LS/74LS173
4-BIT D-TYPE REGISTER
(With 3-State Outputs)

CONNECTION DIAGRAM
PINOUT A

$\overline{OE}_1$	1	16	V_{CC}
$\overline{OE}_2$	2	15	MR
O_0	3	14	D_0
O_1	4	13	D_1
O_2	5	12	D_2
O_3	6	11	D_3
CP	7	10	$\overline{IE}_2$
GND	8	9	$\overline{IE}_1$

DESCRIPTION — The '173 is a high speed 4-bit register featuring 3-state outputs for use in bus-organized systems. The clock is fully edge-triggered allowing either a load from the D inputs or a hold (retain register contents) depending on the state of the Input Enable lines ($\overline{IE}_1$, $\overline{IE}_2$). A HIGH on either Output Enable line ($\overline{OE}_1$, $\overline{OE}_2$) brings the output to a high impedance state without affecting the actual register contents. A HIGH on the Master Reset (MR) input resets the register regardless of the state of the Clock (CP), the Output Enable ($\overline{OE}_1$, $\overline{OE}_2$) or the Input Enable ($\overline{IE}_1$, $\overline{IE}_2$) lines.

- **FULLY EDGE-TRIGGERED**
- **3-STATE OUTPUTS**
- **GATED INPUT AND OUTPUT ENABLES**

LOGIC SYMBOL

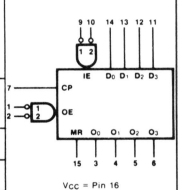

V_{CC} = Pin 16
GND = Pin 8

ORDERING CODE: See Section 9

PKGS	PIN OUT	COMMERCIAL GRADE V_{CC} = +5.0 V ±5%, T_A = 0°C to +70°C	MILITARY GRADE V_{CC} = +5.0 V ±10%, T_A = -55°C to +125°C	PKG TYPE
Plastic DIP (P)	A	74173PC, 74LS173PC		9B
Ceramic DIP (D)	A	74173DC, 74LS173DC	54173DM, 54LS173DM	7B
Flatpak (F)	A	74173FC, 74LS173FC	54173FM, 54LS173FM	4L

INPUT LOADING/FAN-OUT: See Section 3 for U.L. definitions

PIN NAMES	DESCRIPTION	54/74 (U.L.) HIGH/LOW	54/74LS (U.L.) HIGH/LOW
D_0 — D_3	Data Inputs	1.0/1.0	0.5/0.25
$\overline{IE}_1$, $\overline{IE}_2$	Input Enable Inputs (Active LOW)	1.0/1.0	0.5/0.25
$\overline{OE}_1$, $\overline{OE}_2$	3-State Output Enable Inputs (Active LOW)	1.0/1.0	0.5/0.25
CP	Clock Pulse Input (Active Rising Edge)	1.0/1.0	0.5/0.25
MR	Asynchronous Master Reset Input (Active HIGH)	1.0/1.0	0.5/0.25
O_0 — O_3	3-State Outputs	130/10 (50)	65/5.0 (25)/(2.5)

(Courtesy of Fairchild — A Schlumberger Company)

173

TRUTH TABLE

INPUTS					OUTPUT
MR	CP	$\overline{IE}_1$	$\overline{IE}_2$	D_n	Q_n
H	X	X	X	X	L
L	L	X	X	X	Q_n
L	⌐	H	X	X	Q_n
L	⌐	X	H	X	Q_n
L	⌐	L	L	L	L
L	⌐	L	L	H	H

When either $\overline{OE}_1$ or $\overline{OE}_2$ are HIGH, the output
is in the OFF state (high impedenace), however
this does not affect the contents or sequential
operating of the register

H = HIGH Voltage Level
L = LOW Voltage Level
X = Immaterial

LOGIC DIAGRAM

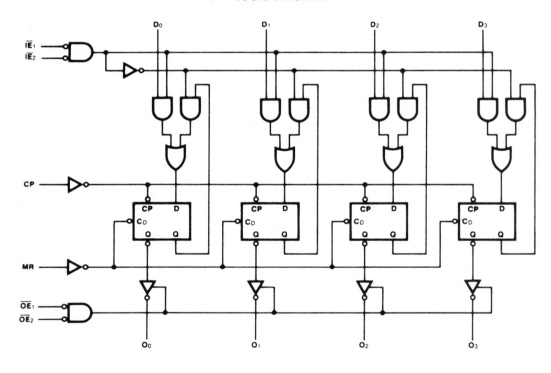

DC CHARACTERISTICS OVER OPERATING TEMPERATURE RANGE (unless otherwise specified)

SYMBOL	PARAMETER	54/74 Min	54/74 Max	54/74LS Min	54/74LS Max	UNITS	CONDITIONS
I_{OS}	Output Short Circuit Current	-30	-70	-20	-100	mA	V_{CC} = Max
I_{CC}	Power Supply Current		72		28	mA	V_{CC} = Max, MR = ⌐_ CP, $\overline{OE}_1$ = 4.5 V $\overline{OE}_2$, $\overline{IE}_1$, $\overline{IE}_2$, D_n = Gnd

AC CHARACTERISTICS: V_{CC} = +5.0 V, T_A = +25°C (See Section 3 for waveforms and load configurations)

SYMBOL	PARAMETER	54/74 C_L = 50 pF R_L = 400 Ω Min	Max	54/74LS C_L = 15 pF Min	Max	UNITS	CONDITIONS
f_{max}	Maximum Clock Frequency	25		30		MHz	Figs. 3-1, 3-8
t_{PLH} t_{PHL}	Propagation Delay CP to O_n		43 31		40 25	ns	
t_{PHL}	Propagation Delay, MR to O_n		27		25	ns	Figs. 3-1, 3-16
t_{PZH} t_{PZL}	Output Enable Time		30 30		20 20	ns	Figs. 3-3, 3-11, 3-12 R_L = 2 kΩ ('LS173)
t_{PHZ} t_{PLZ}	Output Disable Time		14 20		16 16	ns	Figs. 3-3, 3-11, 3-12 R_L = 2 kΩ ('LS173) C_L = 5 pF

AC OPERATING REQUIREMENTS: V_{CC} = +5.0 V, T_A = +25°C

SYMBOL	PARAMETER	54/74 Min	Max	54/74LS Min	Max	UNITS	CONDITIONS
t_s (H) t_s (L)	Setup Time HIGH or LOW D_n to CP	10 10		10 10		ns	
t_h (H) t_h (L)	Hold Time HIGH or LOW D_n to CP	10 10		10 10		ns	Fig. 3-6
t_s (H) t_s (L)	Setup Time HIGH or LOW $\overline{IE}$ to CP	17 17		17 17		ns	
t_h (H) t_h (L)	Hold Time HIGH or LOW $\overline{IE}$ to CP	2.0 2.0		2.0 2.0		ns	
t_w (L)	CP Pulse Width LOW	20		17		ns	Fig. 3-8
t_w (H)	MR Pulse Width HIGH	20		17		ns	Fig. 3-16
t_{rec}	Recovery Time, MR to CP	10		15		ns	

(Courtesy of Fairchild – A Schlumberger Company)

54/74174
54S/74S174
54LS/74LS174
HEX D FLIP-FLOP

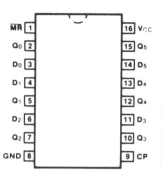

DESCRIPTION — The '174 is a high speed hex D flip-flop. The device is used primarily as a 6-bit edge-triggered storage register. The information on the D inputs is transferred to storage during the LOW-to-HIGH clock transition. The device has a Master Reset to simultaneously clear all flip-flops.

- **EDGE-TRIGGERED D-TYPE INPUTS**
- **BUFFERED POSITIVE EDGE-TRIGGERED CLOCK**
- **ASYNCHRONOUS COMMON RESET**

LOGIC SYMBOL

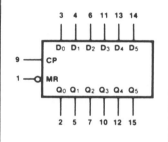

V_{CC} = Pin 16
GND = Pin 8

ORDERING CODE: See Section 9

PKGS	PIN OUT	COMMERCIAL GRADE V_{CC} = +5.0 V ±5%, T_A = 0°C to +70°C	MILITARY GRADE V_{CC} = +5.0 V ±10%, T_A = -55°C to +125°C	PKG TYPE
Plastic DIP (P)	A	74174PC, 74S174PC, 74LS174PC		9B
Ceramic DIP (D)	A	74174DC, 74S174DC, 74LS174DC	54174DM, 54S174DM, 54LS174DM	6B
Flatpak (F)	A	74174FC, 74S174FC, 74LS174FC	54174FM, 54S174FM, 54LS174FM	4L

INPUT LOADING/FAN-OUT: See Section 3 for U.L. definitions

PIN NAMES	DESCRIPTION	54/74 (U.L.) HIGH/LOW	54/74S (U.L.) HIGH/LOW	54/74LS (U.L.) HIGH/LOW
$D_0 — D_5$	Data Inputs	1.0/1.0	1.25/1.25	0.5/0.25
CP	Clock Pulse Input (Active Rising Edge)	1.0/1.0	1.25/1.25	0.5/0.25
$\overline{MR}$	Master Reset Input (Active LOW)	1.0/1.0	1.25/1.25	0.5/0.25
$Q_0 — Q_5$	Flip-Flop Outputs	20/10	25/12.5	10/5.0 (2.5)

FUNCTIONAL DESCRIPTION — The '174 consists of six edge-triggered D flip-flops with individual D inputs and Q outputs. The Clock (CP) and Master Reset ($\overline{MR}$) are common to all flip-flops. Each D input's state is transferred to the corresponding flip-flop's output following the LOW-to-HIGH Clock (CP) transition. A LOW input to the Master Reset ($\overline{MR}$) will force all outputs LOW independent of Clock or Data inputs. The '174 is useful for applications where the true output only is required and the Clock and Master Reset are common to all storage elements.

TRUTH TABLE

INPUTS	OUTPUTS
@ t_n, $\overline{MR}$ = H	@ t_{n+1}
D_n	Q_n
H	H
L	L

t_n = Bit time before positive-going clock transition
t_{n+1} = Bit time after positive-going clock transition
H = HIGH Voltage Level
L = LOW Voltage Level

LOGIC DIAGRAM

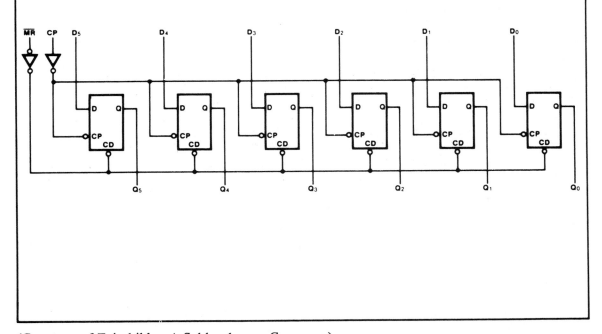

(Courtesy of Fairchild — A Schlumberger Company)

DC CHARACTERISTICS OVER OPERATING TEMPERATURE RANGE (unless otherwise specified)

SYMBOL	PARAMETER	54/74		54/74S		54/74LS		UNITS	CONDITIONS
		Min	Max	Min	Max	Min	Max		
I_{CC}	Power Supply Current		65		144		26	mA	V_{CC} = Max $D_n = \overline{MR}$ = 4.5 V $CP = \_\_\Box\_\_$

AC CHARACTERISTICS: V_{CC} = +5.0 V, T_A = +25° C (See Section 3 for waveforms and load configurations)

SYMBOL	PARAMETER	54/74 C_L = 15 pF R_L = 400 Ω		54/74S C_L = 15 pF R_L = 280 Ω		54/74LS C_L = 15 pF		UNITS	CONDITIONS
		Min	Max	Min	Max	Min	Max		
f_{max}	Maximum Clock Frequency	25		75		30		MHz	Figs. 3-1, 3-8
t_{PLH} t_{PHL}	Propagation Delay CP to Q_n		30 35		12 17		25 22	ns	Figs. 3-1, 3-8
t_{PHL}	Propagation Delay $\overline{MR}$ to Q_n		35		22		35	ns	Figs. 3-1, 3-16

AC OPERATING REQUIREMENTS: V_{CC} = +5.0 V, T_A = +25° C

SYMBOL	PARAMETER	54/74		54/74S		54/74LS		UNITS	CONDITIONS
		Min	Max	Min	Max	Min	Max		
t_s (H) t_s (L)	Setup Time HIGH or LOW D_n to CP	20 20		5.0 5.0		10 10		ns	Fig. 3-6
t_h (H) t_h (L)	Hold Time HIGH or LOW D_n to CP	5.0 5.0		3.0 3.0		5.0 5.0		ns	
t_w (H)	CP Pulse Width HIGH	20		7.0		18		ns	Fig. 3-8
t_w (L)	$\overline{MR}$ Pulse Width LOW	20		7.0		18		ns	Fig. 3-16
t_{rec}	Recovery Time $\overline{MR}$ to CP	25		5.0		12		ns	

54/74178
4-BIT SHIFT REGISTER

CONNECTION DIAGRAM
PINOUT A

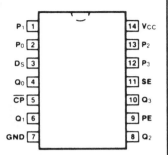

DESCRIPTION — The '178 features synchronous parallel or serial entry and parallel outputs. The flip-flops are fully edge-triggered, with state changes initiated by a HIGH-to-LOW transition of the clock. Parallel Enable and Serial Enable inputs are used to select Load, Shift and Hold modes of operation. The '178 is the 14-pin version of the '179. For detail specifications, please refer to the '179 data sheet.

LOGIC SYMBOL

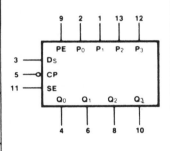

V_{CC} = Pin 14
GND = Pin 7

ORDERING CODE: See Section 9

PKGS	PIN OUT	COMMERCIAL GRADE V_{CC} = +5.0 V ±5%, T_A = 0°C to +70°C	MILITARY GRADE V_{CC} = +5.0 V ±10%, T_A = -55°C to +125°C	PKG TYPE
Plastic DIP (P)	A	74178PC		9A
Ceramic DIP (D)	A	74178DC	54178DM	6A
Flatpak (F)	A	74178FC	54178FM	3I

INPUT LOADING/FAN-OUT: See Section 3 for U.L. definitions

PIN NAMES	DESCRIPTION	54/74 (U.L.) HIGH/LOW
PE	Parallel Enable Input	1.0/1.0
$P_0 — P_3$	Parallel Data Inputs	1.0/1.0
D_S	Serial Data Input	1.0/1.0
SE	Shift Enable Input	1.0/1.0
$\overline{CP}$	Clock Pulse Input (Active Falling Edge)	1.0/1.0
$Q_0 — Q_3$	Flip-flop Outputs	20/10

(Courtesy of Fairchild – A Schlumberger Company)

FUNCTIONAL DESCRIPTION — The '178 contains four D-type edge-triggered flip-flops and sufficient inter-stage logic to perform parallel load, shift right or hold operations. All state changes are initiated by a HIGH-to-LOW transition of the clock. A HIGH signal on the Shift Enable (SE) input prevents parallel loading and permits a right shift each time the clock makes a negative transition. When the SE input is LOW, the signal applied to the Parallel Enable (PE) input determines whether the circuit is in a parallel load or a hold mode, as shown in the Mode Select Table. The SE, PE, D_S and P_n inputs can change when the clock is in either state, provided only that the recommended setup and hold times are observed.

MODE SELECT TABLE

INPUTS			RESPONSE
SE	PE	$\overline{CP}$	
H	X	⎍	Right Shift. $D_S \rightarrow Q_0$; $Q_0 \rightarrow Q_1$, etc.
L	H	⎍	Parallel load $P_n \rightarrow Q_n$.
L	L	X	Hold

H = HIGH Voltage Level
L = LOW Voltage Level
X = Immaterial.

LOGIC DIAGRAM

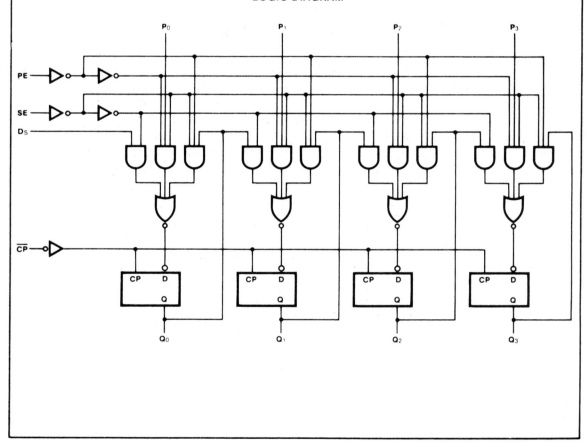

SN54192, SN54193, SN54LS192 SN54LS193,
SN74192, SN74193, SN74LS192, SN74LS193
SYNCHRONOUS 4-BIT UP/DOWN COUNTERS (DUAL CLOCK WITH CLEAR)

DECEMBER 1972—REVISED MARCH 1988

- Cascading Circuitry Provided Internally
- Synchronous Operation
- Individual Preset to Each Flip-Flop
- Fully Independent Clear Input

TYPES	TYPICAL MAXIMUM COUNT FREQUENCY	TYPICAL POWER DISSIPATION
'192,'193	32 MHz	325 mW
'LS192,'LS193	32 MHz	95 mW

SN54192, SN54193, SN54LS192,
SN54LS193 . . . J OR W PACKAGE
SN74192, SN74193 . . . N PACKAGE
SN74LS192, SN74LS193 . . . D OR N PACKAGE
(TOP VIEW)

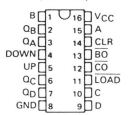

SN54LS192, SN54LS193 . . . FK PACKAGE
(TOP VIEW)

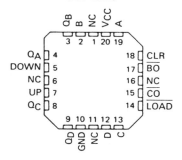

NC - No internal connection

description

These monolithic circuits are synchronous reversible (up/down) counters having a complexity of 55 equivalent gates. The '192 and 'LS192 circuits are BCD counters and the '193 and 'LS193 are 4-bit binary counters. Synchronous operation is provided by having all flip-flops clocked simultaneously so that the outputs change coincidently with each other when so instructed by the steering logic. This mode of operation eliminates the output counting spikes which are normally associated with asynchronous (ripple-clock) counters.

The outputs of the four master-slave flip-flops are triggered by a low-to-high-level transition of either count (clock) input. The direction of counting is determined by which count input is pulsed while the other count input is high.

All four counters are fully programmable; that is, each output may be preset to either level by entering the desired data at the data inputs while the load input is low. The output will change to agree with the data inputs independently of the count pulses. This feature allows the counters to be used as modulo-N dividers by simply modifying the count length with the preset inputs.

A clear input has been provided which forces all outputs to the low level when a high level is applied. The clear function is independent of the count and load inputs. The clear, count, and load inputs are buffered to lower the drive requirements. This reduces the number of clock drivers, etc., required for long words.

These counters were designed to be cascaded without the need for external circuitry. Both borrow and carry outputs are available to cascade both the up- and down-counting functions. The borrow output produces a pulse equal in width to the count-down input when the counter underflows. Similarly, the carry output produces a pulse equal in width to the count-up input when an overflow condition exists. The counters can then be easily cascaded by feeding the borrow and carry outputs to the count-down and count-up inputs respectively of the succeeding counter.

absolute maximum ratings over operating free-air temperature range (unless otherwise noted)

	SN54'	SN54LS'	SN74'	SN74LS'	UNIT
Supply voltage, V_{CC} (see Note 1)	7	7	7	7	V
Input voltage	5.5	7	5.5	7	V
Operating free-air temperature range	−55 to 125		0 to 70		°C
Storage temperature range	−65 to 150		−65 to 150		°C

NOTE 1: Voltage values are with respect to network ground terminal.

TEXAS
INSTRUMENTS

POST OFFICE BOX 655012 • DALLAS, TEXAS 75265

2

TTL Devices

SN54193, SN54LS193, SN74193, SN74LS193
SYNCHRONOUS 4-BIT UP/DOWN COUNTERS (DUAL CLOCK WITH CLEAR)

'193, 'LS193 BINARY COUNTERS

typical clear, load, and count sequences

Illustrated below is the following sequence:

1. Clear outputs to zero.
2. Load (preset) to binary thirteen.
3. Count up to fourteen, fifteen, carry, zero, one, and two.
4. Count down to one, zero, borrow, fifteen, fourteen, and thirteen.

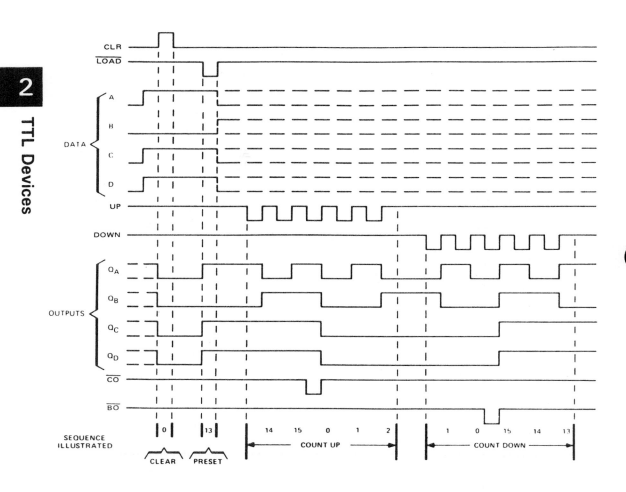

NOTES: A. Clear overrides load, data, and count inputs.

B. When counting up, count-down input must be high; when counting down, count-up input must be high.

2

TTL Devices

2-638

TEXAS
INSTRUMENTS
POST OFFICE BOX 655012 • DALLAS, TEXAS 75265

- Parallel Inputs and Outputs
- Four Operating Modes:

  Synchronous Parallel Load
  Right Shift
  Left Shift
  Do Nothing
- Positive Edge-Triggered Clocking
- Direct Overriding Clear

TYPE	TYPICAL MAXIMUM CLOCK FREQUENCY	TYPICAL POWER DISSIPATION
'194	36 MHz	195 mW
'LS194A	36 MHz	75 mW
'S194	105 MHz	425 mW

SN54194, SN54LS194A, SN54S194 . . . J OR W PACKAGE
SN74194 . . . J OR N PACKAGE
SN74LS194A, SN74S194 . . . D, J OR N PACKAGE

(TOP VIEW)

```
       CLR [ 1   16 ] VCC
    SR SER [ 2   15 ] QA
         A [ 3   14 ] QB
         B [ 4   13 ] QC
         C [ 5   12 ] QD
         D [ 6   11 ] CLK
    SL SER [ 7   10 ] S1
       GND [ 8    9 ] S0
```

SN54LS194A, SN54S194 . . . FK PACKAGE
SN74LS194A, SN74S194 . . . FN PACKAGE

(TOP VIEW)

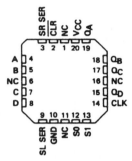

NC – No internal connection

description

These bidirectional shift registers are designed to incorporate virtually all of the features a system designer may want in a shift register. The circuit contains 46 equivalent gates and features parallel inputs, parallel outputs, right-shift and left-shift serial inputs, operating-mode-control inputs, and a direct overriding clear line. The register has four distinct modes of operation, namely:

Inhibit clock (do nothing)
Shift right (in the direction Q_A toward Q_D)
Shift left (in the direction Q_D toward Q_A)
Parallel (broadside) load

Synchronous parallel loading is accomplished by applying the four bits of data and taking both mode control inputs, S0 and S1, high. The data are loaded into the associated flip-flops and appear at the outputs after the positive transition of the clock input. During loading, serial data flow is inhibited.

Shift right is accomplished synchronously with the rising edge of the clock pulse when S0 is high and S1 is low. Serial data for this mode is entered at the shift-right data input. When S0 is low and S1 is high, data shifts left synchronously and new data is entered at the shift-left serial input.

Clocking of the shift register is inhibited when both mode control inputs are low. The mode controls of the SN54194/SN74194 should be changed only while the clock input is high.

TEXAS
INSTRUMENTS

POST OFFICE BOX 225012 • DALLAS, TEXAS 75265

TTL DEVICES

3

TYPES SN54194, SN54LS194A, SN54S194,
SN74194, SN74LS194A, SN74S194
4-BIT BIDIRECTIONAL UNIVERSAL SHIFT REGISTERS

FUNCTION TABLE

CLEAR	MODE		CLOCK	SERIAL		PARALLEL				OUTPUTS			
	S1	S0		LEFT	RIGHT	A	B	C	D	Q_A	Q_B	Q_C	Q_D
L	X	X	X	X	X	X	X	X	X	L	L	L	L
H	X	X	L	X	X	X	X	X	X	Q_{A0}	Q_{B0}	Q_{C0}	Q_{D0}
H	H	H	↑	X	X	a	b	c	d	a	b	c	d
H	L	H	↑	X	H	X	X	X	X	H	Q_{An}	Q_{Bn}	Q_{Cn}
H	L	H	↑	X	L	X	X	X	X	L	Q_{An}	Q_{Bn}	Q_{Cn}
H	H	L	↑	H	X	X	X	X	X	Q_{Bn}	Q_{Cn}	Q_{Dn}	H
H	H	L	↑	L	X	X	X	X	X	Q_{Bn}	Q_{Cn}	Q_{Dn}	L
H	L	L	X	X	X	X	X	X	X	Q_{A0}	Q_{B0}	Q_{C0}	Q_{D0}

H = high level (steady state)
L = low level (steady state)
X = irrelevant (any input, including transitions)
↑ = transition from low to high level
a, b, c, d = the level of steady-state input at inputs A, B, C, or D, respectively.
Q_{A0}, Q_{B0}, Q_{C0}, Q_{D0} = the level of Q_A, Q_B, Q_C, or Q_D, respectively, before the indicated steady-state input conditions were established.
Q_{An}, Q_{Bn}, Q_{Cn}, Q_{Dn} = the level of Q_A, Q_B, Q_C, respectively, before the most-recent ↑ transition of the clock.

schematics of inputs and outputs

'194

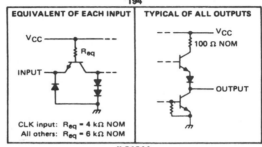

'LS194A

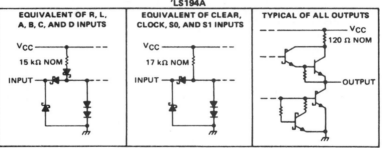

'S194

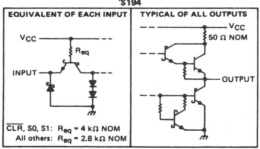

3

TTL DEVICES

3-770

TEXAS
INSTRUMENTS
POST OFFICE BOX 225012 ● DALLAS, TEXAS 75265

logic diagrams (continued)

'LS194A, 'S194

Pin numbers shown on logic notation are for D, J or N packages.

3

TTL DEVICES

TEXAS
INSTRUMENTS
POST OFFICE BOX 225012 • DALLAS, TEXAS 75265

2732A
32K (4K x 8) PRODUCTION AND UV ERASABLE PROMS

- **200 ns (2732A-2) Maximum Access Time ... HMOS*-E Technology**
- **Compatible with High-Speed Microcontrollers and Microprocessors ... Zero WAIT State**
- **Two Line Control**
- **10% V_{CC} Tolerance Available**

- **Low Current Requirement**
  - **−100 mA Active**
  - **−35 mA Standby**
- **int$_e$ligent Identifier™ Mode**
  - **−Automatic Programming Operation**
- **Industry Standard Pinout ... JEDEC Approved 24 Pin Ceramic and Plastic Package**
  - (See Packaging Spec. Order #221369)

The Intel 2732A is a 5V-only, 32,768-bit ultraviolet erasable (cerdip) Electrically Programmable Read-Only Memory (EPROM). The standard 2732A access time is 250 ns with speed selection (2732A-2) available at 200 ns. The access time is compatible with high performance microprocessors such as the 8 MHz iAPX 186. In these systems, the 2732A allows the microprocessor to operate without the addition of WAIT states.

The 2732A is currently available in two different package types. Cerdip packages provide flexibility in prototyping and R & D environments where reprogrammability is required. Plastic DIP EPROMs provide optimum cost effectiveness in production environments. Inventoried in the unprogrammed state, the P2732A is programmed quickly and efficiently when the need to change code arises. Costs incurred for new ROM masks or obsoleted ROM inventories are avoided. The tight package dimensional controls, inherent non-erasability, and high reliability of the P2732A make it the ideal component for these production applications.

An important 2732A feature is Output Enable ($\overline{OE}$) which is separate from the Chip Enable ($\overline{CE}$) control. The $\overline{OE}$ control eliminates bus contention in microprocessor systems. The $\overline{CE}$ is used by the 2732A to place it in a standby mode ($\overline{CE}$ = V_{IH}) which reduces power consumption without increasing access time. The standby mode reduces the current requirement by 65%; the maximum active current is reduced from 100 mA to a standby current of 35 mA.

*HMOS is a patented process of Intel Corporation.

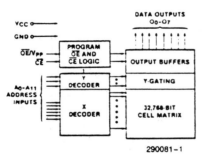

Figure 1. Block Diagram

290081−1

Pin Names

A_0–A_{11}	Addresses
$\overline{CE}$	Chip Enable
$\overline{OE}/V_{PP}$	Output Enable/V_{PP}
O_0–O_7	Outputs

27128 27128A	2764 2764A 27C64 87C64	2716	2732A P2732A		2716	2764 2764A 27C64 87C64	27128 27128A
V_{PP}	V_{PP}			V_{CC}		V_{CC} PGM	V_{CC} PGM
A_{12}	A_{12}					N.C.	A_{13}
A_7	A_7	A_7	A_7 ☐ 1 / 24 ☐ V_{CC}		A_8	A_8	A_8
A_6	A_6	A_6	A_6 ☐ 2 / 23 ☐ A_8		A_9	A_9	A_9
A_5	A_5	A_5	A_5 ☐ 3 / 22 ☐ A_9		V_{PP}	A_{11}	A_{11}
A_4	A_4	A_4	A_4 ☐ 4 / 21 ☐ A_{11}		$\overline{CE}$	$\overline{OE}$	$\overline{OE}$
A_3	A_3	A_3	A_3 ☐ 5 / 20 ☐ $\overline{OE}/V_{PP}$		A_{10}	A_{10}	A_{10}
A_2	A_2	A_2	A_2 ☐ 6 / 19 ☐ A_{10}		$\overline{CE}$	$\frac{CE}{ALE/\overline{CE}}$	$\overline{CE}$
A_1	A_1	A_1	A_1 ☐ 7 / 18 ☐ $\overline{CE}$		O_7	O_7	O_7
A_0	A_0	A_0	A_0 ☐ 8 / 17 ☐ O_7		O_6	O_6	O_6
O_0	O_0	O_0	O_0 ☐ 9 / 16 ☐ O_6		O_5	O_5	O_5
O_1	O_1	O_1	O_1 ☐ 10 / 15 ☐ O_5		O_4	O_4	O_4
O_2	O_2	O_2	O_2 ☐ 11 / 14 ☐ O_4		O_3	O_3	O_3
GND	GND	GND	GND ☐ 12 / 13 ☐ O_3				

NOTE: 290081−2

Intel "Universal Site" compatible EPROM configurations are shown in the blocks adjacent to the 2732A pins.

Figure 2. Cerdip/Plastic DIP Pin Configuration